DARKNESS
AND
LIGHT: Three
Short Works
by Tolstoy

edited by
PETER RUDY

HOLT, RINEHART AND WINSTON
NEW YORK • CHICAGO • SAN FRANCISCO • TORONTO

CONTENTS

INTRODUCTION

*The issue is now quite clear. It is between light and
darkness, and everyone must choose his side.*
G. K. CHESTERTON,
shortly before his death

I

In 1877 Dostoevsky read the latest installment of a novel
appearing serially in *The Russian Herald* and pronounced the
author to be "the God of Art." The novel, whose final chapters
were being published that year, was *Anna Karenina;* the author
was, of course, Leo Tolstoy. This deification surprised no one;
for the most part, the watchdogs of criticism, the writing fra-
ternity, and the public alike were finding extravagant praise to
be the only adequate measure of Tolstoy's current novel. When
Anna Karenina finally appeared in its entirety, the praise rose
to a new high level, and it seemed only natural that the forty-
nine-year-old Tolstoy, having surpassed the great expectations
of the past for his broad and richly textured realism, would
now go on to fulfill, or perhaps to exceed, the still greater expectations of the present for this mode of writing. The expectations were never to be realized. Ironically, even while *Anna
Karenina* was being widely acclaimed, Tolstoy was deeply involved in a spiritual storm that was to end forever the possibility that he would write another *Anna Karenina*. The attitudes
crystallizing during this crisis blocked almost completely the

familiar channel of expression and forced his creativity into a course that he had, up to that time, used only experimentally. Although the readers did not realize it, the Tolstoy that they knew and admired had, for all intents and purposes, ended his career and was about to yield to a Tolstoy with whom they had had only a few brief and largely unsatisfactory encounters. A type of writing that had built a reputation was to be all but abandoned in favor of one that had, in the past, been generally met with indifference or puzzlement.

During the first period of his literary career, the period ending with *Anna Karenina,* most of Tolstoy's fiction consisted of two unequally proportioned ingredients: a heavy concentration of purely reflective material and a relatively light admixture of overt, essentially didactic generalization. In the main, Tolstoy primarily sought to provide the reader with an exciting and credible synthesized reflection of life in all of its great diversity, with all of its shades of good and evil; and to that end he set a high premium on the creation of uniquely individualized, multifaceted personalities within a milieu of interlocking problem situations carefully constructed to suggest the random arrangement found in the world of living men. The tendency toward didactic generalization, very characteristic of Tolstoy's intellectual orientation, was invariably in evidence in these basically reflective works: It manifested itself in repeated character and behavior patterns that were obviously designed to serve as specific illustrations of generalizations and, frequently, also in adjunctive commentaries. But this tendency was kept in check; the two generalizing elements played a distinctly secondary role in the total make-up of his fiction during this period. For one thing, both were quantitatively only a small part of the total narrative; for another, the primarily illustrative trait and behavior patterns were so closely integrated with their purely reflective counterparts that their generalizing force was muted and the author's asides sometimes made to appear peripheral or even extraneous. Most of the fiction of this period, then, was essentially reflective in nature, but laced with a flavoring of overt didactic generalization—satisfying the reader's desire for a broader, though vicarious, participation in life but providing him, in passing, with a few lessons in some of the principles underlying this life. Such was the general structural mode Tolstoy employed in covering a wide variety of subject matter, ranging from the experiences and aspirations of a boy in aristocratic surroundings (*Childhood, Boyhood, and Youth*), to courtship and marriage (*Family Happiness*), to the sham, agony, and grandeur of military life ("The Raid," the Sevastopol tales, "The Wood Felling," "Meeting a Moscow Acquaintance in the Detachment"), to life in rural Russia ("The Snowstorm," *Polikushka*), to an aristocrat's pursuit of happiness at a Caucasian outpost (*The Cossacks*); such were the structural guidelines of those two ambitious composites, each panoramic in its own way, that closed the first period of his literary career: *War and Peace* and *Anna Karenina*.

While Tolstoy poured most of his creative energy during this first period into the production of fiction written in the basically reflective mode, he did experiment with another type of narrative, one that was both very different from and yet very similar to the dominant pattern. This other type of narrative, the basically didactic-illustrative narrative, used the very same elements as the reflective variety but in a reverse ratio; it was obtained by a tilting of the stylistic seesaw. In such fiction the generalizing tendency played the paramount role. There was a generalization or a cluster of generalizations that the author wanted the reader to accept. To achieve this end, he sought to tailor the characters and their behavior so that they would serve as clear-cut illustrations of the abstract idea or idea complex, and he used adjunctive commentaries when he felt the point needed reinforcement. A purely reflective presentation of traits and events was permitted, but, ideally, only in a supporting role, only to the extent that it was necessary for lending credibility and interest to the illustrative material.

Attempts to carry through this type of basically didactic-illustrative narrative[1] were not without difficulties because the author had to resist two opposing tendencies: that of lapsing into an unconvincing parable mode as a result of stressing his point too strongly or that of downgrading his point by introducing too much reflective material in the interests of credibility. The latter problem was the more troublesome for Tolstoy since the reflective tendency was the one that he was used to following. Because of this problem, one of his short stories, "The Raid" started out in the didactic-illustrative vein, as a definition of courage, but then developed into a primarily reflective narrative. Three others stand as examples of stories that almost went the same way. In "Two Hussars" Tolstoy set out to deliver a judgment of two generations, in "A Landowner's Morning" his purpose was to indict the impossible situations created by serfdom, and in "Albert" he wanted to make a point of the world's lack of understanding of the artist, but the supporting reflective material ballooned out. As a result, while his point is dominant, it is just barely so; and the reader is disturbed by the strong pull of the two gravitational systems.

In "Notes of a Billiard Marker," "Lucerne," and "Three Deaths," though, Tolstoy managed to maintain the desired balance—with just enough stress on the didactic-illustrative to throw his generalization into very bold relief, and with just enough emphasis on the reflective to create an aura of reality. When exposed to the raffish stratum of urban life, high-minded but impressionable young men are likely to founder morally; while man needs and enjoys art, he nevertheless persists in treating artists shamefully; there is a right and a wrong way to face one's death—these are the three didactic generalizations for which the stories serve as concrete examples. Most of the descriptive, dialogue, and thought sequences are primarily specific illustrations of parts of these generalizations; the rest,

---

[1] I avoid the use of such terms as *problem story* and *thesis story* because they are too general to suggest the special didactically oriented generalization-content-structure relationship which characterized this phase of Tolstoy's work.

reflective in nature, are designed to reinforce the illustrative material, to give the reader the impression of really viewing life.

The ratio between the basically reflective and the basically didactic-illustrative modes was to be radically reversed by the spiritual storm that swept through Tolstoy's life. This storm, which so decisively altered the course of Tolstoy's creative career, centered about the issue of whether life had a meaning. From his early days Tolstoy had been intoxicated by the sights and sounds of the life about him and had believed that this life had a meaning because it existed for some fundamental purpose. He could never define this purpose to his own satisfaction, but the belief in its existence sustained him. As time went by, Tolstoy was troubled by passing doubts about this conception of a life with some unrevealed purpose; and then, in 1860, the first major storm warning appeared. His brother Nikolai, with whom he was very close, died, slowly and painfully; and a bereaved Tolstoy saw a terrifying vision of a life without an underlying purpose and, hence, without meaning. Life simply existed and then death came and arbitrarily and completely destroyed it. Tolstoy kept repressing this terrifying vision, but the severe storm warnings kept reappearing over the next two years; and, had it not been for his marriage in the fall of 1862, he would have been forced into a decisive confrontation of this problem of life's meaning. With marriage, the crisis was temporarily postponed. His happy family life diverted his attention from the basic problem and, together with his writing, became the focal point of his existence.

Tolstoy was, however, enjoying only a respite. His son Petya died in 1873, his beloved Auntie Tatyana's death followed in 1874, and in the latter year the storm began in earnest. The question of life's meaning began to recur with an ever-increasing frequency, and, to his horror, Tolstoy could find no answer to it except the one suggested earlier by his brother's death. A very depressed Tolstoy was finally forced to admit that life had no meaning because it had no apparent underlying purpose. All he could see was death lying in wait to annihilate every man and all his concerns: "If not today—then tomorrow, sickness and death will come to those I love (they had already come), to me; and nothing will remain except stench and worms. My affairs, whatever they are, will sooner or later all be forgotten, and I simply won't exist. So why make any effort?" This realization affected Tolstoy's attitude toward everything, including his writing and art in general. When he had believed life to have meaning, then the reflection of life in its diversity had afforded him great pleasure; he had loved to see life in the mirror of art. But now that he knew life to be senseless, he could no longer find pleasure in its artistic reflection. The vision of a life of darkness, of a life without meaning, brought Tolstoy to the verge of desperation: "The horror of the darkness was too much for me, and I wanted to free myself of it as quickly as possible with a noose or bullet."

Frantically, Tolstoy turned for help to the natural sciences, to mathematics, to the social sciences, to philosophy; he also sought it in the lives of his peers. All these sources failed him. He was to find a solution to his problem in an unexpected quarter—in the Christian tradition as it existed among the common people of Russia. These people believed that every person comes into the world by God's will; that he is so created by God that he can save or destroy his soul; that the task of man in this life is to save his soul; that to save his soul he must live in a godly fashion; and that to live in a godly fashion he must renounce all the pleasures of life and must labor, humble himself, suffer, and be merciful. Here was a type of life that had a clear-cut purpose, that had a value which was infinite in nature and therefore invulnerable to death; here was a type of life that had a meaning. His decision to accept this life was not an easy one. A strong believer in reason, Tolstoy had to admit that there was a suprarational knowledge, faith, which alone pointed the way to a life with meaning; a seeker of perfection, he realized that in some of its details this life was contaminated by falsehoods and that ahead of him lay a long period of isolating these falsehoods. By the fall of 1879 Tolstoy's new spiritual orientation had crystallized sufficiently for him to begin serious work on a description of it and the process that had led to it; and out of this project grew his *Confession,* finished in the spring of 1882, a dramatic recital of his spiritual blundering and triumph. This resolution of Tolstoy's spiritual crisis had a very significant effect on his literary career, for it forced a radical reversal of the modal ratio that had existed during the first period. It all but blocked one channel of expression, and it expanded another.

As far as Tolstoy was now concerned, there was only one valid way of life, the godly way. The life led by the wealthy, by the educated he considered to be loathsome and meaningless—yet this life had been either the main or an important integral part of the content in most of the primarily reflective writing that dominated the first part of his career. This was the life that he knew most intimately, whose depiction had been in large measure responsible for his reputation. Ironically, after he had devoted most of his creative life to the perfection of a primarily reflective mode, a vital chunk of the subject matter it had mirrored now seemed disgusting and worthless to him. For all practical purposes, the basically reflective mode became the victim of what might be called moral obsolescence. Although the strong force of creative habit sought repeatedly to reassert itself, the strong force of conviction kept it in effective check all but once. Tolstoy was never again to get very far with a basically reflective narrative chronicling the ways of the upper classes. Indeed, in this second and last part of his literary career, only one work belongs to the primarily reflective category and this is "Hadji Murat," the tragic tale of a Caucasian chieftain.

While one aftermath of the crisis was the virtual abandonment of the basically reflective mode, another was the greatly increased use of the primarily didactic-illustrative mode. Tolstoy now felt duty-bound to come to the aid of all those who still continued to walk in darkness. One very effective means to this end was literature. Its emotive power could transmit to the reader the senselessness and horror of the life of darkness, could force him, at least vicariously, through a crisis; its emotive power could suggest the gratification to be found in the life of light. And Tolstoy had at hand a most suitable literary mode for this purpose, the primarily didactic-illustrative mode with which he had experimented earlier in his career. Used properly, it could give intensely concentrated but credible pictures of the life of darkness or of light, pictures that would evoke strong feelings of horror, disgust, scorn, or pity, or that would excite strong approval. During the years that followed, Tolstoy's belletristic work was, with the exception of "Hadji Murat," basically didactic-illustrative in nature. There were short stories: "The Death of Ivan Ilyich," "Kholstomer" (written before the crisis, but now revised in close conformity to his current views), "The Kreutzer Sonata," "Father Sergei," "After the Ball," "The Devil"; there was the novel *Resurrection;* there were plays: *The Power of Darkness, The Fruits of Enlightenment, The Living Corpse;* and all of these works were primarily structured to give propagandizing examples of generalizations from Tolstoy's dichotomous view of the world. The ratio had been reversed.

The primarily reflective mode had produced a *War and Peace* and an *Anna Karenina,* and there were adequate grounds to believe that the basically didactic-illustrative mode would produce at least one comparable masterpiece of fiction or drama. The powerful momentum of conviction, the benefit of previous experimentation with the mode, the highly refined devices (the stylistic bricks and mortar that could be used with either mode) —all of these seemed to give reasonable promise of a second literary career that would rival the first. Unfortunately, that promise was never realized. The effort devoted to his popular stories and dramas (rudimentary, parablelike literature) and to his social, moral, and religious tracts, his continuous involvement in favorite causes, and a nasty domestic situation dissipated his energies, and there were to be no towering peaks paralleling *War and Peace* or *Anna Karenina.* But the best works of the second period certainly rivaled the best that preceded these two novels—and this was no mean accomplishment.

And among the best works of this later period were "The Death of Ivan Ilyich," *The Power of Darkness,* and *The Fruits of Enlightenment.*

II

The selfish life spent in the pursuit of material things, pleasure, and power is a wasted life; the life motivated by a compassionate feeling for one's fellow man is a rich and rewarding life. The first is the life of darkness, the second, the life of light. We meet these ideas in a sermon or a moralistic tract, nod our heads in agreement, and then turn our attention elsewhere. We meet these ideas as the generalizations of "The Death of Ivan Ilyich" and pause at least for a few moments of reflection before turning our attention elsewhere. The pause for reflection is not due to any profundity in Tolstoy's development of these ideas; rather, it is attributable to the emotional force they acquire through his presentation.

"The Death of Ivan Ilyich" begins with an introductory sequence, Part I, that starts and completes one process of entrapment at the same time that it sets another in motion. The first is a process of interest entrapment designed to snare the reader's interest. It is overt and follows the conventional rules of fiction. The second is a process of moral entrapment aimed at getting the reader to admit his commitment to a certain moral position. It is covert and smacks of the methods of an agent provocateur, though of an agent provocateur who is willing to give his victim a sporting chance.

Ivan Ilyich has died. The reader witnesses the reaction of Ivan Ilyich's acquaintances, of his widow, and of his children; he views the body; and he learns that the deceased suffered terribly before dying of an incurable disease. And in the midst of all this, a mystery is introduced. As Ivan Ilyich's associate and close acquaintance, Peter Ivanovich, looks at the body, he is struck by the expression on the face: "On his [Ivan Ilyich's] face there was an expression which said that what was necessary to do had been done, and done properly. Besides, in his expression there was also a rebuke or reminder to the living." The expression has a strong effect on Peter Ivanovich: "This reminder seemed out of place to Peter Ivanovich, or, at least, to have no reference to him. He felt ill at ease, and so he hurriedly crossed himself again and, as it appeared to him, too precipitously and out of keeping with propriety, turned around and walked to the door." A little later, Praskovya Fyodorovna, the widow, calls Peter Ivanovich "a true friend of Ivan Ilyich's," but this fact seems to be contradicted by the behavior of her daughter and son. The daughter bows to Peter Ivanovich "as though he were guilty of something," and when the son notices him, he scowls "sternly and shamefacedly." What is the exact meaning of Ivan Ilyich's expression, of Peter Ivanovich's reaction to it, of the apparently contradictory attitudes of the widow and her children? The other material in Part I points to no definite answers; it merely supplies a basis for interesting speculations along divergent lines. The mystery element temporarily serves a very vital function. Parts II and III are characterized by a summary type of narration without any particularly surprising or dramatic developments, and the mystery element helps to sustain the reader's interest.

The Part I stage of the moral entrapment is executed in a very disarming manner. A narrator describes the reactions of the various characters to Ivan Ilyich's death. It is obvious that the narrator hardly considers these reactions to be ideal, but it is equally obvious that he does not expect ideal behavior in a world which is far from perfect. He is an individual with a very practical attitude framed in a delightful sense of tolerant, mildly mocking humor which seems to say that "people will, after all, be people." We are told that, "on hearing of Ivan Ilyich's death, the first thought of every one of the gentlemen present in the study [Ivan Ilyich's associates] was of the significance which this death might have for transfers or promotions of the judges themselves or of their acquaintances." These remarks are, however, accompanied by the information that

Ivan Ilyich had been ill for several weeks with what was considered to be an incurable disease and that there had already been speculation about the personnel changes which his death would cause, that one of his associates was getting very weary of waiting for the big promotion promised him, and that still another associate had been nagged by his wife about helping her relatives and now saw a chance to do something for her brother. Obviously one could hardly expect an outpouring of grief when all had become used to Ivan Ilyich's death before it occurred, and a long overdue promotion and a nagging wife are understandable pressures. Another reaction to Ivan Ilyich's death was the "feeling of joy that it was 'he' who had died and not 'I.' " But, according to the narrator, this is a feeling that is "always" aroused by the death of a close acquaintance. Certainly no one can blame a person for succumbing to a universal human failing. And still another reaction was the thought of the "very tedious social duties" which the death imposed—one would have to call on the widow and attend the funeral service. "Very tedious" strikes the reader as an apt description of the funerary routine. In this initial presentation of the reactions to Ivan Ilyich's death, the narrator has demonstrated that he is no moralizing prig. Obviously he recognizes the fact that one can expect just so much from human beings. Since the average reader has secretly experienced reactions similar to those of the characters and has secretly used justifications similar to those suggested by the narrator, he is only too happy to fall in with the narrator's sensible attitude and even enjoys the piquancy supplied by the mildly mocking tone. And now that the reader has been shown the comfortable attitude he should take, no further time need be spent on justification; he will automatically supply the justification as long as the behavior conforms to the normal practical standards of decency. The narrator goes on with his description of the behavior that attends Ivan Ilyich's death. There is the attitude of Schwartz, who refuses to be overwhelmed by "depressing impressions," who intends to go on with the session of cards scheduled for that evening. But what purpose would be served if he succumbed to depression or called off the card game? There is the widow's attempt to find out from Peter Ivanovich how she can get more money from the government. But remember? Ivan Ilyich left her nothing; she herself "has a little something, but nothing much." There is Peter Ivanovich's wishful thinking: "But immediately, he himself didn't know how, the habitual thought came to his rescue—the thought that this had happened to Ivan Ilyich, and not to him, and that this should not and could not happen to him. . . ." But who hasn't indulged in such childish self-deception?

The reader is, of course, being misled. From the Tolstoian perspective there can be no justification of this behavior, just short-sighted rationalization. This behavior illustrates certain characteristic aspects of the life of darkness: the pursuit of material things and pleasures; the indifference to one's fellow man that is spawned by these pursuits; a fear of death and the attempt, through one subterfuge or another, to avoid facing the fact of its inevitability, since death makes the attainment of material things and desires seem meaningless. But the narrator has not been altogether unfair to the reader; he has given him an opportunity to put two and two together as far as the meaninglessness of the pursuit of material things is concerned. Peter Ivanovich's reflections provide a hint of Ivan Ilyich's attachment to the material things that made for the nineteenth century equivalent of gracious living; and now Ivan Ilyich lies dead, unable to enjoy the drawing room done in pink cretonne and the clock picked up in a bric-a-brac shop. There is also a statement of the proper attitude one should take toward death in the peasant Gerasim's remarks: "It's God's will. It'll happen to all of us."

The process of moral entrapment is completed during the course of Parts II and III, through a summary account of Ivan Ilyich's life up to the beginning of his illness. This life is the life of an ordinary sensible and decent person who tries to make the best of things in a far-from-perfect world. It is a life that enables the reader to identify himself easily with the hero.

Ivan Ilyich was a decent official. He was devoted to his work and incorruptibly honest in the discharge of his duties. He was usually very conscientious in adhering to the impersonal code prescribed for court officials. In Ivan Ilyich's favor, too, was the fact that while he relished the great and arbitrary power that he possessed, he never abused it. Finally, he was a person with a great deal of initiative in advancing his career.

Ivan Ilyich's personal and social life was also that of an ordinary sensible and decent man. He tried to lead a pleasant, easy-going, gay, and proper life. When domestic strife threatened to make life miserable, he worked out the sort of attitude toward his married life that many sensible men do. ". . . when he met with opposition and querulousness [from his wife], he immediately withdrew to the separate world of his work which he had fenced off for himself and found his pleasure there." One of the great delights of his life was the apartment where they lived, and he had expended a great deal of time and energy in planning and supervising the decorating down to the minutest details. As far as entertainment was concerned, he enjoyed dinner parties attended by people of social standing and, especially, agreeable evenings at cards.

There were some serious blemishes, of course. Early in his life, Ivan Ilyich had sowed some wild oats; he, his wife, and his daughter "discouraged and freed themselves of all kinds of shabby friends and relatives." But a few such blemishes are hardly grounds for condemning a man whose general behavior is decent.

In this main stage of the moral entrapment the narrator has depicted a life led in darkness. Most of Ivan Ilyich's activity is centered about the pursuit of those things which lose all meaning once a person faces, as he inevitably must, the fact that he is mortal: material possessions, pleasure, and power. Also, in following this course Ivan Ilyich commits the cardinal sin of indifference to his fellow man. But the reader is given only two brief and vague hints about the real significance of Ivan Ilyich's life—at the very beginning of the biographical account, the narrator remarks that "the history of Ivan Ilyich's life was most simple, and most common, and most terrible," and later there is the reference to the *Respice-finem* inscription on the hero's watch-fob charm. Furthermore, the narrator indulges in sallies of mild, mocking humor that actually divert the reader from the real significance of Ivan Ilyich's behavior. There is, for example, the amusing treatment of Ivan Ilyich's taste in home furnishings.

The moral entrapment is not, however, an end in itself. It is actually one of the two parts of a favorite Tolstoian device, the double view. This device consists of presenting the reader with one presumably correct view of a character, situation, or idea and then correcting it with another and contradictory view. Having shown the reader a life which seems to be sensible and decent (considering the imperfect nature of the world), a practical life with which the reader readily identifies his own, Tolstoy now proceeds to a devastating exposure of this life as both meaningless and pernicious. The reader accompanies his fictional alter ego, Ivan Ilyich, on the latter's torturous journey from the first intimation that his illness might be fatal to the absolute certainty that he will die. The reader sees illness and the specter of death compelling a very unwilling Ivan Ilyich to first realize and then admit that his life was wrong.

Ivan Ilyich had devoted his adult life to the pursuit of material things, pleasure, and power; but now, as death gradually became a personal reality, these lost all meaning for him. He could not maintain any interest in the material objects he had acquired. He would be rearranging things in the drawing room when his wife would say: "Let the servants do it; you'll hurt yourself again." And instantly he would be reminded of death, which was slowly but inexorably advancing upon him: "*It* would appear, and he would still hope that *it* would vanish; but then he would involuntarily become aware of his side—the pain would still be there and would still be nagging in the same way, and he would no longer be able to forget it; and *it* would boldly stare at him from behind the flowers. What was the point of it all?" Then "he would go to his study, would lie down, and would again be left all alone with *it*. He would be face to face with *it,* but there was nothing he could do about *it*. All he could do was to look at it and grow cold with horror." The sweetness of Ivan Ilyich's pleasure activities turned to wormwood. There is an exhilarating moment during an evening at cards but "suddenly Ivan Ilyich feels that nagging pain, that taste in his mouth, and he sees something preposterous about being able to find any pleasure in a slam when this is going on." He makes a mistake and sees how his partner suffers, "while he himself doesn't care. And it's terrible for him to think why he doesn't care." And at the end of the evening "Ivan Ilyich is left alone with the consciousness that his life is poisoned for him and poisons the life of others, and that this poison is not receding, but keeps on penetrating his being more and more." In the past Ivan Ilyich's legal work had always been a source of great pleasure and he had relished the power with which it endowed him. Now this was no longer true. In court he would try to carry on as before, "but suddenly, in the middle of everything, the pain in his side, paying no attention to the stage of the proceedings, would begin *its* enervating proceedings. Ivan Ilyich would concentrate on the matter at hand, would keep driving away the thought of the pain, but it would continue its work; and *it* would come and stand right in front of him and look at him, and he would be petrified, and the light in his eyes would go out, and he would again begin to ask himself: 'Is it possible that *it* alone is the truth?' " Ivan Ilyich's life was wrong, then, because it was wasted on the pursuit of ephemera.

This life of his was wrong for another reason. In pursuing ephemera, Ivan Ilyich had practiced an indifference to other human beings. As a court official he had treated people as legal cases; as a husband he had solved his marital problems by working out "an attitude" that permitted him to lead a comfortable life but ruled out the possibility of any but the most superficial relationship with his wife. He had practiced an indifference to others; now, in the early stages of his illness, it is his turn to learn how it feels to be on the receiving end of indifference, and the experience is a shattering one. In a pointed and devastating parody of Ivan Ilyich's behavior in court, "a famous doctor" treats him as a mere medical case.

Earlier Ivan Ilyich's wife had been a victim of "an attitude" which he had worked out, "an attitude" grounded in his indifference to her problems; now, in an ironic reversal, he becomes the victim of "an attitude" which she works out, an attitude stemming from her indifference to his problem: "Praskovya's outward attitude toward her husband's illness, which she expressed to others and to him, was that Ivan Ilyich had himself to blame for this illness and that this whole illness was a new annoyance which he was creating for his wife. Ivan Ilyich felt that her remarks just came out involuntarily, but this didn't make it any easier for him."

The more serious Ivan Ilyich's illness grows, the greater is the indifference to him and the greater his sensitivity to this indifference. He feels that he is "alone, without a single person who might understand and take pity on him." Toward the end, Ivan Ilyich is existing in a limbo of loneliness to which indifference has relegated him. It is a "terrible loneliness," "a loneliness than which none more complete could exist anywhere, either at the bottom of the sea or in the earth."

The evidence accumulates relentlessly, and Ivan Ilyich gradually comes to realize that his life was wrong because it was spent in the pursuit of meaningless goals and because he had been guilty of a cardinal sin, an indifference to his fellow men. But it is one thing to realize that one's life has been wrong and another to admit it, and Ivan Ilyich struggles desperately to avoid an admission of the truth. It is only at the very end that his resistance crumbles and he makes the unqualified admission: "Yes, it was all wrong. . . ."

For a moment the dying Ivan Ilyich is caught in a void, for

he has renounced one way of life and not found another. "What is the right thing?" he asks himself, and, as if in answer, the son kisses his hand and begins to cry. A compassionate feeling for one's fellow human beings is "the right thing." And this compassionate feeling overwhelms Ivan Ilyich; he feels sorry for his son and wife and tries to beg forgiveness of her for a lifetime of indifference. On the threshold of death, a happy Ivan Ilyich has begun a life of light.

Ivan Ilyich's discovery and acceptance of "the right thing" is very rapid. It does not, however, strike the reader as an artificial contrivance. The reason for this is that even as Tolstoy was exposing the sham of Ivan Ilyich's life he was putting his hero (and, of course, the reader) through a preparatory conditioning for an acceptance of "the right thing." He had given a dramatic sampling of "the right thing" by depicting the peasant Gerasim's compassionate treatment of Ivan Ilyich and by showing the comfort the latter derived from it. Now, when Ivan Ilyich renounces his previous way of life, it is only natural for him to grasp for the one principle of behavior that he knows to be good.

The main structural girders of "The Death of Ivan Ilyich" are interest entrapment, the double view (whose first stage is here aimed at a moral entrapment), and preparatory conditioning. Through this combination of devices the reader is drawn into a deep personal involvement with the hero's waywardness, suffering, and triumph. But important as this framework is, it still accounts only in part for the effectiveness of the story. A network of supplementary devices, the very same ones that Tolstoy had used in the first period of his creativity, is also responsible for a great deal of the narrative's force.

Association of ideas is put to versatile use. Sometimes it is employed for anticipatory characterization. For example, Peter Ivanovich and the widow enter the drawing room "done in pink cretonne." A few lines later he recalls how "Ivan Ilyich had decorated this drawing room and had consulted him in regard to this very same pink cretonne with its green leaves."

In this unobtrusive manner the author is able to pass on to the reader bits of advance information about Ivan Ilyich. The associative device is also effective for transitional purposes. The author wishes to illustrate through a brief burst of hysteria the toll that Ivan Ilyich's mental anguish has taken, and the associative device is used as a bridge between two emotional states. One moment Ivan Ilyich is calmly thinking about his predicament: "What do you want now? To live? To live how? To live as in court when the bailiff announces: 'The judges are coming!' " Then he repeats the familiar bailiff's cry twice and is immediately projected into an imaginary courtroom situation with himself on trial for the sort of life he has led: " 'Here they are: the judges! But I'm not guilty!' he shrieked in anger. 'Why am I on trial?' " A little later on, the device serves to trigger reminiscences of Ivan Ilyich's childhood days, of the period before he went astray: "One after another there arose before him pictures of his past. This process of recollection always began with what was most recent and went back to what was most remote, to his childhood, and there it stopped. If Ivan Ilyich thought of the stewed prunes which he had been offered that day, he recalled the raw, wrinkled French prunes of his childhood, their particular taste, and the abundance of saliva when he reached the stone; and along with this recollection of the taste there arose a whole series of memories of that time: his nurse, his brother, his toys. 'I shouldn't think of this—it's too painful,' Ivan Ilyich would say to himself, and would again come back to the present. A button on the sofa and wrinkles on the morocco. 'The morocco is expensive, not durable; there was a quarrel because of it. But it was a different kind of morocco and a different kind of quarrel when we tore father's portfolio, and were punished, and mama brought us patties.' And again his thoughts stopped at his childhood. . . ."

Another versatile device is speculative interpretation, a device that consists of the "translation" of a glance, gesture, or remark. This device enables the author to establish a channel of communication between characters on a matter that could not

be discussed openly. For example, when Peter Ivanovich visits
the dead Ivan Ilyich's home, Schwartz's glance informs him that
"this business of the service for the dead for Ivan Ilyich can by
no means be a sufficient reason for declaring the order of the
session disturbed—in other words, nothing can keep us, this
very evening, from opening and snapping a pack of cards.
. . ." Later on, as Peter Ivanovich is accompanying the widow
to the dining room, Schwartz's glance tells him: "There goes
the vint! Don't be mad at us if we find another partner. When
you get away, we may play a five-handed game." As a result
of the information gained in this fashion, Peter Ivanovich, after
leaving the home of the deceased, proceeds directly to Fyodor
Vasilevich's, confident that the card game has not been canceled, and is able "to come in as the fifth." Speculative interpretation can also be used to illustrate a character's frame of
mind, as in this scene between the footman and an Ivan Ilyich
who is disturbed by the fact that he can no longer lead a normal
life and is a nuisance to others:

> "Do you wish to order some tea, sir?"
> *"He has to have things going on as usual; gentlemen should
> drink tea in the morning,"* he [Ivan Ilyich] thought, but he only
> said: "No."
> "Do you wish to go over to the sofa?"
> *"He has to tidy up the room and I'm in his way—I'm filthiness
> and disorder,"* he thought, but he only said: "No, leave me alone."

To dramatize the intensity of a character's emotional state
or mental struggle, Tolstoy uses a variety of devices. There is
the subjective coloration of perception by emotion. Thus, when
Ivan Ilyich leaves the doctor's office with the impression that
something is seriously wrong with him, everything he sees is
colored by his gloomy mood: "Everything in the streets seemed
sad to Ivan Ilyich. The cab drivers were sad, the houses were
sad, the passers-by, the shops were sad." Personification is also
employed to emphasize an emotional state. Terrified by the
thought that his illness is a fatal one, Ivan Ilyich begins to
visualize death as a being that stands before him, that stares

at him, that tries to get him to look straight into its eyes. Particularly effective for highlighting emotion is the dream symbolism introduced toward the end of the story. Through this dream symbolism Tolstoy translates Ivan Ilyich's spiritual dilemma into a terrifying primitive physical impasse. In his drugged state Ivan Ilyich dreams that something has pushed him part way into a "narrow, black, and deep sack" and is trying to make him get into it completely. He is resisting the force and, yet, he would like to get into the sack. The sack represents the even more agonizing state in which Ivan Ilyich believes he will find himself once he renounces the principles by which he has lived; the something pushing him into the sack is the specter of death, which is relentlessly showing him the meaninglessness of his life and forcing him into a renunciation of it; Ivan Ilyich's resistance to getting into the sack stands for his continued justification of the principles by which he has been guided; his desire to get into it represents his feeling that he should renounce these principles. Still another device that Tolstoy uses for dramatic emphasis is the internal dialogue. Thus, instead of merely describing a thought sequence of Ivan Ilyich's, Tolstoy will cast it in the form of a conversation between the hero and his soul. It is through such devices that Tolstoy dramatizes individual moments of Ivan Ilyich's agony.

Of vital importance for "The Death of Ivan Ilyich" is reality-simulation, the use of seemingly irrelevant or else naturalistic detail to give the narrative added credibility. In real life a meeting between two people seldom goes by without the intrusion of some extraneous matter that distracts them, at least briefly, from the business at hand. It is this sort of realistic totality that Tolstoy tries to suggest by inserting the interruptions into the drawing-room scene at the beginning of the story. The widow has led Peter Ivanovich into the drawing room in order to be able to talk with him alone. But before she can begin to discuss what she has in mind, there is the humorous incident in which she catches her mantilla on the table and Peter Ivanovich has his feud with the pouffe springs, the scene with the butler, and her remarks in explanation of her interest in the arrangements for the funeral. Real life, too, is characterized by certain unpleasant physical processes and phenomena, and Tolstoy uses these in moderation to lend realism to his story: Praskovya Fyodorovna blows her nose and has halitosis, a live Ivan Ilyich has bowel movements, and a dead Ivan Ilyich gives off an odor.

On reading "The Death of Ivan Ilyich," one senses that the stylistic texture is both quite similar to and yet quite different from the works that made Tolstoy's reputation, the works written in the reflective mode. Both the similarity and difference are attributable to Tolstoy's purpose. He wanted to show the emotional-mental experiences of his characters, and in pursuing this end he repeatedly used, and as brilliantly as he ever had, those techniques which were particularly suitable for depicting the inner life. Since his characters' *physical* characteristics, behavior patterns, and surroundings were very much a secondary consideration, the expository devices employed for these are less in evidence.

III

You sit in a terrifying darkness slashed by a single shaft of pure white light. The darkness steadily errodes the shaft of light, and it seems that soon you will be overwhelmed by darkness. Then suddenly the shaft explodes and destroys the darkness. This is the effect that *The Power of Darkness* will have on you. Greed, lust, murder, revenge, and infanticide are triumphing and there is no room for decency. Then, unexpectedly, decency comes into its own. The play is a masterpiece of literary brutality and not recommended for those with weak nerves.

The first four acts of *The Power of Darkness* are devoted to a frightening demonstration of the chain reaction of evil, of how evil keeps spawning more evil. As the play opens, the forces of evil are already firmly established. Even though he is seriously ill, the rich peasant Peter lives only for practical gain.

His second wife, Anisya, hates him for his tight-fistedness, is having an affair with the hired man Nikita, and lives only for the day when her husband will die and she will be able to marry her lover. Nikita is interested only in comfort and the gratification of his sexual desires. Into this situation comes Matryona, Nikita's mother, who is dedicated to material things. This combination of greed, hatred, and lust results in murder. Under Matryona's direction, Anisya poisons her husband. It would seem that now, with the disagreeable Peter out of the way, and with Anisya and Nikita married, there should be an end to evil deeds; however, the chain reaction continues. Both Nikita and Akulina, Peter's daughter by his first wife, learn of the murder. Their reaction is an intense hatred of Anisya and they take a sexual revenge against her by having a love affair. This hatred and revenge set the wheels in motion for infanticide. Akulina gives birth to a baby. To avoid a scandal, which would upset their plans for getting rid of Akulina by marrying her off, Anisya and Matryona force a horrified Nikita to kill his own child.

In the course of these first four acts, only one person takes a resolute stand against the forces of evil, and this is Nikita's mild-mannered father, Akim, who represents the best of the godly tradition of Russia. Early in the play he makes a a desperate effort to get Nikita back onto the path of righteousness; he wants him to marry the girl he seduced and then abandoned for Anisya. Arguing his case against the "practical" Matryona, who is adamantly opposed to such a marriage, who has, as a matter of fact, already purchased the powders that will kill Peter, Akim points out that the godless way leads only to grief. But Akim's strictures have no effect on the course of events. Evil appears to be victorious.

The fifth act begins, and the chain reaction seems to be continuing. Akulina is about to be married off under false pretenses and a now remorseful Nikita is contemplating suicide. But then, suddenly, the power of light overcomes the power of darkness. The remarks of his hired hand, Mitrich, provide Nikita with a

formula that will enable him to face life. It is Mitrich's belief
that one should be truthful, without fear of any unpleasant consequences that might ensue. Armed with this principle, Nikita
appears before the guests gathered at the prenuptial celebration
and abjectly confesses and repents. This act frees him from the
power of evil and cuts short any further operation of the chain
reaction that started in the first act.

A fascinating moral problem, a procession of electrifying
horrors, the violent clash of personalities, the intense agony of
Akim and, later, of Nikita—these are the elements of *The
Power of Darkness* that claim the primary attention of an audience. But Tolstoy's sometimes wry and sometimes blistering
comments on matters as diverse as money lending and foundling homes do not go unnoticed. There is the sophisticated
Mitrich's description of interest on capital as a device for
fleecing helpless people; there is this denunciation of the ignorance and superstition that weighs upon the peasant women of
Russia and turns the innocent little Anyutkas into murderous
Matryonas; there is his depiction of foundling homes as simply
convenient disposal facilities for those who have been indiscreet
enough to have an illegitimate child.

Two aspects of the literary mechanics in *The Power of Darkness* are particularly interesting. The first of these is Tolstoy's
skill in keeping those of his characters who are deeply involved
in evil from degenerating into monsters. The author maintains
credibility by showing occasional flashes of basic decency in
them. Thus, Nikita bursts into tears when the dying Peter begs
his forgiveness. At the end of Act III, after his father has up-
braided him for the life he is leading, Nikita lies down to sleep
with the words "Oh, I feel bad, I feel so bad!" Even while
overseeing the murder of the illegitimate child, Matryona cau-
tions Anisya not to forget to baptize it. And then there is that
very wistful remark of Matryona's that proves she is not just an
"Iago in skirts": "I'd like to get along without sinning, but what
are you going to do?"

The other especially interesting aspect of this play from the standpoint of literary mechanics is Tolstoy's demonstration of two very different approaches to the depiction of the infanticide at the end of Act IV, for this crime is also shown in a variant scene. As Scene 1 ends, Matryona and Nikita are in the farmyard at night. She and Anisya, who has just stepped out, have been trying to get a very reluctant Nikita to dig a grave in the cellar for his illegitimate child. In the original Scene 2, Anisya returns and a starkly brutal sequence begins. Anisya berates Nikita for his reluctance, threatens to go to the constable if he doesn't cooperate, and gloats at the prospect of his learning how it feels to be a murderer. After crushing the child to death, Nikita rushes about in a frenzy, threatening Anisya and his mother and imagining that he still hears the child whining. This Scene 2 attempts to depict all the horror of the situation directly; it leaves nothing to the imagination. The action of the variant Scene 2 takes place in the hut. The audience learns of the baby's murder through a very effective combination of indirect exposition, direct exposition, fragmentary presentation, and suspense interludes. Anisya's little daughter Anyutka and Mitrich are alone in the hut. At first the audience experiences the grim events in the farmyard through the reactions of the lovable and innocent Anyutka. She has seen and understood enough of what has been going on to be frightened. Now she hears people going out to the barn, the crying of the baby, and the digging in the cellar. Mitrich tries unsuccessfully to calm her down. Then the audience sees one of the participants in the crime—Anisya is on the stage briefly, looking for a cross with which to baptize the infant. When Anisya leaves, the audience is again given Anyutka's reaction to the situation. After that, as the audience wonders what will really happen in the farmyard—remember, Nikita was balking at the end of Scene 1— Mitrich tells Anyutka a story. Once again Anyutka refers to the events in the farmyard. This is followed by another interlude of suspense, as Mitrich inveighs against the ignorance and superstition that reigns among the peasant women of Russia. Suddenly there is shouting, and a distraught Nikita rushes in with Matryona. From his remarks the audience knows that Nikita has murdered the baby. Nikita rushes out, followed by Matryona, and the audience sees the effect of the revelation on Anyutka:

> ANYUTKA   Grandpa dear, they've strangled it!
> MITRICH (*angrily*)   Go to sleep, I tell you. Oh you, darn you! I'll give it to you with a broom! Go to sleep, I tell you.
> ANYUTKA   Grandpa dear! Someone's grabbing me by the shoulders; someone's grabbing me, grabbing me with his paws. Grandpa dear, so help me God, I'm getting away from here right away. Grandpa dear, let me get up on the oven! For God's sake, let me up! He's grabbing me . . . grabbing me. . . . O-oh! (*Rushes to the oven.*)

The indirect exposition through the reactions of Anyutka underscores the enormity of the events in the farmyard—the audience sees the events through the eyes of innocence; the direct exposition through the abrupt appearances of Anisya and then of Nikita and Matryona give the audience some first-hand contact with the principals in the crime at this climactic point; the exposition through selected fragments and the suspense intervals serve as powerful stimulants to the imagination. All of these factors combine to make this variant a far more superior artistic product than the original, grossly naturalistic scene.

IV

The Fruits of Enlightenment is like that popular toy, the magical piece of plastic that shows one picture when it is tilted toward the viewer and another when it is tilted away from him. The play can be regarded as a rather jolly comedy whose setting is the house of one Leonid Fyodorovich Zvezdintsev, a wealthy aristocrat of the late nineteenth century. There appears to be very little that is disagreeable in the play. Zvezdintsev himself is a rather vague gentleman engrossed in spiritualism. His wife, Anna Pavlovna, is a high-strung woman with a hysterical fear of microbes. They have only two children, both grown up. Vovo, the son, is devoted to such momentous pursuits as dog breeding; Betsy, the daughter, is a normal girl interested in the usual social pastimes. In the Zvezdintsev entourage there are such characters as the doctor, Peter Petrovich, who dances a tongue-in-cheek attendance on Anna Pavlovna; Vovo's friend Petrishchev, a gay devotee of puns and charade entertainments; two pompous "scientists"—the hypnotist Grossmann and Professor Krugosvetlov, who has an allegiance to spiritualism matched only by Zvezdintsev's; and the stout Marya Vasilevna, who has an absolute genius for irrelevancy. None of these people appears to be vicious; all of them are highly amusing. There is also an interesting assortment of town and country peasants. Among these are the gentle Fyodor Ivanych, Zvezdintsev's valet; the effervescent and shrewd Tanya; the lecherous footman Grigori Mikhailych; and three peasants who have come from the country to purchase land from Zvezdintsev and cut a comic figure with their quaint rustic mannerisms. The basic plot is a rather simple one. The three peasants arrive and attempt unsuccessfully to buy some land from Zvezdintsev, but he is advised by the spirits not to sell. While the three peasants wait about, provoking the ire of the antiseptic Anna Pavlovna and exchanging remarks about the masters with their equals, Tanya successfully dupes Zvezdintsev, in the course of a séance, into signing a purchase agreement. The peasants get their land and Tanya becomes engaged to the son of one of them. Not a few people have viewed *The Fruits of Enlightenment* in this fashion. And this is readily understandable, but it is not in accord with Tolstoy's intention. Tolstoy had in mind not a jolly comedy but a blistering indictment of the conditions that were inexorably leading to the cataclysmic events of twentieth century Russia; he was casting in dramatic form some of the principal ideas from his polemical *What Then Must We Do?* And once one tilts the magical piece of plastic in the right direction, one can see the depth of the social criticism.

The Zvezdintsev's, their peers, and their hangers-on are living the life of darkness. For one thing, they are wasting their time, energy, and substance in worthless pursuits—Zvezdintsev and

Professor Krugosvetlov in their blind commitment to spiritualism and Anna Pavlovna in her relentless war on microbes and
her addiction to cards. For another, as the Woman Cook points
out, they are gluttonous: "They've got all those sweet wines,
vodkas, fizzling liquors—a different kind for each course. They
eat and wash it down, eat and wash it down. . . . God bless
us, as soon as they open their eyes, they have to have their
samovar, teas, coffee, chicolate. No sooner have they finished
two samovars than they need a third. And then comes lunch,
then dinner, and then coffee again. They no sooner get up from
the table than they've again got to have tea. And then snacks
are served: candy, jams—and there's no end to it. They even
eat when they're laying in bed." Obsessed by foolish ideas and
preoccupied with the satisfaction of their selfish desires, the
Zvezdintsevs and their like cause suffering to the helpless. The
visiting footmen describe how parents refuse to visit dying children for fear of microbes. We have the testimony of Zvezdintsev's former cook: "I roasted at the stove for thirty years. And
then they didn't need me anymore—so, croak like a dog! You
just wait for them to take pity!" There is the Woman Cook's
story of what happens to girl servants in the Zvezdintsev household when they get into trouble: "And once she's gone astray,
the masters don't want her. They get rid of her right away, and
get a fresh one to take her place. That's what happened to poor
Natalya—she went astray, and right away they threw her out.
She had a baby, got sick, and last spring she died in the hospital.
And what a fine girl she was!" Anna Pavlovna's harassment of
the butler Yakov and her rudeness to the three peasants;
Zvezdintsev's refusal to sell the land to the three peasants,
though he realizes that they need it if they are to survive—these
are further examples of inhumanity that Tolstoy cites. Nor does
the younger generation hold forth any promise. The son squan-
ders money on dogs, prates of the fortunes to be made in growing mint, and insults his social inferiors; the daughter's sole concern is her social life. Their friends are cut of the same cloth.
   In the process of proving his point that the upper classes

were intellectually and morally bankrupt and the source of so much suffering to others, Tolstoy had and took the opportunity to outline some of the admirable qualities of the peasantry, qualities that characterize the way of light. Through his peasant characters he demonstrated the great warmth existing under gruff or taciturn exteriors, the common sense, the persistence, the resourcefulness, and the sense of dignity. Among these people there is found, too, a great love for the land and a scorn for the artifice of the "civilized" life. And all of this is done without any idealization, for all of these peasants have their very definite shortcomings.

Three devices in the play deserve special mention because of their effectiveness. One of these is the "atomizing" device, which consists of the presentation of an object or event through the listing of its component parts. In *The Fruits of Enlightenment* it becomes a fine satirical weapon. For example, the maid Tanya describes her mistress' corset without using the word "corset": "Well, there's this thing made of bone, like a jacket, and it goes up to about here. Well, you pull it in with cords, just like when you spit on your hands and tighten up a harness." Another device is virtually a Tolstoian trademark since he makes such frequent use of it in his pre- and postcrisis works. This is the labeling characteristic, a gesture, word, or expression that a character repeats on successive occasions. Two of the visiting peasants are endowed with such labeling characteristics. The First Peasant loves to use "denifitively"; the Third Peasant keeps repeating the plaintive refrain: "We have little land: there isn't enough room for a chicken, you know, let alone for cattle." In the case of the First Peasant, the device calls attention to his desire to impress other people with his learning. The Third Peasant's refrain, of course, keeps emphasizing the desperate plight of the peasants. Finally, there is the use of association of ideas as a device to depict the rattle-brained personality of Marya Vasilevna. For example, Professor Krugosvetlov's remark about "the loss of vital energy" during an hypnotic trance sets off the following chain of ideas: "You say there's a loss of strength? Well, I wanted to say that when I was travelling by carriage. . . . The roads were terrible then—you wouldn't remember that—but I noticed it. And, say what you will, all our nervousness is caused by the railroads. For example, I can't sleep while travelling—for the life of me, I just can't get to sleep. . . . I'll miss one, two, three nights of sleep, and still won't be able to fall asleep."

P. R.

Evanston, Illinois
September 1965

NOTES

A Glance into the Writer's Laboratory

What is true of so many of Tolstoy's other works is also true of "The Death of Ivan Ilyich," *The Power of Darkness,* and *The Fruits of Enlightenment:* In each case, along with the end product of the creative process, we also possess an exceptionally vivid history of the process itself. The diaries and correspondence of Tolstoy and the memoirs of those close to him yield a great deal of general information about the conception and development of his works. The preserved drafts give the details of the laborious process by which the raw literary material was shaped and reshaped. Pieced together, all of this information provides an unusually intimate view of the artist at work: It opens a window into the writer's laboratory. The following account gives the main outline of the development of these three works—a "glance" into Tolstoy's laboratory.

The creative history of "The Death of Ivan Ilyich" really begins in 1881. Tolstoy had been acquainted with a certain Ivan Ilyich Mechnikov, the Tula prosecutor, and had always held him in very high regard, thinking him to be an exceptionally decent and intelligent person. Mechnikov developed cancer and suffered unspeakable agonies. During his illness he spent long hours discussing the banality and futility of his past life. He died in July 1881. The torments and the reflections of the doomed man made an understandably forceful impression on a Tolstoy, who had become obsessively sensitive about the fact that death was an inevitable mockery of the materialistic values by which he himself had once lived and by which so much of mankind was continuing to live. Here, in the history of Mechnikov's last months on earth, was a rough outline for the dramatic projection of a problem that Tolstoy considered to be so critical. But the gestation period was to be a long one. Several years passed and little progress was made in the actual writing of the story.

A traumatic experience in 1885 provided the stimulus for concentrated work on "The Death of Ivan Ilyich." In that year, the pattern of a man doomed to death by disease was repeated, and this time the impression was even stronger, for the person involved was close to Tolstoy. In January, Tolstoy learned from a doctor that his friend Leonid Urusov was suffering from an incurable disease. Tolstoy's reaction to this news emphasized what was to become one of the basic themes of "The Death of Ivan Ilyich": man's strong irrational desire to ignore the fact of death's inevitability. "God sentenced all of us to death at birth," Tolstoy wrote, "but when a doctor tells us this, it strikes us as something new." Alternating between hope and despair, Urusov lingered another eight months.

This constant reminder of impending death spurred Tolstoy's interest in what he called "a description of the ordinary death of an ordinary man." In August 1885 there began a period of intensive work that lasted into October. Thereafter the pace slackened. The story was finally sent to the printer in January 1886, presumably finished. But when Tolstoy received the proofs, he made so many and such extensive changes that the copy returned to the printer amounted to a new draft. It was the latter part of March of that year before the second set of proofs was corrected and the story was ready for publication.

Since "The Death of Ivan Ilyich" is so simple in structure and mode of narration, consisting as it does of a death plus a flashback described with almost Biblical simplicity, one might very easily underestimate the effort that this story cost its author. But the truth of the matter is that, after a deceptively smooth beginning, the story went through the myriad adjustments and readjustments that frequently characterized the developmental stages of Tolstoy's fiction. Two main lines of development stand out among the many convolutions: one resulting from a search for a suitable general structure, the other from a desire to give individual narrative elements their proper emphasis.

It was Tolstoy the moralist-artist who conceived the initial general plan of "The Death of Ivan Ilyich"; it was Tolstoy the artist-moralist who quickly saw its inadequacies and set about reshaping it. When he started the actual writing, Tolstoy had a very definite didactic purpose in mind: He wanted to warn the Ivan Ilyichs of Russia against their self-centered, self-seeking way of life. This purpose determined the general structure of the story in its initial developmental stage. The warning was to be sounded through a dying man's observations about the truth in life, and a diary seemed the ideal framework: The remarks could be of a highly intimate nature and they could range a variety of topics without any need for artificial transitional devices. Some sort of prefatory explanation would, of course, be desirable, and this was to consist of a short introductory section narrated by Mikhail Semyonovich (the future Peter Ivanovich).

At first this general plan seemed satisfactory, and the writing of the introductory section proceeded without any apparent difficulties. Mikhail Semyonovich informs the reader that he learned of Ivan Ilyich's death at the courthouse, that he paid a visit to the home of the deceased, and that the widow gave him the dead man's diary. With the introduction out of the way, Tolstoy began the first entry of the diary, the main section. In it the dying Ivan Ilyich reveals his "horrible, unbearable spiritual suffering." It is the consciousness of the falsehood in life that torments Ivan: "Everything about me is a lie. My wife is a lie, my children are a lie, and I myself am a lie." But Ivan still aspires toward the truth. And while he yet has the strength, he will try, for his own benefit and that of others, to describe the truth in his diary.

But before he finished this first entry, Tolstoy began to have second thoughts about the main section. His intent was to sound a warning to a sophisticated audience. But had he chosen an effective means for achieving this end? Obviously the readers he wanted to reach would dismiss the diary as a thinly disguised sermon. The project was in danger of becoming self-defeating.

It was at this point that Tolstoy the artist-moralist took firm control and began to alter the main section. He introduced a story element into it. In the final remark of the first diary entry, Ivan Ilyich informs the reader that he will first give a description of "how all this happened" to him. Now the plan appeared to be moving in the direction of a pattern that Tolstoy had used successfully in "Lucerne" many years before: A character describes his experiences and follows them with an explicative commentary. But as the newly introduced story element took more definite shape in his imagination, Tolstoy began to realize its potentiality. This story element could, all by itself and without a trace of sermonizing, convey his message with extreme effectiveness. There would first be a review of Ivan Ilyich's life from his law school days to the beginning of his illness. During this period of his life Ivan Ilyich would be a very obvious middle-class Everyman mirroring the practical values and conventional behavior patterns of the reader. There would, however, be no effort to probe the fundamental issues. A narrative tone of good-natured, mildly mocking humor would merely flit superficially over the surface. The reader would readily admit that this was a witty and agreeable treatment of the sort of life he himself led. And then the hellish nightmare of Ivan Ilyich's illness would begin, and, before it was over, the life which the reader had identified with his own would be thoroughly exposed as a horrible sham.

When Tolstoy decided to use this narrative as the main section (and this happened only after an alternative had been considered and discarded), he was forced to drop Ivan Ilyich's diary as an expository device: It would hardly be in character for the dying hero to adopt and maintain an urbanely tolerant attitude toward his earlier life when he knew how terribly wrong it had been. As a result, the narrator of the introductory part, Mikhail Semyonovich, also became the narrator of the main section. Tolstoy now has Mikhail inform his readers that he read Ivan Ilyich's diary, was horrified by it, collected additional information about his friend, and is now presenting the biographical account that he compiled. But then Tolstoy visualized a dramatic ending in which Ivan Ilyich, no longer able to communicate with the world about him, finally arrives at a resolution of his problem. Obviously an omniscient narrator was now necessary for the main section. For the sake of consistency, the same mode of narration had to be used in the introduction, and all references to Ivan Ilyich's now superfluous diary had to be eliminated.

One main aspect of the work on "The Death of Ivan Ilyich" was, then, a series of changes in the general narrative structure. Frequently proceeding simultaneously with it, and often directly provoked by it, was the other main activity: a gradual, intensive refinement of the component narrative elements. And this refinement consisted of two opposing movements: exclusion and addition.

On the one hand, there was a ruthlessly thorough exclusion of material that, while interesting in itself, would have proved both superfluous and distractive as far as the principal narrative line was concerned. For example, in the first draft of the story, Ivan Ilyich, after being passed over for promotion, obtains a position that involves him in a complex of almost Job-like misfortunes; also, a forced and embarrassing stay with unsympathetic relatives is developed at considerable length. The first sequence does not appear in the final draft; the second does, but it is scaled down drastically. Had these changes not been made, the narrative center of gravity in the third section would have been shifted: The image of a man efficiently overcoming

all obstacles in pursuit of his ends would have been badly marred
had there been any intimation that Ivan Ilyich was, at this point,
capable of floundering about under the pressure of circumstances.

On the other hand, the process of refinement consisted of a
progressive saturation with detail designed to heighten the intensity of various scenes and to reinforce lines of narrative
exposition. Many of the elements that contribute significantly
to the effectiveness of the final version are either completely
absent from the first draft or else appear there in rudimentary
form. The references to the odor of putrefaction in the death
chamber and the pathetic figure of Ivan Ilyich's son waiting for
the service to begin—deft touches used to recreate the atmos-
phere of death—were later additions. So was the touch of humorous byplay with the recalcitrant pouffe during Peter Ivanovich's visit to the widow, an element that plays a vital role in
simulating a "realistic totality." Nor does the first draft contain
that initial tantalizing hint in Part I—the "rebuke or reminder
to the living" in the face of the dead judge. Ivan Ilyich's
desire always to belong to the best social circle, his enjoy-
ment of power over people, his impersonal attitude toward
others in the performance of his duties, and his use of work as
an escape from the unpleasantness of the domestic situation are
facets of his behavior that existed in the first version but were
built up in significance only over the course of subsequent revisions.

Like "The Death of Ivan Ilyich," *The Power of Darkness*
originated in an incident that actually occurred; however, in the
first case, Tolstoy, starting with the account of Mechnikov's
illness and death, had both to create a suitable general structure
and to develop it in detail, while in the second, a considerable
amount of this work was done for him by a murder trial of
1880. "I took the plot," Tolstoy said, "almost in its entirety
from an actual criminal case tried in the Tula District Court.
The details of this case were given to me by my close friend

Davydov, the then prosecuting attorney and now presiding judge of the Court. . . ."

The case Tolstoy was referring to was that of Efrem Koloskov and his wife. Efrem was an intemperate peasant; his wife, Martha, had been a widow and had a sixteen-year-old daughter, Elena, by her first husband. The trouble started as a result of Efrem's more than stepfatherly interest in Elena: he pressed his attentions on her without any success, and then finally raped her. This was followed by what might best be described as a period of successive rapes, and in November 1879 Elena gave birth to a child. Acting on Efrem's orders, the wife took the baby to the cellar, where Efrem was to kill it. But the murder was much easier in the planning than in the execution. Efrem went through much hesitation and anguish before he finally placed a board over the infant and crushed it. The baby did not die at once, and a distraught Efrem could hear its crying for hours afterward. He finally buried it in the back yard. Two months passed. A husband had been found for Elena and the wedding date had been set. But on the wedding day, Efrem hid in the barn and refused to bless the couple before the departure for church. When he was finally persuaded to leave the barn, he fell on his knees and made a public confession. Both Efrem and his wife were arrested, tried, and sentenced to penal servitude.

Tolstoy was fascinated by the Koloskov case, so much so that he visited the unfortunate Efrem on two occasions; however, the dramatic raw material provided by the trial in October 1880 lay dormant until 1886. In August of that year Mikhail Lentovsky, the director of the Skomorokh Theater in Moscow, approached Tolstoy with a plea for support. Since the Skomorokh was part of the "popular theater" movement, dedicated to bringing drama to the common people at prices within their means, Tolstoy responded with the promise of a play. But concentrated work on the play did not begin until October.

The choice of the Koloskov case as the basis for a play at

this time was a very natural one for Tolstoy to make. This material could be readily shaped to serve two important purposes: first, to provide the "popular theater" audiences with a dramatic moral lesson, and second, to give a stinging rebuttal to the official pap that purported to show the enlightenment prevailing in rural Russia on the twenty-fifth anniversary of the abolition of serfdom.

By the latter half of November, after the various acts had gone through six to eight revisions, Tolstoy considered the play finished. But a complication arose and it led to further work in December. There had been adverse reactions from literary and theatrical people who had seen the play and thought the fourth act too horrific for the stage. Remarking that he wished to spare "their delicate nerves," Tolstoy wrote an alternate ending for the fourth act, and this, in turn, forced significant changes in the fifth act.

When he started to write *The Power of Darkness,* Tolstoy was already over one major hurdle: The Koloskov tragedy had provided him with a serviceable preliminary sketch of plot and characters. Nevertheless, a great deal of work remained before him. To make the illicit romance of Nikita and Anisya credible, their ages were lowered drastically below those of their real-life counterparts. To make Nikita's public confession more convincing, he was depicted as an unstable but basically good man —a far cry from his blackguard prototype. The theme that evil spawns more evil had to be reinforced, and this was accomplished by introducing the poisoning of the first husband. There was a need for a running commentary at certain critical points in the play, and so Akim and Mitrich, patterned after peasants Tolstoy had known, were created. This work on the play, involving as it did the concentrated utilization of both his imaginative and critical powers, was arduous, but it was something that Tolstoy was well used to and did not present any problems out of the ordinary. In two other respects, dramatic technique and peasant speech, Tolstoy did, however, face special problems.

As Tolstoy pointed out, when he first began work on *The*

Power of Darkness, he employed the techniques that were second nature to him—those of a novelist. But shortly he perceived the essential difference between a novel and a play. In writing the latter, one could not set one's characters to thinking aloud nor could one rely on reminiscences for a revelation of their personalities—this would be both dull and unrealistic; instead, one had to depend upon crystallized emotions and thoughts. If the work of a novelist or short story writer could be compared to that of a painter, then the dramatist's task was like that of a sculptor. It was sculptured personalities in mutual collision that the theater demanded. Tolstoy confessed that he had not been entirely successful in restraining the novelist in himself, that he had "pasted a few monologues into *The Power of Darkness,*" although even as he was doing this he realized that it was the wrong thing. "It's difficult for an old novelist to refrain from this," he commented wryly, "just as it's difficult for a coachman to hold his horses back when they're coming down a mountain and a heavy coach is pushing them forward."

In working on the play, Tolstoy also had the special problem of sustaining the vivid peasant speech of his characters through five acts. The danger of dealing with this idiom on an extended scale was that one could only too easily lapse into an artificial quaintness. Fortunately, Tolstoy had long been interested in the characteristic features of peasant speech—its colorful words, expressions, and proverbs. He had combed through lexical and literary sources, he had listened attentively to the common folk, and everything distinctive had been jotted down. A great deal of this material was now absorbed by the play: "I plundered my notebooks in order to write *The Power of Darkness,*" he remarked on one occasion. As he worked on the revisions, he kept changing the language until it was completely saturated with the peasant idiom. It was hard work, but well worth it: In its genuine ring, vividness, and almost lyrical quality, the language has been compared favorably with that of the great dramatist Ostrovsky.

The Fruits of Enlightenment can also be traced to an incident from real life. Here, however, the incident provided neither the core idea, as in the case of "The Death of Ivan Ilyich," nor a fairly detailed preliminary sketch, as in the case of *The Power of Darkness;* it merely served as a triggering device for Tolstoy's imagination. This is the way in which the core idea for *The Fruits of Enlightenment* came into being: Tolstoy had long considered spiritualism to be a superstition of the educated class; he had, in fact, already expressed his strong opinion on this subject in fiction—(in *Anna Karenina* he had Levin inform Countess Nordston that spiritualism shows "the so-called educated class" to be no more advanced than the peasants with their superstitions). Sometime in the first half of the 1880s, a scornful Tolstoy and his friend Davydov—the one who had told him about the Koloskov case—went to a séance at the home of Prince Nikolai Lvov. The séance was unsuccessful and the next day Tolstoy remarked to Davydov that spiritualism was either a form of self-deception to which both the medium and the séance participants subjected themselves or simply a fraud perpetrated by professionals. Applying these two elements, self-deception *and* fraud, to the séance he had witnessed (in the preliminary sketches of the play, Lvov and his guest Samarin, the later Zvezdintsev and Sakhatov, are still called by their own names), Tolstoy conceived the core idea for a satirical comedy.

The actual writing of *The Fruits of Enlightenment* turned into a protracted and frustrating experience. In November 1886 Tolstoy wrote the first act and part of the second, and then he laid the play aside. Work on it was not resumed until the latter part of March 1889. In a brief spurt of determination lasting into April, Tolstoy revised what he had done earlier and "finished" the play. For several months after that, there were half-hearted efforts to return to the play, but little was accomplished. The last stage of the writing began in December of that year. He agreed to let his daughter Tatyana put on an amateur performance of the play, and when the rehearsals began, he became deeply involved in the work of revision. After almost every rehearsal he would introduce further changes: Certain roles were extended and even ad libs were incorporated. The performance took place on December 30, but the momentum of revision continued beyond that date. Work on the play was not completed until April 1890. By this point, *The Fruits of Enlightenment* had gone through the equivalent of some eight drafts. An interesting aspect of the play's creative history is the fact that Tolstoy was so disgruntled with the results he was obtaining. "Very bad" and "trash" were among the derisive comments he made about the comedy at different stages of its development.

Tolstoy's negative attitude toward the play while he was working on it was in large measure attributable to the compositional difficulties its dual purpose presented. Not only did he want to ridicule out of all countenance the preoccupation of the well-to-do with false ideas, he also wanted to show how these people, in ordering their lives according to such false ideas, caused others, especially the common people, to suffer. But the problem was that the second theme was blunted by the first: The greater part of the play was devoted to the follies of the Zvezdintsevs—the father's obsession with spiritualism, the mother's hysteria about germs, the son's interest in borzois, and the daughter's involvement in the forthcoming charade entertainment. The material indicating the family's moral irresponsibility in dealing with its servants and the delegation of three country peasants was quantitatively modest and tended to be obscured. Then too, the idea of the insulted and injured peasant class was further canceled out by the crafty footman Grigori and that clever manipulator, the maid, Tanya. Both of these characters were more than equal matches for the Zvezdintsevs. Could one seriously believe that the latter were capable of hurting any peasant who had all his wits about him? Furthermore, the speech andd behavior of the visiting country peasants, who were supposed to evoke pity, were so very much out of place in the sophisticated town house that the trio could easily be played as comic characters. Fearing that his second theme—the pernicious effect of the Zvezdintsevs of Russia—would be obscured, Tolstoy devoted a great deal of effort to bolstering it at various stages of the writing. For example, he made Anna Pavlovna's behavior toward the three peasants and the servants significantly more insulting; he converted a single remark of the Third Peasant into the famous plaintive refrain about the straitened circumstances of the common man; he introduced those two unfortunate victims of the Zvezdintsevs, Yakov the butler and the Old Cook, and also that comical victim, the Coachman; and he also added the footmen's discussion of the callous behavior of germfearing aristocrats toward their dying children. Such changes were made in order to throw into greater relief the misery caused by the Zvezdintsevs and their like, who persisted in living according to modish "enlightened" ideas.

It would, of course, be foolhardy for anyone to attempt a definition of Tolstoy's creative methodology on the basis of these or any other works, for the truth of the matter is that there were as many Tolstoian methodologies as Tolstoian works. In reality, each work by Tolstoy had its own distinctive "compositional personality." But four important general aspects of Tolstoy's genius can be observed even in this cursory survey of the creative history of "The Death of Ivan Ilyich," *The Power of Darkness,* and *The Fruits of Enlightenment:* (1) he had the ability to sense the thematic and dramatic potential of material that he found in the life about him; (2) he had a fantastically prolific imagination and an acute critical sense, both operating in perfect balance; (3) he had the faculty of visualizing each element of a story or play in terms of its immediate effectiveness and in terms of the thematic and structural totality of the work; and (4) he had the gift of infinite patience.

The Ordeal of Two Plays

Equally as interesting as the creative history of many of Tolstoy's works is the reception that they found, and both *The Power of Darkness* and *The Fruits of Enlightenment* are good cases in point. Some of the attention directed at the two plays was sensible, but some was not. The ordeal that they endured at the hands of pettifogging officials, carping critics, and inadequate or doctrinaire directors and actors would have spelled oblivion for lesser works.

By the end of 1886, *The Power of Darkness* was well on its way to publication and staging: the proofs had been corrected and preliminary arrangements were in progress for its production at the Aleksandrinsky Theater in St. Petersburg. Then the censor struck! Both the publication and performance of the play were forbidden. As a friend informed Tolstoy, the deletions during the censor's review were so heavy that the "original fourth act was completely castrated." In an effort to popularize the play and thus to pressure the censor into lifting the ban, Tolstoy's acquaintance Stakhovich began to give readings of it before influential court groups in January 1887. Within a month, permission was granted for the publication of the play and for its staging at the Aleksandrinsky. Furthermore, the Czar (Alexander III), who had sat in on one of Stakhovich's readings, had pronounced the play to be "a wonderful thing" and had expressed the desire to attend the dress rehearsal.

To all outward appearances, events then proceeded smoothly. The play was published in the early part of February and was soon being read throughout Russia. At the Aleksandrinsky, rehearsals were in full swing and the costumes and scenery were being readied. But a secret move to reinstate the ban was developing. The chief of the Central Board for Publications, one Eugene Feoktistov, wrote to Eugene Pobedonostsev, the powerful head of the Holy Synod, informing him that the Czar had given permission for the play's performance in the Imperial theaters. Feoktistov expressed his dissatisfaction with this turn of events and sent along a copy of the play. On reading *The Power of Darkness,* Pobedonostsev lost no time in letting the Czar know of his revulsion: "I have just read L. Tolstoy's new play and I can't recover from the horror. And I'm told that it's supposedly being readied for presentation in the Imperial theaters and that the parts are already being learned. I don't know whether your Highness knows about this play. I don't know of anything like it in any literature." Pobedonostsev's style flared into rhetoric: "The writer's artistry is remarkable, but what an abasement of that artistry! What a lack of—even worse than that—what a negation of an ideal; what a debasement of the moral sense; what an insult to good taste! My God, what have we lived to see in the realm of art! The day on which Tolstoy's play is presented in the Imperial theaters will be the day of the final degeneration of our stage. . . ."

"The day of the final degeneration of our stage" was postponed. The Czar capitulated, and in March 1887 his minister of internal affairs issued a court order forbidding "the sale in streets, squares, and other public places, and also by peddlers, of a pamphlet called *The Power of Darkness, or When the Claw Is Caught, the Whole Bird Is Lost,* a play by Count L. N. Tolstoy." The performance at the Aleksandrinsky Theater was "indefinitely postponed." It was to be 1895 before the ban was lifted, and even then certain harassing limitations were imposed on the play. By the time its public performance was permitted in Russia (there was a restricted amateur performance in 1890), *The Power of Darkness* was already familiar to theatergoers in most European capitals.

Critical reaction to the play both before and after it appeared on the stage tended to be polarized. Such writers as Garshin, Goncharov, Chekhov, and Gorky thought it was very effective drama. In theatrical circles it generally received an exceedingly positive reception: Nemirovich-Danchenko, for example, was never to forget how overwhelmed he and his colleagues were when they first read *The Power of Darkness*. There were those, though, who had little or no use for the play and made a determined effort to popularize their views. Influential leaders in the "popular theater" movement considered it too didactic and grim for the common people. Reviewers characterized it as disgusting, as an outrageous slander against the Russian people, as a specimen of banality, as something that appealed primarily to the trashy element of the population. The negative voices made the loudest noise, but the audiences paid little heed to them. Whenever the play was competently produced, audience response was enthusiastic, sometimes tumultuously so; and at the Skomorokh Theater, catering to the common people, the spectators frequently became so involved with the events on the stage that they shouted out their advice, praise, and disapproval to the characters.

Not only did *The Power of Darkness* survive a gauntlet of antagonistic censors and critics it also rode out two other hazards. One of these was inadequate acting; the other, doctrinaire interpretation.

In the latter part of 1895, the play was running at the Maly and Aleksandrinsky theaters in St. Petersburg, and at the Korsh, Maly, and Skomorokh theaters in Moscow. In all but the Korsh production, first-rate actors were employed; however, the constant complaint was that, except in the case of the Skomorokh, most of the actors gave competent but superficial portrayals. It appears that the actors and their directors simply knew too little of the speech, mannerisms, and general behavior of Tula peasants. This problem continued to dog subsequent productions. For example, in his 1902 Moscow Art Theater presentation, Stanislavsky tried to avoid this defect through an in-depth study of the play's locale and by bringing two Tula peasants to the theater as models for the actors; but the same problem persisted: Most of the actors were not able to do full justice to Tolstoy's peasants. To this day, *The Power of Darkness* remains a play in search of a troupe capable of an over-all excellence in performing it.

The other hazard that *The Power of Darkness* has encountered on the stage is doctrinaire interpretation. In the period up to the Revolution, the play was put on as a moral drama, an ethnographic drama, a crime drama, and a psychological drama. There was even a mystical-symbolist treatment: from 1910 until after the Revolution, Gaiderburov's Traveling Theater staged it as a struggle of the human spirit against the forces of darkness prevailing among men. In the Soviet period, the play has generally been interpreted primarily as a dramatic social document of patriarchal village life in the pre-Revolutionary era. Heavy emphasis is placed on those scenes depicting the widespread stultifying ignorance, the evils flowing from the pursuit of money and property, and the native wisdom of Akim and Mitrich; there is a de-emphasis of the moral and, frequently, of the psychological struggle. Not only is *The Power of Darkness* a play in search of a troupe, it is also a play in search of a balanced interpretation, one that would bring out its full potential as a moral-psychological-symbolic-ethnographic-crime-and-social drama.

Like its predecessor, *The Fruits of Enlightenment* also had its bout with censorship, but only as far as stage presentation was concerned (it was published in November 1890 without much ado). At first, permission was granted for limited presentation. There were complaints from highly placed individuals that Tolstoy was ridiculing the nobility in the comedy, and, as a result, the Central Board for Publications banned *The Fruits of Enlightenment* from all stages. Primarily because he felt that the prohibition artificially made the play seem more significant than it really was, the minister of foreign affairs, Durnovo, recommended to the Czar that the ban be rescinded. The Czar, however, concluded that the play was inappropriate for the theater and permitted only amateur performances. In February 1891, Stanislavsky directed a successful "amateur" production of the play, and this spurred a determined campaign by a group of St. Petersburg actors to have it approved for presentation in the Imperial theaters. Approval was granted in September of that year, and in subsequent years other types of theaters were allowed to produce the play.

But the treatment that *The Fruits of Enlightenment* received at the hands of officialdom was mild compared to that which it was accorded by many reviewers. There were those who thought the play an effective exposé of the Zvezdintsevs of Russia, but their voices were virtually drowned out by the vitriolic outpouring of those who considered it an abomination.

It was characterized as something that did not deserve serious attention, as something that was better suited for the amateur than the serious theater, as something that violated all the fundamental norms of comedy; it was called "a satire without any sting, a comedy without any comic quality, an observation without a conclusion." It was reproached for having no clearly defined central idea, was attacked by some simply because it put the common man in a more favorable light than his betters, and there was also the criticism that Tolstoy, carried away by the point he was trying to make, had lost all sense of proportion and had turned his characters into caricatures bearing no resemblance to real people. There were also charges that Tolstoy was demonstrating a deep hostility to science.

The Fruits of Enlightenment and its author even earned the distinction of a "dramatic rebuttal." In 1894 a play called *The Flowers of Enlightenment,* written by one V. M. Sikevich, began its run in Moscow. A rather tasteless parody, it had as its characters thinly disguised caricatures of Tolstoy, his wife, and their daughter Mary, as well as counterparts of Tanya, Fyodor Ivanych, Grigori, and the Woman Cook from *The Fruits of Enlightenment*. The character representing Tolstoy was depicted as stupid, hypocritical, and a crashing bore. He wandered about the stage, mouthing garbled versions of Tolstoy's ethical ideas, exhorting the household to follow his moral strictures, and making passes at the maid on the sly. For a while, this "antidote" to *The Fruits of Enlightenment* enjoyed a measure of notoriety; some theatrical companies even included both plays in their repertoire.

Soviet critics have generally held the play in high estimation, considering it a forceful documentation of the class disparities and conflicts existing in nineteenth-century Russia. On occasion, though, revivals have brought forth negative reviews characterizing the play as a dated, trite, and oversimplified sermon without much claim to serious attention.

During its stage history, *The Fruits of Enlightenment* has suffered at the hands of actors and directors who have mismanaged certain roles. Some companies turned the Zvezdintsevs, their friends, or both into farcical characters; other groups presented Zvezdintsev and his wife as rather decent fools. In both cases, Tolstoy's intent was negated. It is difficult for an audience to condemn caricatures or sympathetically drawn fools for the mischief they create. There has also been a problem with the roles of the three peasants. They have sometimes been played as comic characters and even as comic swindlers. One notorious case of a "comic-rogue" interpretation occurred in the Moscow Maly Theater production of 1891, and it drew a sharp reaction from Tolstoy. The actors playing the three peasants pulled out all the comic stops and the audience reacted with roars of laughter. A highly annoyed Tolstoy accused the actors of caricaturing the parts. He pointed out that the speeches of the peasants reflect a sorrowful complaint and, sometimes, even an attempt at a protest, that their words are supposed to evoke sympathy for their desperate predicament and not, under any circumstances, laughter. In writing the play, he had been on the side of the peasants, he stated, and here on the Maly stage they had been converted into scoundrels rivaling Grossmann. As one might expect, the tendency to play the Zvezdintsevs and their friends as harmless fools and the three peasants as buffoons was most common in the pre-Revolutionary era; the tendency to use caricature for the Zvezdintsev circle has appeared most frequently in Soviet productions.

"The truth will come into its own, and sooner or later all people will recognize it," Tolstoy once wrote. This statement could serve as an apt commentary on the various hazards that *The Power of Darkness* and *The Fruits of Enlightenment* have encountered over the years.

THE DEATH OF IVAN ILYICH

I

In the large courthouse, during a pause in the case of the Melvinskys, the judges and the prosecuting attorney met in the study of Ivan Egorovich Shebek and got into a conversation about the famous Krasovsky case. Fyodor Vasilevich grew excited, proving that it was not subject to their jurisdiction, while Ivan Egorovich stuck to his opinion. Peter Ivanovich, not having entered the discussion at the start, was not taking any part in it, but was looking through the *Gazette,* which had just come in.

"Gentlemen!" he said. "Ivan Ilyich is dead."

"Really?"

"Here, read it," he said to Fyodor Vasilevich, handing him the fresh paper, which still smelled of printer's ink.

Within a black border was the following announcement: "Praskovya Fyodorovna Golovin with deep sorrow informs relatives and acquaintances of the death of her beloved husband, Ivan Ilyich Golovin, a member of the Appelate Court, on February 4th of this year, 1882. The funeral will be on Friday at one P.M."

Ivan Ilyich was an associate of the gentlemen present and they all liked him. He had been ill for several weeks; it was said that his disease was incurable. His position had been left open for him, but it had been thought that in case of his death Alekseev might be appointed in his place and that either Vinnikov or Shtabel might get Alekseev's place. So, on hearing of Ivan Ilyich's death, the first thought of every one of the gentlemen present in the study was of the significance which this death might have for transfers or promotions of the judges themselves or of their acquaintances.

"Now I'll probably get Shtabel's place or Vinnikov's," thought Fyodor Vasilevich. I was promised that long ago, and this promotion will mean an eight hundred ruble raise for me, in addition to the expense account."

"Now I'll have to petition for my brother-in-law's transfer from Kaluga," thought Peter Ivanovich. "The wife will be very glad. Now she'll no longer be able to say that I'm not doing anything for her relatives."

"I never did think that he'd get out of bed again," said Peter Ivanovich aloud. "It's a shame."

"But what was really the matter with him?"

"The doctors couldn't diagnose it. That is, they did, but each of them differently. When I saw him the last time, I thought he was getting better."

"And here I hadn't called on him since the holidays. I was meaning to all the time."

"Well, did he have any property?"

"I think his wife has a little something, but nothing much."

"Yes, I'll have to go there. But they live terribly far away."

"From your house, you mean. From your house everything is far away."

"You see, he can't forgive me for living across the river," Peter Ivanovich said, smiling at Shebek. And they began to talk about the long distances between the various parts of the city, and went back to the court session.

In addition to the reflections evoked in everyone by this death, reflections about the transfers and possible changes in the service likely to result, the very fact of the death of a close acquaintance aroused in everyone who learned of it, as it always does, a feeling of joy that it was "he" who had died and not "I." "Just think, he died, but, see, I didn't," everyone thought or felt. In addition, close acquaintances, Ivan Ilyich's so-called friends, couldn't help but remember that now they would have to perform some very tedious social duties and go to the funeral service and call on the widow to express their condolences.

The closest of all to him were Fyodor Vasilevich and Peter Ivanovich.

Peter Ivanovich had been his classmate in law school and considered himself under obligation to Ivan Ilyich.

At dinner Peter Ivanovich gave his wife the news of Ivan Ilyich's death and his views about the possibility of transferring the brother-in-law to their circuit, and then, without lying down to rest, he put on his dress coat and drove to Ivan Ilyich's.

At the entrance to Ivan Ilyich's apartment stood a carriage and two cabs. Downstairs, in the hall, a tinselled coffin-lid with tassels and burnished galloons leaned against the wall, near the coat-rack. Two ladies in black were taking off their fur coats. He knew one of them, Ivan Ilyich's sister; the other was a stranger to him. Peter Ivanovich's friend Schwartz was coming downstairs, and, catching sight of the newcomer from an upper step, he stopped and winked to him, as if to say: "Ivan Ilyich has managed things stupidly; you and I do things better."

Schwartz's face with its English side-whiskers and his whole lean figure in the dress coat had, as always, an elegant solemnity about them, and this solemnity, which always contradicted Schwartz's playful character, was particularly piquant at this point. This was what occurred to Peter Ivanovich.

Peter Ivanovich let the ladies precede him, and slowly followed them up the staircase. Schwartz did not start down again, but remained upstairs. Peter Ivanovich knew why—he evidently wanted to settle with him where they would play vint[1] that day. The ladies went on up the stairs to see the widow, and Schwartz, with seriously compressed, firm lips and a playful glance, used a

---

[1] A card game.

motion of his brows to direct Peter Ivanovich to the right, to the room where the body lay.

Peter Ivanovich entered, as is always the case, perplexed as to what he would have to do there. One thing he knew—that under such circumstances it never did any harm to cross oneself. But he wasn't quite sure whether he should also make an obeisance at the same time, and so he chose a middle course—on entering the room, he began to cross himself and made a motion that somewhat resembled a bow. At the same time, as much as the motion of his hands and of his head permitted, he surveyed the room. Two young men, one of them a high school student—he thought they were nephews—were leaving the room, crossing themselves. An old woman stood motionless and a lady with strangely arched eyebrows was telling her something in a whisper. A church assistant in a Prince Albert, a brisk, determined man, was loudly reading something with an expression which precluded any contradiction; Gerasim, the peasant who served as a butler's helper, passed in front of Peter Ivanovich with light steps, strewing something on the floor. When he saw this, Peter Ivanovich at once became aware of the faint odor of the decaying corpse. During his last visit to Ivan Ilyich, Peter Ivanovich had seen this peasant in the study; he had been performing the duties of a nurse, and Ivan Ilyich had been particularly fond of him. Peter Ivanovich kept crossing himself and bowing slightly in a direction intermediate between the coffin, the church assistant, and the icons on the table in the corner. Afterward, when this motion of making the sign of the cross with his hand appeared to him to have gone on too long, he stopped and began to examine the corpse.

The dead man was lying, as dead men always lie, quite heavily, in corpse-like fashion sinking his stiff limbs into the cushions of the coffin, with his eternally bent head on the pillow; he thrust forward, as dead men always do, his yellow, waxen forehead with bald patches on the sunken temples and a protruding nose which seemed to be pressing against the upper lip. He was very much changed and thinner than when

Peter Ivanovich had seen him the last time, but, as is the case with all dead men, his face was more handsome and, above all, more impressive than it had been when he was alive. On his face there was an expression which said that what was necessary to do had been done, and done properly. Besides, in this expression there was also a rebuke or reminder to the living. This reminder seemed out of place to Peter Ivanovich, or, at least, to have no reference to him. He felt ill at ease, and so he hurriedly crossed himself again and, as it appeared to him, too precipitously and out of keeping with propriety, turned around and walked to the door.

Schwartz was waiting for him in the next room, standing with his legs wide apart and with both his hands playing behind his back with his top hat. One glance at Schwartz's playful, natty, and elegant figure refreshed Peter Ivanovich. Peter Ivanovich understood that he, Schwartz, was above such things and did not surrender to depressing impressions. His very glance said: "This business of the service for the dead for Ivan Ilyich can by no means be a sufficient reason for declaring the order of the session disturbed—in other words, nothing can keep us, this very evening, from opening and snapping a pack of cards, while the footman puts four fresh candles on the table. There is altogether no reason for supposing that this business could keep us from passing this evening in an agreeable fashion." Indeed, he said so in a whisper as Peter Ivanovich passed by, proposing that they meet for the game at the house of Fyodor Vasilevich. But apparently it was not Peter Ivanovich's fate to have a game of vint that evening. Praskovya Fyodorovna, a short, fat woman, who, in spite of all efforts to the contrary, had nevertheless been expanding from the shoulders downwards, dressed all in black, with her head covered with lace, and with the same strangely arched eyebrows as those of the lady who was standing in front of the coffin, came out of her quarters with some other ladies and, taking them to the door of the room where the dead man lay, said: "The service will begin shortly. Please go in."

Schwartz made an indefinite bow and stopped, evidently neither accepting nor declining the offer. When Praskovya Fyodorovna recognized Peter Ivanovich, she sighed, went up close to him, took his hand, and said: "I know that you were a true friend of Ivan Ilyich's." And she looked at him, expecting an appropriate response to these words. Peter Ivanovich knew that, just as it was necessary to cross himself there, so here it was necessary to press her hand, to sigh, and to say: "Believe me!" And he did this. And having done it, he felt that the desired result was achieved—both he and she were touched.

"Let's go, since the service hasn't begun. I have to talk with you," said the widow. "Give me your arm."

Peter Ivanovich gave her his arm, and they went off to the inner rooms, past Schwartz, who gave Peter Ivanovich a sad wink. "There goes the vint! Don't be mad at us if we find another partner. When you get away, we may play a five-handed game," said his playful glance.

Peter Ivanovich sighed still more deeply and more sadly, and Praskovya Fyodorovna pressed his hand gratefully. Entering her drawing room, which was done in pink cretonne and was illuminated by a dim lamp, they sat down at the table—she on a sofa and Peter Ivanovich on a low pouffe with bad springs and an unevenly yielding seat. Praskovya Fyodorovna wanted to warn him to take another seat, but found such a warning out of keeping with her present condition, and changed her mind. Seating himself on this pouffe, Peter Ivanovich recalled how Ivan Ilyich had decorated this drawing room and had consulted him in regard to this very same pink cretonne with its green leaves.

As the widow had passed by the table on her way to the sofa (the room was altogether too full of knick-knacks and furniture), the black lace of her black mantilla had caught on the carving of the table. Peter Ivanovich had raised himself in order to disentagle it, and the liberated pouffe had begun to vibrate under him and to push him. The widow had begun to free the lace herself, and Peter Ivanovich had sat down again, suppressing the rebellious pouffe. But the widow hadn't freed the lace entirely, and Peter Ivanovich had raised himself again, and again the pouffe had rebelled and even clicked. When all this had ended, she had taken out her clean cambric handkerchief and had begun to cry. But the episode with the lace and the struggle with the pouffe had taken the spirit out of Peter Ivanovich, and he sat scowling.

This awkward situation was interrupted by Sokolov, Ivan Ilyich's butler, who came to report that the plot in the cemetery which Praskovya Fyodorovna had chosen would cost two hundred rubles. She stopped crying and, giving Peter Ivanovich a martyred look, said in French that it was very hard for her. Peter Ivanovich made a silent sign which expressed the firm belief that it could not be otherwise.

"Go ahead and smoke," she said in a magnanimous and at the same time crushed voice, and proceeded to busy herself with Sokolov about the price of the plot. While lighting up, Peter Ivanovich heard how very thoroughly she inquired about the different prices of land and settled on the plot which she was going to take. Having finished with the matter of the plot, she also made arrangements about the singers. Sokolov went away.

"I do everything myself," she said to Peter Ivanovich, pushing aside the albums which were lying on the table; and, observing that the ashes might damage the table, she promptly moved the ash tray over to Peter Ivanovich and said: "I consider it hypocrisy to pretend that my grief prevents me from attending to practical matters. On the contrary, if there's anything which can . . . well . . . not console, but distract me, it's the cares concerning him." She again took out her handkerchief, as though getting ready to cry; but suddenly, as though getting control of herself, she shook herself and began to speak calmly. "But I want to ask you about a certain matter."

Peter Ivanovich made a bow, without permitting the springs of the pouffe, which at once began to stir under him, to get away.

"The last few days he suffered terribly."

"He suffered very much?" asked Peter Ivanovich.

"Oh, terribly! Not just during the last minutes, but for hours before the end came, he never stopped screaming. Three days in a row he screamed incessantly. It was unbearable. I can't understand how I stood it. You could hear him three rooms away. Oh, what I endured!"

"And was he really conscious?" asked Peter Ivanovich.

"Yes," she whispered, "to the last minute. He said good-by to us a quarter of an hour before his death, and also asked us to take Volodya away."

The thought of the suffering of this man, whom he had known so well, first as a gay boy, as his schoolmate, and later, when he was grown up, as his partner, suddenly terrified him, in spite of the disagreeable consciousness of his own hypocrisy and that of the woman. He again saw that forehead and that nose pressing against the lip, and he felt terrified about himself.

"Three days of horrible suffering, and death. Why, this could happen to me now, any minute," he thought, and for a moment he felt terrified. But immediately, he himself didn't know how, the habitual thought came to his rescue—the thought that this had happened to Ivan Ilyich, and not to him, and that this should not and could not happen to him; that in thinking this way he was succumbing to a gloomy mood, something which he should not do, as was evident from Schwartz's face. And having reflected thus, Peter Ivanovich calmed down and began to inquire with interest about the details of Ivan Ilyich's end, as though death were an accident peculiar only to Ivan Ilyich but by no means to him.

After various remarks about the details of the really terrible physical suffering which Ivan Ilyich had endured (these details Peter Ivanovich learned only from the way the torments of Ivan Ilyich had affected the nerves of Praskovya Fyodorovna), the widow apparently found it necessary to pass on to business.

"Oh, Peter Ivanovich, it's so hard, so terribly hard, so terribly hard!" And she started to cry again.

Peter Ivanovich sighed and waited for her to blow her nose.

When she had done so, he said: "Believe me. . . ." And she again became voluble and revealed what was evidently her chief business with him. This business consisted of questions about how to obtain money from the government on the occasion of her husband's death. She made it appear as though she were asking Peter Ivanovich's advice in regard to the pension; but he saw that she already knew down to the minutest details what even he himself didn't know—all that could be gotten out of the government as a result of this death. But what she really wanted to find out was if it weren't possible in some way to get even a little more money. Peter Ivanovich tried to think of some way to do this, but, after reflecting a little and, for the sake of propriety, scolding our government for its stinginess, he said that he thought nothing more could be gotten from it. Thereupon she sighed and obviously began to look for a way to get rid of her visitor. He understood this, put out his cigarette, got up, pressed her hand, and went out into the hall.

In the dining room with the clock to which Ivan Ilyich had taken such a fancy in a bric-a-brac shop that he had bought it, Peter Ivanovich met a priest and also a few acquaintances who had come to the service, and he saw Ivan Ilyich's daughter, a pretty young woman, with whom he was acquainted. She was dressed all in black. Her very slim waist seemed even slimmer. She had a gloomy, determined, almost angry look. She bowed to Peter Ivanovich as though he were guilty of something. Behind the daughter, and with the same offended look, stood a wealthy young man whom Peter Ivanovich knew. He was an examining magistrate and her fiancé, as Peter Ivanovich had heard. Peter Ivanovich bowed dejectedly to them and was on the point of passing into the room of the dead man, when from under the staircase appeared the little figure of a high school boy, Ivan Ilyich's son, who bore a striking resemblance to his father. This was little Ivan Ilyich, just as Peter Ivanovich remembered him in law school. His eyes, red from crying, were such as one generally sees in impure boys of thirteen or fourteen. When he noticed Peter Ivanovich, the boy scowled sternly and shamefacedly. Peter Ivanovich nodded to him and entered the room of the dead man. The service began: candles, groans, incense, tears, sobs. Peter Ivanovich stood frowning, looking at his feet in front of him. He didn't glance at the dead man even once, and to the very end didn't succumb to these debilitating influences, and was one of the first to leave the room. There was no one in the hall. Gerasim, the peasant who served as a butler's helper, dashed out of the deceased's room, rummaged with his powerful hands among all the fur coats in search of the one which belonged to Peter Ivanovich, and handed it to him.

"Well, Gerasim, my boy?" said Peter Ivanovich, just to be saying something. "A shame, isn't it?"

"It's God's will. It'll happen to all of us," said Gerasim, displaying his white, solid peasant teeth; and like a man performing a strenuous job, he opened the door briskly, called the coachman, helped Peter Ivanovich in, and jumped back to the porch, as though considering what else he should do.

It was especially pleasant for Peter Ivanovich to breathe the pure air after the odor of the incense, the dead body, and the carbolic acid.

"Where to, sir?" asked the coachman.

"It isn't late yet. I'll drop in on Fyodor Vasilevich."

And Peter Ivanovich departed. And indeed, he found them at the end of the first rubber, so that it was easy for him to come in as the fifth.

II

The history of Ivan Ilyich's life was most simple, and most common, and most terrible.

Ivan Ilyich died at the age of forty-five, when he was a member of the Appelate Court. He was the son of an official who had made himself that sort of career in various ministries and departments of St. Petersburg which brings people to a position where, although it becomes evident that they are no

good for the performance of any essential duty, they nevertheless can't be fired on account of their long past service and
their rank, and so they receive imaginary, fictitious posts and
non-fictitious thousands, from six to ten, with which they live
to a ripe old age.

Such had been the privy councillor,[2] the useless member of
all kinds of useless government offices, Ilya Efimovich Golovin.

He had three sons. Ivan Ilyich was his second. The oldest
had made himself a career similar to that of his father, only in
a different ministry, and was already rapidly approaching that
stage in the Service when one automatically gets a salary. The
third son was a failure. He had repeatedly ruined his chances
in various positions and was now serving with the railroads;
and his father and brothers, and especially their wives, not only
disliked meeting him, but, except when it was absolutely necessary, didn't even mention the fact of his existence. His sister
was married to Baron Gref, who was the same type of St.
Petersburg official as his father-in-law.

Ivan Ilyich was *le phenix de la famille,* as they said. He was
not as cold and as precise as the older son, and not as desperate
as the younger. He was midway between them—a clever, lively,
agreeable, and decent man. He attended law school together
with his younger brother. The younger brother didn't graduate,
and was expelled in his fifth year. Ivan Ilyich graduated high in
his class. Even in law school he was already the sort of man
that he was to be later on during his whole life—a capable,
gaily good-natured, and affable man, but one who strictly carried out what he considered to be his duty; and he considered
his duty to be all that which was so considered by men in the
highest positions. Neither as a boy nor as a grown man did he
curry favor with anyone, but from his earliest youth he was
attracted like a fly to the light to men who occupied the highest positions in society, adopted their manner and views of life,
and established friendly relations with them. All the passions of

[2] A Civil Service rank.

childhood and youth had come and gone without leaving any great traces on him; he abandoned himself to sensuality and ambition, and—toward the end, when he was well along in school—to liberalism, but all this was done within certain limits that were faithfully prescribed by his instinct.

While studying law he had committed acts which had beforehand seemed to him to be very vile and which had inspired him with contempt for himself at the time that he was committing them; but later, when he observed that such acts were also committed by distinguished people, and were not considered by them to be bad, he didn't acknowledge them to be good, but, rather, completely forgot about them and didn't torture himself with reminiscences.

Having graduated from law school and qualified for the tenth Civil Service grade, and having received money for an outfit from his father, Ivan Ilyich ordered clothes at Charmeur's, attached to his watch fob a small charm with the inscription *Respice finem,* said good-by to the head of the school and to his tutor, dined with his friends at Donon's, and, with a new smart trunk, linen, clothes, shaving and toilet accessories, and a travelling rug—all of them ordered and bought in the best shops—departed for the province to take a position which his father had procured for him, that of a governor's aide for special assignments.

In the province Ivan Ilyich at once arranged the same easy and pleasant way of life for himself that he had enjoyed in law school. He served, made a career for himself, and at the same time amused himself pleasantly and decently; now and then he travelled to the various districts on official business, bore himself with dignity both toward those who stood above him and those who stood beneath him, and with precision and incorruptible honesty, which he could not help but be proud of, carried out the business entrusted to him, mainly matters concerning the Old Believers.[3]

[3] A persecuted religious group which adhered to the older rites and customs of Orthodoxy.

In official affairs he was, despite his youth and tendency toward light-hearted gaiety, extremely reserved, formal, and even severe; but in social affairs he was often playful and witty, and always good-natured, decent, and a *bon enfant,* as was said of him by his chief and his chief's wife, at whose house he was like one of the family.

In the province there was also a liaison with one of the ladies who had thrust herself upon the stylish lawyer; there was also a modiste; there were also drinking bouts with visiting aides-de-camp, and trips to a distant street after supper; there was also a subserviency to the chief, and even to the chief's wife; but all this had about itself such an elevated tone of respectability that none of it could be called by any bad words—it was all merely what the French refer to with their saying *Il faut que jeunesse se passe.* Everything took place with clean hands, in clean shirts, with French words, and, what was most important of all, in the very highest society, consequently with the approval of highly placed people.

Thus Ivan Ilyich served for five years, and then there was a change in the Service. New judicial organs came into being; new men were needed.

And Ivan Ilyich became such a new man.

Ivan Ilyich was offered the position of examining magistrate, and Ivan Ilyich accepted it, despite the fact that this position was in another province and he had to give up established relations and establish new ones. His friends saw Ivan Ilyich off, had a group picture taken, presented him with a silver cigarette case, and he departed for the new position.

As an examining magistrate, Ivan Ilyich was the same sort of individual as he had been when he was an aide for special assignments: *comme il faut,* decent, one who knew how to keep his official duties separate from his private life, and one who inspired general respect. The post of examining magistrate was itself much more interesting and attractive for Ivan Ilyich than the one he had formerly held. In his former position it had been a pleasure for him, wearing Charmeur's uniform, to walk with

an easy gait past the trembling petitioners who were waiting for
an audience and past the officials, who envied him, and to go
right into the chief's office and sit down with him for tea and a
cigarette; but there had been few people directly subject to his
authority. These had included only district police officers and
Old Believers, whenever he was sent out on some special business; and he had been fond of treating such people, who were
dependent on him, politely, almost chummily, and of making
them feel that here he, who might crush them, was treating
them in a friendly and simple manner. There had been few
such people at that time.

But now that he was an examining magistrate, Ivan Ilyich
felt that all, all without exception—the most important and
most self-satisfied people—were in his power, and that he
needed only to write certain words on a paper with a certain
heading, and this important, self-satisfied man would be brought
to him in the capacity of a defendant or witness, and if Ivan
Ilyich didn't want to let him sit down, this man would have to
stand before him and answer his questions. Ivan Ilyich never
misused this power of his; on the contrary, he tried to temper
its expression; but the consciousness of this power and the
possibility of tempering it were the most interesting and attractive aspects of his new position. On the job, namely, in the
course of investigations, Ivan Ilyich very soon acquired the
technique of ignoring all those circumstances which had no
relevance to his duties and of putting every extremely com-
plicated matter into such a form that only the bold outline appeared on paper, that his personal view was completely ex-
cluded, and, above all, that every necessary formality was
observed. This was a new field. And he was one of the first men
to put the Statutes of 1864 into practical application.

On moving to the new town in the capacity of examining
magistrate, Ivan Ilyich made new acquaintances and connec-
tions, arranged matters for himself anew, and assumed a somewhat different tone. He adopted an attitude of rather dignified
aloofness towards the provincial authorities; chose the best

circle, consisting of members of the legal profession and the wealthy gentry living in town; and assumed a tone of slight dissatisfaction with the government, of moderate liberalism, and of cultured public spiritedness. Besides this, without making any changes in the elegance of his dress, in this new position Ivan Ilyich stopped shaving his chin and let his beard grow as it wished.

In this new town Ivan Ilyich's life again arranged itself in a most agreeable manner—the social circle which found fault with the governor was friendly and decent, the salary was larger, and not a small degree of pleasure was added to life by whist, which Ivan Ilyich began to play. He was good company in a game of cards; he was fast and very shrewd in his calculations, so that on the whole he was always winning.

After two years of service in the new town, Ivan Ilyich met his future wife. Praskovya Fyodorovna Mikhel was the most attractive, clever, and brilliant girl of the circle in which Ivan Ilyich moved. To the other amusements and relaxations from the labors of an examining magistrate, Ivan Ilyich added a playful, casual relationship with Praskovya Fyodorovna.

Ivan Ilyich used to dance when he was an aide for special assignments; but as an examining magistrate, he rarely danced. He now danced only in order to show that "though I'm serving in the new judicial system and in the fifth grade of the Civil Service, I can nevertheless prove that, when it comes to dancing, I'm better than anybody else at this sort of thing." So he occasionally danced with Praskovya Fyodorovna towards the end of the evening, and it was mainly during these dances that he overwhelmed Praskovya Fyodorovna. She fell in love with him. Ivan Ilyich didn't have any clear and definite intention of getting married, but when the girl fell in love with him, he put this question to himself: "Well, why shouldn't I get married?"

Praskovya Fyodorovna came of good gentry stock, wasn't bad looking, and had a little property. Ivan Ilyich could expect a more brilliant match, but this one wasn't bad either. Ivan

Ilyich had his salary, and she, so he hoped, would have as much again. It would be a good connection; she was a sweet, pretty, and completely respectable woman. To say that Ivan Ilyich got married because he fell in love with his fiancée and found her sympathetic to his views of life would be as unjust as to say that he got married because the people of his social circle approved of the match. Ivan Ilyich got married for two reasons: he was doing something agreeable for himself in acquiring such a wife and, at the same time, he was doing what people in the highest positions considered to be correct.

And so Ivan Ilyich got married.

The whole process of getting married and the first period of married life, with its conjugal caresses, new furniture, new dishes, and new linen, passed very pleasantly until his wife's pregnancy, so that Ivan Ilyich began to think that his marriage would not only not impair the nature of the easy, agreeable, gay, and always proper life which was approved of by society and which Ivan Ilyich regarded as peculiar to life in general, but that it would even intensify this way of living. But then, beginning with the early months of his wife's pregnancy, there appeared something new, unexpected, disagreeable, oppressive, and improper, something which it had been impossible to expect and was impossible to get rid of.

Without the least provocation, as it seemed to Ivan Ilyich, *de gaité de coeur,* as he said to himself, his wife began to disturb the pleasure and propriety of life—she was jealous of him without any cause whatsoever, demanded his attentions, complained about everything, and involved him in disagreeable and vulgar scenes.

At first Ivan Ilyich hoped to free himself of the unpleasantness of this situation by means of that same easy and decorous attitude toward life which had helped him out in the past—he tried to ignore his wife's disposition; he continued to live easily and agreeably, as before, inviting his friends over for cards and going to the club or to his friends. But one day his wife began to upbraid him so energetically with vulgar words, and continued to scold him so persistently every time that he didn't comply with her demands, having apparently firmly determined not to stop until he submitted, that is, stayed at home and was bored like she herself, that Ivan Ilyich was horrified. He realized that married life, at least with his wife, didn't always contribute to the pleasures and propriety of life, but, on the contrary, frequently disturbed them, and that it was therefore necessary for him to defend himself against these disturbances. Ivan Ilyich began to search for a way to accomplish this. His work was the one thing which impressed Praskovya Fyodorovna, and, using his work and the duties resulting from it as a means, Ivan Ilyich began the struggle with his wife, fencing off his independent world.

With the birth of a child, with the attempts to nurse it and the various failures in this matter, with the real and imaginary diseases of the child and the mother, when Ivan Ilyich's help was demanded though he knew nothing about these things, the need for Ivan Ilyich to fence off a world for himself apart from his family became even more urgent.

As his wife became more irritable and more exacting, Ivan Ilyich more and more shifted the center of gravity of his life to his work. He began to love his work more and became more ambitious than he had been before.

Very soon, not more than a year after his marriage, Ivan Ilyich realized that married life, though offering certain comforts to life, was, in reality, a very complex and difficult matter, toward which, in order to perform one's duty, that is, to lead a decent life approved by society, it was necessary to work out a definite attitude, just as in the case of one's job.

And Ivan Ilyich worked out such an attitude toward his married life. From his domestic life he demanded nothing but those comforts of dining at home, of a well-kept house, of a conjugal bed, which she could give him, and, above all, a propriety that conformed to the external forms determined by public opinion. For the rest, he also sought a cheerful pleasantness. He was thankful when he found it; but when he

met with opposition and querulousness, he immediately withdrew to the separate world of his work which he had fenced
off for himself and found his pleasure there.

Ivan Ilyich was esteemed as a good official, and after three
years he was made an assistant prosecuting attorney. His new
duties, their importance, the possibility of summoning to court
and imprisoning any person, the publicity given his speeches,
the success which Ivan Ilyich had in this work—all this attracted him more and more to his job.

They had more children. His wife became more and more irritable and querulous, but the attitude toward domestic life
which Ivan Ilyich had worked out made him practically imper-
vious to her querulousness.

After seven years of service in one town, Ivan Ilyich was
transferred to another province in the capacity of prosecuting
attorney. They moved, they had little money, and his wife
didn't like the place to which they had moved. Though his
salary was larger than before, the cost of living was higher; besides, two of the children died, and so domestic life became even
more unpleasant for Ivan Ilyich.

Praskovya Fyodorovna blamed her husband for all the problems they encountered in this new place where they were now
living. Most of the subjects of conversation between husband
and wife, especially the education of the children, led to topics
which recalled former quarrels, and quarrels were apt to flare
up at any moment. There remained only those rare periods of
love-making which overwhelmed the pair, but which didn't
last long. Those were islets where they anchored for a while,
but then they set out again upon a sea of hidden enmity which
found its expression in their mutual alienation. This alienation
might have hurt Ivan Ilyich if he had thought that this shouldn't
be so; but he now recognized this situation not only as normal,
but even as the aim of the domestic role which he played. His
aim consisted of freeing himself more and more from unpleasantness and giving it the character of innocuousness and
propriety; and he was achieving this by spending less and less

time with his family; and when he was compelled to be with it, he tried to make his position secure by having outsiders present.

The most important thing for Ivan Ilyich was that he had his work. All his interest in life was centered in the world of official-dom. And this interest absorbed him. The consciousness of his power, of the possibility of ruining any man he wanted to ruin, even the superficial pomp attending his entrance into court and his meetings with subordinates, his success in the eyes of his superiors and subordinates, and, above all, the mastery with which he conducted his cases and of which he was conscious—all this made him happy and, together with his conversations with friends, dinners, and whist, filled his life. So, in general, Ivan Ilyich's life continued to proceed as he thought that it should proceed: agreeably and with propriety.

Thus he lived another seven years. His oldest daughter was now sixteen, another child had died, and there was a high school boy, the subject of contention. Ivan Ilyich had wanted to send him to law school, but Praskovya Fyodorovna, to spite him, had sent the boy to a high school. The daughter studied at home and was coming along well; the boy wasn't a bad student either.

III

Such was Ivan Ilyich's life during the seventeen years since his marriage. He was an old prosecuting attorney, who had declined several transfers in the expectation of a more desirable place, when there unexpectedly occurred a disagreeable circum-stance which completely upset the calm of his life. Ivan Ilyich was expecting the position of presiding judge in a university town; but Goppe somehow got ahead of him and received this post. Ivan Ilyich was annoyed by this, began to make unpleasant remarks, and quarrelled with him and with his immediate su-periors; they began to treat him coldly and he was again passed over when the next appointment was made.

That was in 1880. That year was the most difficult in Ivan Ilyich's life. In that year it appeared that, on the one hand, the salary was not large enough to live on and that, on the other, all had forgotten him, and that what seemed to him to be a most grave and most cruel personal injustice, appeared to others to be an entirely common affair. Even his father didn't consider it his duty to help him. He felt that all had abandoned him, considering his situation with a salary of thirty-five hundred rubles most normal and even desirable. He alone knew that with the consciousness of those injustices which had been done him, and with the eternal nagging of his wife, and with the debts which he had begun to accumulate by living beyond his means—he alone knew that his situation was far from being normal.

To economize, he took a leave of absence that summer and went with his wife to spend the summer in the country, at the place of Praskovya Fyodorovna's brother.

In the country, deprived of his work, Ivan Ilyich for the first time experienced not only boredom, but also an intolerable despondency, and he decided that it was impossible to live in this manner and that it was necessary to take decisive measures of some sort.

After spending a sleepless night pacing up and down the terrace, Ivan Ilyich decided to go to St. Petersburg to try for another position; and, in order to punish *them,* those who were incapable of appreciating him, to transfer to another ministry.

The next day he went to St. Petersburg, despite the efforts of his wife and brother-in-law to dissuade him.

He went there for one thing—to get a position with a salary of five thousand. He was no longer interested in any particular ministry, trend, or type of work. All he needed was a position, a position with five thousand, in the administration, in the banking system, with the railroads, in Empress Mary's institutions, even in customs—but it had to be five thousand, and he had to leave the ministry in which they were incapable of appreciating him.

And this trip of Ivan Ilyich's was actually crowned by a remarkable, unexpected success. In Kursk, F. S. Ilyin, an ac-

quaintance of his, got into the first-class car and informed him
of the contents of the latest telegram received by the governor
of Kursk. Shortly there would be a reorganization in the ministry—Ivan Semyonovich was being appointed to Peter Ivanovich's place.

The proposed reorganization had, in addition to its significance for Russia, a special significance for Ivan Ilyich, since by
effecting the promotion of Peter Petrovich and, apparently, of
his friend Zakhar Ivanovich, it was extremely favorable for
Ivan Ilyich. Zakhar Ivanovich was Ivan Ilyich's classmate and
friend.

The news was confirmed in Moscow. And on arriving in St.
Petersburg, Ivan Ilyich located Zakhar Ivanovich and received
the promise of a definite place in his former ministry of justice.

A week later he wired his wife: "Zakhar has replaced Miller.
I will receive appointment on presentation of first report."

As a result of this change in personnel, Ivan Ilyich unexpectedly received an appointment in his former ministry which
advanced him two grades above his comrades; he got a salary
of five thousand and thirty-five hundred for travelling expenses.
His resentment against former enemies and against the whole
ministry was completely forgotten, and Ivan Ilyich was quite
happy.

Ivan Ilyich returned to the country gay and satisfied, something that he had not been for a long time. Praskovya Fyodorovna also cheered up and a truce was established between
them. Ivan Ilyich told how all had lionized him in St. Petersburg, how all those who were his enemies had been put to
shame and were now groveling before him, how he was envied
his position, and especially how much they all liked him in St.
Petersburg.

Praskovya Fyodorovna listened to all this, and pretended
that she believed it, and did not contradict him in anything; she
was busy with plans for the new living arrangements in the city
to which they were moving. Ivan Ilyich saw with delight that
these plans were his plans, that they agreed with one another,

and that his disrupted life was once more resuming its real, characteristic course of gay agreeableness and propriety.

Ivan Ilyich came back for only a short time. On the tenth of September he had to start work, and, besides, he needed time to settle down in the new place, to move everything from the province, to buy and to order quite a few things—in short, to arrange matters as he himself had decided and in almost precisely the same manner as had been decided by Praskovya Fyodorovna.

Now that everything had turned out so successfully and he and his wife agreed on their aims and, besides, lived together so little, they got along with one another better than they had since the first years of their married life. Ivan Ilyich intended to take his family away at once, but, on the insistence of his sister and brother-in-law, who suddenly became unusually amiable and intimate with Ivan Ilyich and his family, Ivan Ilyich departed by himself.

Ivan Ilyich departed, and the happy mood produced by his success and his agreeable relations with his wife, one intensifying the other, didn't leave him at all. He found a charming apartment, precisely what husband and wife had been dreaming of. Large, lofty reception rooms in the old style, a comfortable, magnificent study, rooms for his wife and daughter, a classroom for his son—everything was as if purposely planned for them. Ivan Ilyich himself attended to the decorating: he chose the wallpaper, bought additional furniture, especially antiques, which he considered to be particularly *comme il faut,* and upholstery material; and everything grew and grew, and approached that ideal which he had set for himself. When he had half-arranged matters, the results surpassed his expectations. He visualized that *comme il faut,* elegant, and non-vulgar character which everything would assume when it was ready. While falling asleep, he imagined what the reception room would be like. As he looked at the drawing room, which was not yet finished, he already saw the fireplace, the screen, the shelves, and those little chairs scattered here and there, those dishes and plates along the walls, and the bronzes all set up in their proper places. He rejoiced at the thought of how he would surprise Pasha and Lizanka,[4] who also had good taste in such things. They weren't expecting it at all. He was particularly fortunate in finding and buying at a low price some antiques which gave everything a distinctively aristocratic air. In his letters he purposely underplayed everything in order to astonish them. All this interested him so much that even his new position, though he liked it, interested him less than he had expected. During court sessions he had moments of absent-mindedness: he wondered what kind of valances to hang on the curtains, straight or gathered. He became so involved in all of this that he frequently puttered around himself; he even re-arranged the furniture and himself tried the curtains out on different windows. One day he got up on a ladder to show an upholsterer, who didn't get the idea, how he wanted something draped; he slipped and fell, but, since he was a strong and agile man, he kept his balance, merely striking his side against the knob of the window-frame. The bruise ached a little while, but this soon stopped. Ivan Ilyich felt particularly gay and healthy at this time. He wrote: "I feel about fifteen years younger." He had intended to be through with the work in September, but it lasted until the middle of October. But then, the effect was charming; not only he said so, but also all who saw it.

In reality, he behaved like all those not quite wealthy people who want to look like wealthy people, and so end up looking only like each other: there were damasks, dark wood, flowers, rugs, and bronzes; everything was dark and burnished —it was all the sort of thing which all people of a certain class have in order to resemble all people of a certain class. And everything in his apartment was so much on this order that it wasn't worth one's attention; but to him all of this seemed to be something special. When he met his family at the railroad sta-

---

[4] *Pasha* is a diminutive of *Praskovya,* and *Lizanka* of *Elizaveta* (*Elizabeth*).

tion and brought it home to his lit-up and fixed-up apartment, and a footman in a white necktie opened the door into the hall decorated with flowers, and when they then entered the drawing room and the study and gasped with delight—he was very happy, led them around everywhere, luxuriated in their praises, and beamed with pleasure. That same evening, at tea, when Praskovya Fyodorovna asked him, among other things, how he had fallen, he laughed and gave them an impersonation of how he had come flying down and had frightened the upholsterer.

"I'm not an athlete for nothing. Another man would have been killed, but I barely hit myself right here; when you touch it, it hurts, but it's already going away: it's just a bruise."

And they began to live in their new apartment, which, as is always the case when people have completely settled down, was just one room short of being big enough, and with their new income, which, as is always the case, was only a little, some five hundred rubles, short of being adequate; and all went very well. It went especially well at first, when everything was not yet arranged and it was still necessary to look after things —now to buy something, now to order something, now to re-arrange something, now to repair something. Even though there were some disagreements between husband and wife, nevertheless both were so satisfied and had so much to do that everything ended without any great quarrels. When there was nothing more to arrange, it became a little boring and there was a feeling that something was lacking; but at this point they made new acquaintances, formed new habits, and life was again full.

After spending the morning in court, Ivan Ilyich would come home for dinner, and at first he was usually in a good humor, though this was occasionally marred somewhat, namely, by the state of the apartment. (Every spot on the tablecloth and on the damask, every broken curtain cord irritated him. He had put so much work into the arrangement of things that every bit of destruction pained him.) But, in general, Ivan Ilyich's life went on in the way that he felt it should proceed: easily, agreeably, and with propriety. He got up at nine, drank his coffee, read the newspaper, then put on his uniform and went to court. There the harness in which he worked was all ready for him; he got into it immediately. There were petitioners, inquiries at the office, the office itself, the sessions—public and administrative. In the course of all this it was necessary to be able to exclude all that raw and vital material which always impairs the regular flow of official affairs—it was necessary not to permit any but official relations with people, and the basis for such relations must be nothing but official, and the relations themselves must be nothing but official. For example, a man comes and wants to find out something. Ivan Ilyich can have no relations with such a man in an unofficial capacity; but if this man approaches him in his official capacity as a member of the court—that is, if the relationship is such as can be expressed on a piece of paper with a heading on it—then within the limits of such a relationship Ivan Ilyich does everything, absolutely everything possible, and at the same time observes a semblance of amicable human relations, in other words, politeness. As soon as the official relationship comes to an end, every other relationship also ends. This ability to keep his official life distinct and to avoid mixing it with real life Ivan Ilyich possessed in the highest degree, and through long practice and talent he had perfected it to such a degree that at times he even permitted himself, like a virtuoso, as though in jest, to mix human and official relations. He took this liberty because he felt himself always able, whenever it should be necessary, again to isolate what was official and to reject what was human. Ivan Ilyich did this sort of thing not only easily, agreeably, and with propriety, but even artistically. During recesses he smoked, drank tea, and chatted a little about politics, a little about general matters, a little about cards, and most of all about appointments. And he would return home tired, but with the feeling of a virtuoso who has performed his part—that of one of the first violins in the orchestra—with precision. When he came home, the daughter and her mother were either out calling somewhere or they had guests; the son was in school, preparing his lessons with tutors and industriously studying such things as are studied in a high school. All went well. After dinner, if there were no guests, Ivan Ilyich sometimes read a book which people were discussing a great deal, and in the evening sat down to business, that is, he read documents and took care of other legal work, comparing depositions and finding applicable statutes for them. This neither bored him nor gave him pleasure. It was boring only when he could have been playing vint; but when there was no vint, this was, after all, better than sitting alone or with his wife. His pleasures consisted of small dinners to which he invited men and women of social standing and of such pastimes with them as would resemble the usual pastimes of such people, just as his drawing room resembled all other drawing rooms.

Once they even had an evening party, a dance. Ivan Ilyich was gay and everything went well, except that he had a big quarrel with his wife on account of the cake and candy. Praskovya Fyodorovna had her own plan, but Ivan Ilyich insisted that everything he bought from an expensive confectioner, and he bought a lot of cake; and the quarrel was due to the fact that there was cake left over, while the confectioner's bill came to forty-five rubles. The quarrel was a big one, and disagreeable, so much so that Praskovya Fyodorovna ended up by calling him a fool and a whining bore. And he clutched his head and in his anger made some mention of divorce. But the evening itself was a gay one. The best society was present, and Ivan Ilyich danced with Princess Trufonov, the sister of the one who was famous as the founder of the society called Relieve My Misfortune.

The official joys were the joys of pride; the social joys were the joys of vanity; but Ivan Ilyich's real joys were the joys of playing vint. He confessed that after everything, after any joyless incidents in his life, the one joy which, like a candle, outshone all the the rest was to sit down with good players and soft-spoken partners to a game of vint, by all means a four-

handed game ("a five-handed game is annoying, though I pretend that I like it a lot"), and to carry on a clever, serious game
("when the cards come your way"), then to eat supper and
drink a glass of wine. And after a game of vint, Ivan Ilyich used
to lie down to sleep in a very good frame of mind, especially
if he had won a little ("to win a lot is disagreeable").

Thus they lived. Their social circle consisted of the best
people, and both important and young people called on them.

Husband, wife, and daughter were in complete agreement in
their opinion of the circle of their acquaintances, and with
tacit unanimity they discouraged and freed themselves of all
kinds of shabby friends and relatives who descended upon
them with flattery in their drawing room with the Japanese
plates along the walls. Soon these shabby friends stopped de-
scending upon them, and the Golovins were left with nothing
but the very best society. Young men courted Lizanka; and
the examining magistrate Petrishchev, the son of Dmitri Ivanovich Petrishchev and the only heir to his fortune, began to be
particularly attentive to Lizanka, so that Ivan Ilyich had already
had a talk with Praskovya Fyodorovna about this matter—
about whether they shouldn't take them out for a troika drive
or arrange a theatrical performance for them.

This is the way they lived. And everything went on in this
way, without any change, and everything was very fine.

IV

All were well. One couldn't call ill-health that of which Ivan
Ilyich now and then spoke: the peculiar taste in his mouth and
a kind of uncomfortable feeling in the left side of his abdomen.

But it so happened that this uncomfortable feeling began to
grow and to turn, not as yet into a pain, but into a consciousness of a constant pressure in his side and an irritable disposition. This irritable disposition, which kept on intensifying and
intensifying, began to spoil the pleasure of the easy and proper
life which had been established in the Golovin family. Husband

and wife began to quarrel more and more often, and soon the easiness and pleasure disappeared, and propriety alone was maintained, but with difficulty. The scenes again became more frequent. Again there were left some islets, but only a few of these, on which husband and wife could meet without an explosion.

And Praskovya Fyodorovna now said, not without reason, that her husband was hard to get along with. With her usual habit of exaggerating, she said that he had always had such a terrible disposition, that one had to have her goodness to have stood this for twenty years. It's true that the quarrels now began with him. His fault-finding always began immediately before dinner, and frequently just as he was beginning to eat, with the soup course. Now he would notice that some dish was chipped, now that the food wasn't just right, now that his son had put his elbow on the table, now that there was something wrong with his daughter's hairdo. And he blamed Praskovya Fyodorovna for everything. At first Praskovya Fyodorovna would retort and say disagreeable things to him, but once or twice he flew into such a rage at the beginning of dinner that she realized this was an illness which was brought on by the taking of food; and she restrained herself—she no longer retorted, but merely rushed through dinner. Praskovya Fyodorovna regarded her humility as a great credit to herself. Having decided that her husband had a terrible disposition and had made her life miserable, she began to pity herself. And the more she pitied herself, the more she hated her husband. She began to wish that he would die, but she couldn't wish this, because if he did, then there would be no salary. And this caused her to be even more exasperated with him. She considered herself terribly unfortunate because even his death couldn't save her, and she kept on getting irritated and kept on concealing her irritation, and this concealed irritation intensified his irritation.

After a scene in which Ivan Ilyich had been particularly unjust, and after which, in the course of explanations, he had said that he was indeed irritable, but that this was due to his illness, she told him that if he were ill he should receive treatment and demanded that he go to a famous doctor.

He went. Everything was as he had expected; everything was done as such things are always done. The waiting and the doctor's affected importance, which was familiar to him—it was the same which he knew in himself in court—and the tapping, and the auscultation, and the questions requiring previously determined and obviously unnecessary answers, and the significant air which suggested that "you just put yourself in our hands and we'll take care of everything—we know exactly how to take care of everything, everything in the same way for every man, whoever he may be." Everything was exactly as in court. Just as he assumed an air in dealing with defendants, just so the famous doctor also assumed an air.

The doctor said: "So and so shows that there is so and so inside of you; but if this should not be confirmed by the investigation of so and so, we shall have to assume so and so. But if we assume so and so, then. . . ." And so on. Ivan Ilyich was interested in one question alone: Was his condition dangerous or not? But the doctor ignored this irrelevant question. From the doctor's point of view, this question was pointless and not subject to consideration; there existed only a weighing of the probabilities—a floating kidney, chronic catarrh, and appendicitis. It was not a question of Ivan Ilyich's life, but a dispute as to whether it was a floating kidney or appendicitis. And Ivan Ilyich saw the doctor decide this dispute brilliantly in favor of appendicitis, with the proviso that the urinalysis might give new indications and that then the matter would be reconsidered. All this was precisely what Ivan Ilyich had himself done thousands of times just as brilliantly in the case of defendants. The doctor made his summation in the same brilliant manner, and looked triumphantly, even gaily, over his glasses at the defendant. From the doctor's summation, Ivan Ilyich drew the conclusion that things were bad, and that it was a matter of indifference to him, the doctor, and also, very likely, to all people, while he himself felt terrible. And this conclusion was painful for Ivan Ilyich, arousing in him a feeling of great pity for himself and of great anger at this doctor who was indifferent to such an important question.

But he didn't make any comment, but got up, put the money down on the table, and said, sighing: "No doubt we sick people often ask you irrelevant questions. Is this illness usually dangerous or not?" [5]

The doctor looked at him sternly with one eye, over his glasses, as though saying: "Defendant, if you don't keep within the limits of the questions put to you, I shall be obliged to order your removal from the courtroom."

"I have already told you what I consider necessary and proper," said the doctor. "Analysis will reveal anything further." And the doctor bowed.

Ivan Ilyich went out slowly, gloomily seated himself in the sledge, and drove home. All the way he continued analyzing everything which the doctor had said, trying to translate all those confusing, obscure scientific words into simple language and to find in them an answer to the question: "Am I in bad shape, in very bad shape, or is there nothing to worry about yet?" And it seemed to him that the meaning of everything the doctor had said was that he was in bad shape. Everything in the streets seemed sad to Ivan Ilyich. The cab drivers were sad, the houses were sad, the passers-by, the shops were sad. And this pain, this dull, nagging pain which never stopped for a second, seemed to have acquired another, a more serious significance as a result of the doctor's obscure remarks. Ivan Ilyich now observed it with another, a grim feeling.

He came home and began to tell his wife about it. His wife listened to him, but in the middle of the account his daughter entered with her hat on; she was getting ready to go out with her mother. Reluctantly she sat down to listen to this boring news, but she couldn't stand it for long and so her mother didn't hear the end of it.

[5] Ivan Ilyich's illness has generally been "diagnosed" as cancer.

"Well, I'm very glad," said his wife. "So now be sure to take the medicine regularly. Give me the prescription. I'll send Gerasim to the druggist." And she went to get dressed.

He hadn't paused for a breath while she was in the room, and he sighed heavily when she left. "Well," he said, "maybe there's really nothing to worry about yet."

He began to take medicine, to carry out the doctor's orders, which were changed as a result of the urinalysis. But at this point it so happened that some confusion arose in the matter of this analysis and in what was to follow it. It was impossible for him to get to the doctor himself, and it turned out that something was happening that was different from what the doctor had told him. Either the doctor had forgotten something, or had lied, or was hiding something from him.

But, nevertheless, Ivan Ilyich began to carry out the doctor's instructions faithfully, and at first found consolation in performing this duty.

Since his visit to the doctor, Ivan Ilyich's chief occupation had become the faithful execution of the doctor's instructions on hygiene and the taking of medicine and the observation of his pain and of all the functions of his organism. People's illnesses and health became the chief interest of Ivan Ilyich. When anyone in his presence spoke about sick people, about those who had died or had recuperated, especially about the type of illness which resembled his own, he, trying to conceal his agitation, listened, inquired, and made deductions about his own illness.

The pain did not subside, but Ivan Ilyich tried to make himself believe that he was better. And he was able to deceive himself as long as nothing excited him. But the moment there was some unpleasantness with his wife, some failure in his work, bad cards in vint, he immediately felt the full force of his illness. Formerly he had endured these failures, expecting that "I'll soon correct what has gone wrong; I'll triumph and end up with success, with a grand slam." But now every failure sapped his strength and plunged him into despair. He told himself: "Here

I've just begun to get better and the medicine has already begun to take effect, and now comes this damned bad luck or unpleasantness. . . ." And he was furious at the bad luck or at the people who were causing him unpleasantness and killing him; and he felt that this anger was killing him, but he was unable to avoid it. It would seem that it should have been clear to him that this bitterness of his against circumstances and people intensified his illness, and that, therefore, he ought to pay no attention to unpleasant incidents; but his reasoning was completely opposite—he said that he needed peace, noted everything which disturbed this peace, and became irritable with every least disturbance. What made his condition worse was that he read medical books and consulted doctors. The deterioration proceeded so evenly that he was able to deceive himself when he compared one day with another—there was little difference. But when he consulted doctors, it seemed to him that he was growing worse, and very rapidly at that. And in spite of this, he constantly consulted doctors.

That month he went to another celebrity. This other celebrity told him almost the same thing as the first celebrity, but put the questions differently. And the consultation with this celebrity only redoubled Ivan Ilyich's doubt and fear. A friend of a friend of his, a very good doctor, diagnosed the illness as something still completely different, and, although he promised a cure, his questions and speculations confused Ivan Ilyich even more and intensified his doubts. A homeopath diagnosed the illness in a still different way and gave him some medicine, and he took it for a week secretly. But after a week he felt no relief and lost confidence in all former treatments and in the present one too, and became still more despondent. Once a woman whom he knew told him of healing done with icons. Ivan Ilyich caught himself listening attentively and believing that this could be done. This incident frightened him. "Is it possible I've grown so feeble mentally?" he asked himself. "Nonsense! It's all bosh! I must not panic, but, having chosen one doctor, must follow his course of treatment strictly. And this is what

I'll do. Now it's settled. I won't think about it and will stick to the one treatment until summer. Then it'll be obvious. Enough of this shilly-shallying!"

It was easy to say this, but impossible to carry it out. The pain in his side kept on tormenting him and seemed to be increasing and becoming incessant; the taste in his mouth kept on getting stronger; he thought a disgusting smell came from his mouth; and his appetite and his strength kept declining. It was impossible for him to deceive himself—something terrible, new, and more significant than anything that had ever taken place in Ivan Ilyich's life was now going on in him. And he alone knew of it, and all those about him didn't understand, or didn't want to understand, and thought that everything in the world was going on as before. This tormented Ivan Ilyich more than anything else. He saw that the people at home, especially his wife and daughter, who were in the very midst of their social calls, didn't understand a thing about it and were annoyed because he was so cheerless and so exacting, as though it were his fault. Even though they tried to conceal this, he saw that he was a drag on them, but that his wife had worked out a certain attitude toward his illness and adhered to it regardless of what he said and did. This attitude was as follows:

"You know," she would say to her friends, "Ivan Ilyich can't follow the prescribed course of treatment strictly, like all decent people do. Today he'll take his drops, and eat what he's ordered to, and will go to bed at a reasonable hour; tomorrow, if I don't watch him, he'll suddenly forget to take his medicine, will eat some sturgeon (and he isn't allowed to), and will even sit up playing vint until one o'clock."

"Well now, when did I do that?" Ivan Ilyich would say with annoyance. "Once at Peter Ivanovich's."

"And yesterday with Shebek."

"But I couldn't have slept anyway, because of the pain."

"Well, whatever the problem is, you'll never get well this way. You just torment us."

Praskovya Fyodorovna's outward attitude toward her husband's illness, which she expressed to others and to him, was that Ivan Ilyich had himself to blame for this illness and that this whole illness was a new annoyance which he was creating for his wife. Ivan Ilyich felt that her remarks just came out involuntarily, but this didn't make it any easier for him.

In court Ivan Ilyich noticed, or thought that he noticed, the same strange attitude toward himself—now it seemed to him that people peered at him as at a man who was soon to vacate his position; now his friends would suddenly begin, in a friendly way, to tease him about his suspiciousness, as though this thing, this something terrible and horrible, something unheard-of, which had started in him and was incessantly draining his vitality and irresistibly drawing him somewhere, were a most pleasant subject for a joke. He was particularly irritated by Schwartz, who, with his playfulness, vivacity, and *comme-il-faut* ways, reminded Ivan Ilyich of what he himself had been ten years before.

Friends come to have a game, and they sit down to play. The cards are dealt; the new cards are limbered up, and the diamonds are placed with the diamonds: seven of them. His partner says "No trumps" and supports two diamonds. What more could one wish for? It ought to be gay and lively—a slam. And suddenly Ivan Ilyich feels that nagging pain, that taste in his mouth, and he sees something preposterous about being able to find any pleasure in a slam when this is going on.

He looks at Mikhail Mikhailovich, his partner, as the latter energetically strikes the table and politely and condescendingly refrains from sweeping up the tricks, but, instead, pushes them over to Ivan Ilyich in order to give him the pleasure of taking them in without going to much trouble or stretching his hand out too far. "Does he really think that I'm so feeble that I can't stretch my hand out far?" thinks Ivan Ilyich; and he forgets what is trumps, unnecessarily trumps his own cards, and loses the slam by three points; and, worst of all, he sees how Mikhail Mikhailovich suffers, while he himself doesn't care. And it's terrible for him to think why he doesn't care.

All see that it's hard for him, and they say to him: "We can stop if you're tired. Take a rest." Rest? No, he isn't at all tired. They finish the rubber. All are gloomy and silent. Ivan Ilyich feels that it's he who has cast this gloom over them, and he can't dispel it. They eat supper and leave, and Ivan Ilyich is left alone with the consciousness that his life is poisoned for him and poisons the life of others, and that this poison is not receding, but keeps on penetrating his being more and more.

And it is with this consciousness, and also with physical pain, and also with a feeling of terror that he has to lie down in his bed and often be unable to sleep the greater part of the night because of the pain. And in the morning he has to get up again, to dress, to go to court, to speak, to write; and if he doesn't go to court, he has to stay home all the twenty-four hours of the day, each of which is torture. And he has to live this way on the verge of ruin, alone, without a single person who might understand and take pity on him.

V

Thus passed a month, and two months. Shortly before New Year's his brother-in-law arrived in town and stopped at their place. Ivan Ilyich was in court. Praskovya Fyodorovna was out shopping. Coming into his study, Ivan Ilyich found his brother-in-law there, a healthy sanguine man who was unpacking his suitcase himself. On hearing Ivan Ilyich's steps, he raised his head and looked at him in silence for a second. This look revealed everything to Ivan Ilyich. The brother-in-law opened his mouth and was on the point of exclaiming, but checked himself. This action confirmed everything.

"Well, have I changed?"

"Yes . . . there is a change."

And after this, no matter how much Ivan Ilyich led his brother-in-law on to talk about his appearance, his brother-in-law would say nothing about it. Praskovya Fyodorovna came home, and the brother-in-law went to see her. Ivan Ilyich locked the door and began to look at himself in the mirror, at first full-face and then in profile. He took the photograph of himself and his wife and compared it with what he saw in the mirror. The change was tremendous. Then he bared his arms as high as the elbows, looked at them, pulled down the sleeves, sat down on an ottoman, and grew more gloomy than the night.

"I must not, I must not," he said to himself. He jumped up, went over to the table, picked up a law case, and began to read it—but he couldn't. He opened the door and went into the reception room. The door to the drawing room was closed. He went up to it on tiptoe, and began to listen.

"No, you're exaggerating," said Praskovya Fyodorovna.

"What do you mean, exaggerating? Don't you see—he's a dead man. Look into his eyes. There's no light in them. But what's the matter with him?"

"Nobody knows. Nikolaev [that was the other doctor] said something, but I don't know what. Leshchetitsky [that was the famous doctor] said, one the contrary. . . ."

Ivan Ilyich walked away, went to his room, lay down, and began to think: "A kidney, a floating kidney." He recalled everything that the doctors had told him about how it had become detached and was moving about. And, with an effort of his imagination, he tried to catch this kidney and to stop it, to secure it. So little was needed for that, he thought. "No, I'll go and see Peter Ivanovich again." [This was the friend whose friend was a doctor.] He rang, ordered the horse to be hitched up, and got ready to go.

"Where are you going, *Jean?*" his wife asked with a particularly sad and unusually kind expression.

This unusually kind expression embittered him. He glanced at her gloomily.

"I have some business with Peter Ivanovich."

He drove to the house of the friend who had a friend who was a doctor. And with him he drove to the doctor. He found him in and talked with him for a long time.

By analyzing anatomically and physiologically the details of what, according to the doctor's opinion, was going on in him, he understood it all.

There was a thing, a little thing in his appendix. All this might change for the better. Strengthen the energy of one organ, weaken the activity of another, absorption will occur, and everything will improve.

He was a little late for dinner. He ate dinner, chatted gaily, but couldn't for a long time go back to his room and work. Finally he went to his study and immediately sat down to work. He read cases and worked; but the consciousness of the fact that there was a postponed, important, intimate matter, to which he would devote himself after he was through, did not leave him. When he was through with his work, he remembered what this intimate matter was: his thoughts about the appendix. But he didn't abandon himself to them; he went to the drawing room for tea.

There were guests there, and they talked, and played the piano, and sang; the examining magistrate, his daughter's choice, was there. According to Praskovya Fyodorovna, Ivan Ilyich had a better time that evening than ever; but he didn't forget, even for a minute, that there were some postponed important thoughts about the appendix.

At eleven o'clock he said good-night and went to his room. Ever since the beginning of his illness he had slept by himself in a little room near his study. He went there, undressed, and picked up a novel by Zola; but he didn't read it—he was thinking. In his imagination the desired improvement in his appendix took place. There was an absorption, an excretion, and the regular function was being reëstablished. "Yes, that's the way it is," he said to himself. "All you have to do is help Nature." He thought of his medicine. He raised himself, took the medicine, and lay down on his back, waiting to see how the medicine would help him and how it would relieve his pain. "Just take it regularly and avoid harmful influences; I'm already beginning to feel a little better, much better." He began to probe his side—it wasn't painful to the touch. "Yes, I don't feel it; it's really much better now." He put out the light and lay on his side. "The appendix is improving; absorption is going on." Suddenly he felt the familiar, old, dull, nagging pain: persistent, deliberate, and serious. In his mouth there was the same familiar, abominable taste. His heart sank; his head felt muddled. "My God, my God!" he muttered, "again and again, and it will never stop." And suddenly he saw the matter in an entirely different light. "The appendix! The kidney!" he said to himself. "It's not a question of the appendix or the kidney, but of life and . . . death. Yes, there was life, and now it's going away, going away, and I can't stop it. Yes. Why deceive myself? Isn't it obvious to all except me that I'm dying, and that it's only a question of the number of weeks and days—it might happen even now. There was light, but now there's darkness. I was here, but now I'm going there! Where?" He was chilled, and his breath stopped. He heard only the beating of his heart.

"I shall be no more, so what will there be? There will be nothing. But where shall I be when I am no more? Is this death? No, I don't want to die." He got out of bed hurriedly, wanted to light a candle, fumbled with trembling hands, dropped the candle with the candlestick on the floor, and again fell back on the pillow. "What's the use? It makes no difference," he said to himself, peering into the darkness with wide-open eyes. "Death. Yes, death. And not one of them knows, or wants to know; and they have no pity. They're playing. [From beyond the door he heard the distant peal of a voice and a ritornello.] It makes no difference to them, but they too will die. Fools! First I, and then they; they'll come to the same end. And here they're having a good time. Beasts!" His anger was choking him. He felt agonizingly and intolerably miserable. It couldn't be that all were always doomed to experience this terrible fear. He raised himself.

"Something isn't quite right; I have to calm myself; I have to think everything over from the very beginning." And he began to think. "Yes, there was the beginning of my illness. I struck my side, and there wasn't any change that day and the next; it ached a little, then more, then the doctors, then the depression, then the despair, again the doctors. And I kept coming closer and closer to the abyss. I kept losing strength. Closer, closer. And I wasted away—there is no light in my eyes. And here is death, and I spend my time thinking of my appendix. I'm worrying about a cure for my appendix, but this is death. Is it really death?" Again he was seized by terror; he was gasping for breath; he bent over, tried to find the matches, and pressed with his elbow against the night table. It was in his way and hurt him, so he became angry with it and in his annoyance pressed harder and knocked the stand over. And in despair, gasping, he fell on his back, expecting death at once.

At this time the guests were departing. Praskovya Fyodorovna was seeing them off. She heard something fall and came into the room.

"What's the matter?"

"Nothing. I knocked it over accidentally."

She went out and brought a candle. He was lying there, breathing heavily and very fast, like a man who has just run a verst, and staring fixedly at her.

"What's the matter, *Jean?*"

"Noth—ing. I—knocked—it—over." *"What's the use of telling her? She won't understand,"* he thought.

She really didn't understand. She righted the stand, lit a candle for him, and hurried away. She had to see a guest off.

When she returned, he was still lying on his back, looking at the ceiling.

"What's the matter? Are you feeling worse?"

"Yes."

She shook her head and sat there a while.

"You know, *Jean,* I wonder whether we shouldn't send for Leshchetitsky?"

This meant sending for the famous doctor and not sparing any expense. He smiled malignantly and said: "No." She sat a while, and then went up to him and kissed him on the forehead.

As she kissed him, he hated her with all his being, and he had to make an effort to keep from pushing her away.

"Good night. God grant you sleep."

"Yes."

VI

Ivan Ilyich saw that he was dying, and he was in constant despair.

In the depth of his heart Ivan Ilyich knew that he was dying; but, far from becoming used to this idea, he simply didn't understand, was absolutely unable to understand it.

That example of a syllogism which he had studied in Kiesewetter's logic book, "Caius is a man; all men are mortal; therefore Caius is mortal," had always seemed to be applicable only to Caius, but in no way to him. That was the man Caius, and man in general; and this was completely true of them. But he was not Caius, and not man in general; he had always been a being completely, completely different from all others. He had been Vanya,[6] with his mama, with his papa, with Mitya and Volodya, with his toys, with a coachman, with a nurse; then with Katenka, with all the joys, sorrows, and delights of childhood, boyhood, youth. Had Caius ever smelled that odor of the striped leather ball which Vanya had loved so? Had Caius kissed his mother's hand in the same way, and had the silken folds of his mother's dress rustled in the same way for Caius? Had he rioted about the patties at law school? Had Caius been in love in the same way as he had? Had Caius been able to preside over a session like he could?

"And Caius is indeed mortal, and it's proper for him to die; but for me, Vanya, Ivan Ilyich, with all my feelings and thoughts, for me it's a different matter. It simply can't be that

[6] *Vanya* is a diminutive of *Ivan*.

I'll have to die. That would be too terrible." That was the way he felt about it.

"If I had to die like Caius, I would know it; an inner voice would tell me so; but this has not been the case with me at all, and I and all my friends—we understood that it's not at all the same as with Caius. But now see what's happening!" he said to himself. "It can't be. It can't be, but it is. How is this? How do you understand this?"

And he was unable to understand, and tried to dispel this thought as being false, incorrect, and morbid and to supplant it with other, correct, healthy thoughts. But this thought—not merely a thought, but, as it were, a reality—again returned and confronted him.

And he summoned other thoughts, one after the other, to replace this thought, hoping to find support in them. He tried to return to former patterns of thought, which had formerly screened the thought of death from him. But, strange to say, all that had formerly screened, concealed, and destroyed the consciousness of death now could no longer produce this effect. Of late Ivan Ilyich passed the greater part of his time in these endeavors to reëstablish the former patterns of feeling which had screened death from him. At times he would say to himself: "I'll busy myself with my work; after all, it used to be my life before." And he would go to court, driving all doubts away from himself. He would get into discussions with his colleagues and would sit down, from force of old habit casting an absent-minded, pensive glance at the crowd and leaning with both his emaciated arms on the rests of the oak chair. Just as always, he would lean over to a colleague, shift the documents, whisper; and then, suddenly casting an upward glance and sitting up straight, he would pronounce the customary words and begin the case. But suddenly, in the middle of everything, the pain in his side, paying no attention to the stage of the proceedings, would begin *its* enervating proceedings. Ivan Ilyich would concentrate on the matter at hand, would keep driving away the thought of the pain, but it would continue its work; and *it* would come and stand right in front of him and look at him, and he would be petrified, and the light in his eyes would go out, and he would again begin to ask himself: "Is it possible that *it* alone is the truth?" And his associates and subordinates would be surprised and distressed that he, such a brilliant and subtle judge, was getting confused and making mistakes. He would shake himself, would try to pull himself together, and would somehow manage to bring the session to a close; and he would return home with the sad realization that his judicial work could not, as it had done before, conceal from him that which he wished to conceal and that he could not get rid of *it* by means of his judicial work. And worst of all was the fact that *it* drew his attention toward itself, not in order to get him to do something, but only to make him look at it, straight into its eyes—look at it and suffer inexpressibly, without doing anything.

And, trying to escape from this situation, Ivan Ilyich would seek various consolations, other screens; and these other screens would appear and, for a short time, seem to save him; but very soon they would again be, not destroyed, but made transparent, as though *it* penetrated everything and as though nothing could screen *it*.

During this last period he would enter the drawing room which he had himself decorated, that drawing room where he had fallen, for which he—as he thought with a bitter humor—for the arrangement of which he had sacrificed his life, because he knew that his illness had begun with that injury; he would enter and see that something had scarred the polished table. He would look for the cause of this and find it in the album's bronze ornamentation, which was bent back at the edge. He would pick up the album, an expensive one—he had arranged it himself with love—and would be annoyed at the untidiness of his daughter and her friends—there were tears and photographs were turned upside down. He would carefully put it all back into order and would bend the ornamentation back into its original shape.

Then he would think of moving this whole *établissement* with the albums to another corner, near the flowers. He would call a footman. Either his daughter or his wife would come to help him; they would not agree, would contradict him; he would argue and get angry; but all this was good, for then he wouldn't think of *it*—*it* was not visible.

But just then, as he moved the things himself, his wife would say: "Let the servants do it; you'll hurt yourself again"; and suddenly *it* would appear through the screen—he would see *it*. *It* would appear, and he would still hope that *it* would vanish; but then he would involuntarily become aware of his side— the pain would still be there and would still be nagging in the same way, and he would no longer be able to forget it; and *it* would boldly stare at him from behind the flowers. What was the point of it all?

"And it's true that I lost my life here, at this curtain, just as if I had been storming a fortress. Is it possible? How terrible and how stupid! It can't be! It can't be, but it is."

He would go to his study, would lie down, and would again be left all alone with *it*. He would be face to face with *it*, but there was nothing he could do about *it*. All he could do was to look at it and grow cold with horror.

VII

It's impossible to say how it all happened in the third month of Ivan Ilyich's illness because it all happened imperceptibly, step by step; but what happened was that his wife, and his daughter, and his son, and the servants, and his acquaintances, and the doctors, and, above all else, he himself knew that the whole interest of others in him consisted in knowing whether he would soon and finally vacate his position, free the living from the constraint produced by his presence, and himself be freed from his sufferings.

He slept less and less; he was given opium, and they began morphine injections. But this didn't make it easier for him. The dull depression which he experienced in his half-sleeping state at first gave him the relief provided by something new, but later it became as agonizing as the unalleviated pain, or even more so.

They prepared special food for him in accordance with the doctor's instructions; but he found this food to be more and more tasteless, more and more repulsive.

Special arrangements were also made for his bowel movements, and this was always a torture for him. It was a torture because of the filth, the indecency, and the smell, and because of the consciousness that another person had to take part in it.

But it was in this most disagreeable matter that Ivan Ilyich found his consolation. The peasant who served as the butler's helper, Gerasim, always came to carry out the excrement. Gerasim was a clean, fresh young peasant, who had put on weight as a result of his city diet. He was always cheerful and calm, and was always neatly dressed in the Russian fashion. At first the sight of this man doing this revolting work embarrassed Ivan Ilyich.

Once, after getting off of the bedpan and being unable to pull up his pants, he dropped down into an easy chair and looked in horror at his bare, feeble thighs with their sharply defined muscles.

Gerasim, in heavy boots, spreading about him the pleasant odor of tar from his boots and of the freshness of the winter air, came into the room with light, firm steps. He wore a clean hempen apron and a clean cotton-print shirt, the sleeves of which were rolled up on his bare, strong, young arms. Without looking at Ivan Ilyich—obviously repressing the joy of life which shone in his face, in order to avoid offending the sick man—he walked up to the bedpan.

"Gerasim," said Ivan Ilyich in a feeble voice.

Gerasim gave a start, evidently afraid that he had done something wrong, and with a quick movement turned toward the sick man his fresh, kind, simple, youthful face, which was just beginning to show signs of a beard.

"What do you wish?"

"I suppose this is unpleasant for you. You must excuse me. I can't help it."

"Why it's nothing at all, sir." And Gerasim's eyes lit up, and he showed his youthful, white teeth. "Why shouldn't there be a little work? You're sick."

And with his strong, agile hands he did his usual work, and went out, stepping lightly. And in five minutes he returned, stepping as lightly as before.

Ivan Ilyich was still sitting in the same position in the chair.

"Gerasim," he said, when the man had put down the clean, washed bedpan, "please come here and help me."

Gerasim went up to him.

"Lift me up. It's hard for me to do it alone, and I've sent Dmitri away."

Gerasim went up to him; with the same lightness with which he walked, Gerasim put his strong arms around Ivan Ilyich, skillfully and gently lifted and supported him, with one hand pulled up his pants, and wanted to put him down again in the chair. But Ivan Ilyich asked to be led to the sofa. Gerasim, without an effort, and without seeming to press against him, led him, almost carried him, to the sofa, and seated him on it.

"Thank you. How skillfully and well you do everything."

Gerasim smiled again, and was on the point of leaving. But Ivan Ilyich felt so comfortable with him that he didn't want to let him go.

"Here's something you can do: Please move that chair up to me. No, that one—under my feet. I feel more comfortable when my legs are raised."

Gerasim brought the chair, put it down in the right spot on the floor without making any noise, and raised Ivan Ilyich's legs onto the chair. It seemed to Ivan Ilyich that he felt better while Gerasim was raising his legs.

"I feel better when my legs are higher," said Ivan Ilyich. "Put that cushion under them."

Gerasim did this. He raised the legs and put the cushion

down. Again Ivan Ilyich felt better while Gerasim was holding his legs. When Gerasim put them down, he thought he felt worse.

"Gerasim," he said to him, "are you busy now?"

"Not at all, sir," said Gerasim, who had learned from city folk how to talk to gentlemen.

"What else do you have to do?"

"What else do I have to do? I've done everything, and only have to chop some wood for tomorrow."

"If that's the case, hold my legs up a little higher for a while. Can you do that?"

"Why not? I can."

Gerasim raised his legs higher, and it seemed to Ivan Ilyich that he didn't feel any pain at all in this position.

"And what about the wood?"

"Don't worry, sir. There'll be time enough for that."

Ivan Ilyich told Gerasim to sit down and hold his legs, and he chatted with him. And, strange to say, it seemed to him that he felt better as long as Gerasim was holding his legs.

From that time on Ivan Ilyich began to call Gerasim in sometimes, and had Gerasim hold his legs on his shoulders, and liked to talk with him. Gerasim did this easily, gladly, simply, and with a kindness which touched Ivan Ilyich. Health, strength, vitality in all other people offended Ivan Ilyich; only Gerasim's strength and vitality didn't upset Ivan Ilyich—they soothed him.

Ivan Ilyich's chief torment was the lie—that lie, for some reason accepted by all, to the effect that he was only sick and not dying, and that he only needed to be calm and to be treated, and that then some very good thing would result. He knew full well that, no matter what they might do, nothing would come of it but still more agonizing suffering and death. And he was tormented by this lie; he was tormented by the fact that they would not admit what everybody, and he too, knew, but wanted to lie about him in this terrible situation of his, and wanted and compelled him to take part in this lie. The lie, this lie perpe-

trated against him on the eve of his death, the lie destined to
reduce this terrible, solemn act of his death to the level of all
their visits, curtains, sturgeon at dinner . . . was terribly painful for Ivan Ilyich. And, strange to say, often, while they were
making their jokes about him, he was within a hair's breadth
of shouting to them: "Stop lying. Both you and I know that I'm
dying, so at least stop lying." But he never had the courage to
do this. He saw that the terrible, horrible act of his dying was
reduced, by all those about him, to the level of an accidental
unpleasantness, partly to that of an impropriety (something like
the way they treat a man who, on entering a drawing room,
gives off a bad odor), and this was done in the name of that
very same "propriety" which he had served all his life; he saw
that no one would pity him because no one wanted even to
understand his position. Gerasim alone understood this position
and pitied him. And for this reason Ivan Ilyich felt comfortable
only with Gerasim. He felt comfortable when Gerasim sometimes held his legs for whole nights at a stretch and didn't want
to go to bed, saying: "Don't worry, Ivan Ilyich, I'll get some
sleep later on"; or when he suddenly added, passing over to
the familiar *thou*: "If thou wert not a sick man, it would be
different; but, as it is, why shouldn't I serve thee?" Gerasim
alone didn't lie; it was obvious from his whole behavior that
he alone understood what the matter was, and didn't consider it
necessary to conceal this, and simply pitied his emaciated master. Once, when Ivan Ilyich was sending him away, he said
straight out: "We're all going to die. Why shouldn't we go to a
little trouble ourselves?" With these words he expressed the
idea that he didn't find his work burdensome, for the very
reason that he was doing it for a dying man, and that he hoped
someone would also do the same thing for him when his time
came.

Besides this lie, or as a result of it, Ivan Ilyich was tormented most of all by the fact that no one pitied him the way
he wanted to be pitied. At certain moments, after prolonged
suffering, Ivan Ilyich wanted most of all, no matter how much

he would have been ashamed to admit it—he wanted someone to pity him like a sick child. He wanted to be petted, kissed, cried over—as they pet and console children. He knew that he was an important member of the court and that his beard was turning grey, and that, therefore, this was impossible; but, nevertheless, he wanted this. In his relations with Gerasim there was something close to this, and so his relations with Gerasim consoled him.

Ivan Ilyich feels like crying, wants to be petted and cried over; and here comes his colleague, the judge Shebek; and instead of crying and being petted, Ivan Ilyich assumes a serious, stern, pensive look and automatically expresses his opinion about the significance of the decree of the Court of Cassation, and stubbornly sticks to it.

This lie, around him and in him, did more than anything else to poison the last days of Ivan Ilyich's life.

VIII

It was morning. It was morning because Gerasim had left and Peter the footman had come in his place, put out the candles, drawn one curtain aside, and had very quietly begun to tidy up the room. Was it morning? Was it evening? Friday? Was it Sunday? None of this made the slightest difference—it was always one and the same thing: the nagging, agonizing pain which didn't subside for a moment; the consciousness of a life which kept receding hopelessly, but which hadn't receded completely as yet; the same terrible, hateful death which kept on approaching and which alone was reality; and always the same lie. What sense was there to days, weeks, and hours of the day?

"Do you wish to order some tea, sir?"

"He has to have things going on as usual—gentlemen should drink tea in the morning," he thought, but he only said: "No."

"Do you wish to go over to the sofa?"

"He has to tidy up the room and I'm in his way—I'm filthi-

ness and disorder," he thought, but he only said: "No, leave me alone."

The footman bustled about a little while. Ivan Ilyich stretched out his arm. Peter came up, ready to help him.

"What do you wish, sir?"

"My watch."

Peter got the watch, which was lying near at hand, and gave it to him.

"Eight-thirty. They haven't got up yet?"

"Not yet, sir. Vasili Ivanovich [that was his son] has gone to school, and Praskovya Fyodorovna left orders to be awakened if you ask for her. Should I do it, sir?"

"No, it isn't necessary." *"Maybe I should try some tea,"* he thought. "Yes, some tea . . . bring me some tea."

Peter started to go out. Ivan Ilyich became terrified about being left alone. *"How can I keep him here? Yes, the medicine."* "Peter get me the medicine." *"Why not? Maybe the medicine will help me yet."* He took a spoonful and swallowed it. *"No, it won't help me. It's all nonsense, a fraud,"* he decided the moment he felt the familiar, saccharine, hopeless taste in his mouth. *"No, I can't believe it any more. But this pain, why this pain? If it would only stop for just a minute."* And he groaned. Peter came back. "No, go. Bring me some tea."

Peter went away. When Ivan Ilyich was left alone, he groaned, not so much from the pain, terrible though it was, as from despondency. "Always the same and the same, all these endless days and nights. If it would only come sooner. If what came sooner? Death, darkness. No, no. Anything is better than death!"

When Peter came in with the tea on a tray, Ivan Ilyich looked at him in perplexity a long time, unable to make out who he was or what he wanted. Peter was confused by this look. And when Peter became confused, Ivan Ilyich came to his senses. "Yes," he said, "the tea . . . fine, put it down. Just help me to wash and to put on a clean shirt."

And Ivan Ilyich began to wash. Stopping to rest from time to time, he washed his hands and face, brushed his teeth; he began to comb his hair, and looked in the mirror. He became terrified; especially terrifying was the way in which his hair clung limply to his pale forehead.

As his shirt was being changed, he knew that he would feel even more terrified if he glanced at his body, and so he didn't look at himself. But finally it was all finished. He put on his dressing gown, wrapped himself in a shawl, and sat down in a chair to his tea. For a minute he felt refreshed, but as soon as he began to drink the tea, there again was that same taste, that same pain. With an effort he finished his tea and lay down, stretching his legs. He lay down and dismissed Peter.

Always the same. Now a drop of hope would sparkle, and now a sea of despair would suddenly rage, and always the pain, always the pain, always the despondency, and always one and the same thing. It's terribly depressing to be alone, and he wants to call someone in, but he knows in advance that it would be even worse in the presence of others. "If I just had some morphine again—if I could just lose consciousness. I'll tell him, the doctor, to think of something else. It can't go on this way; it can't."

One hour, two hours pass in this way. But now there's the bell in the hall. Maybe it's the doctor. Indeed, it is the doctor: fresh, brisk, fat, jolly, with an expression that says: "Now there you've gone and gotten frightened by something, but we'll soon take care of everything for you." The doctor knows that this expression is out of place here, but he has put it on once and for all and can't take it off, like a man who puts on his dress coat in the morning and goes out calling.

The doctor rubs his hands in a brisk, reassuring manner.

"I'm frozen. It's really cold today. Just let me get warmed up," he says with an expression which seems to imply that all they have to do is wait a little until he gets warmed up, and as soon as he's warm he'll fix everything.

"Well then, how are you?"

Ivan Ilyich feels that the doctor would like to say: "How are things going?" but that even he feels that it wouldn't do to speak in this manner, and so he says: "How did you pass the night?"

Ivan Ilyich looks at the doctor with an expression that asks the question: "Won't you ever feel ashamed of lying?" But the doctor doesn't want to understand the question.

And Ivan Ilyich says: "Just as terribly as ever. The pain doesn't pass away, doesn't subside. If there were just some relief!"

"Oh now, you patients are always like that. Well, sir, I think I'm warm enough now, and even that most particular Praskovya Fyodorovna would have no basis for objecting to my temperature. Well, sir, good morning." And the doctor shakes his hand.

And, dropping his former playfulness, the doctor begins, with a serious expression, to examine the patient, feels his pulse, takes his temperature, and the tapping and auscultation begin.

Ivan Ilyich knows very well and without any doubt that all this is nonsense and a pure fraud; but when the doctor kneels, leans over him, puts his ear now higher up and now lower down, and with a significant expression on his face performs various gymnastic motions over him, Ivan Ilyich submits to this as he used to submit to the speeches of the lawyers after he had already come to realize full well that they always lie and why they lie.

The doctor, kneeling on the sofa, was still tapping in search of something when Praskovya Fyodorovna's silk dress rustled at the door and she was heard reproaching Peter for not having informed her of the doctor's arrival.

She comes in, kisses her husband, and immediately proceeds to prove that she got up long ago and that it was only through a misunderstanding that she hadn't been present when the doctor came.

Ivan Ilyich looks at her, studying her from head to foot, and silently reproaches her for her whiteness, and plumpness, and the cleanliness of her hands and neck, the gloss of her hair, and the sparkle of her vivacious eyes. He hates her with the full force of his being. And her touch makes him suffer by releasing a flood of hatred for her.

Her attitude toward him and his illness was still the same. Just as the doctor had worked out a certain attitude for himself toward his patients, an attitude which he was no longer able to discard, so she had worked out a certain attitude toward Ivan Ilyich: that he was not doing something that he should be doing, that he himself was at fault, and that she was lovingly reproaching him for this; and she was no longer able to discard this attitude toward him.

"Well, you know, he won't listen to me. He doesn't take his medicine on time. But worst of all, he lies in a position which is undoubtedly harmful for him—with his legs raised." She told the doctor how he made Gerasim hold his legs up.

The doctor's contemptuously kind smile said: "Well, what's to be done? These patients sometimes get such silly ideas. But we can forgive them."

When the examination was finished, the doctor looked at his watch; and Praskovya Fyodorovna announced to Ivan Ilyich that she didn't care how he felt about it, but that she had asked the famous doctor to come today. He and Mikhail Danilovich (that was the name of their regular doctor) would examine Ivan Ilyich together and have a consultation.

"Now please don't object. I'm doing this for my own sake," she said ironically, giving him to understand that she was doing everything for his sake and was saying this only to deprive him of the right to refuse her. He was silent, and frowned. He felt that this lie which surrounded him was becoming so involved that it was now difficult to make anything out.

All that she did for him was entirely for her own sake, and she told him that she was doing for herself everything that she really was doing for herself, as though it were such an incredible thing that he ought to understand it as the opposite.

And the famous doctor really did arrive, at eleven-thirty. Again there were auscultations and significant discussions, in his presence and in another room, about the kidney and the appendix, and questions and answers with such significant looks that attention was focused not on the real problem of life and death, which now alone confronted him, but on the problem of the kidney and the appendix, which were somehow not acting as they ought to, and which, for this reason, Mikhail Danilovich and the celebrity were about to attack and compel to get better.

The famous doctor departed with a serious, but not hopeless look. And in reply to the timid question which Ivan Ilyich directed to him, with eyes raised to him and shining with terror and hope, as to whether there was any possibility of recovery, he replied that he could not guarantee it, but that it was possible. The glance of hope with which Ivan Ilyich saw the doctor off was so pitiful that, seeing it, Praskovya Fyodorovna even burst into tears as she was leaving the study in order to give the famous doctor his fee.

The elation produced by the doctor's encouragement did not last long. Again the same room, the same pictures, curtains, wallpaper, bottles, and the same pain-ridden, suffering body. And Ivan Ilyich began to groan; they gave him an injection, and he lost consciousness.

When he came to, it was beginning to get dark; they brought him his dinner. With an effort, he took some broth; and again the same thing, and again the approaching night.

After dinner, at seven o'clock, Praskovya Fyodorovna came into his room. She was dressed for an evening's entertainment, with large, uplifted breasts and traces of powder on her face. Only that morning she had reminded him that they were going to the theater. Sarah Bernhardt was in town, and they had a box which he had insisted that they take. He had now forgotten about this, and her attire offended him. But he concealed his sense of insult when he remembered that he himself had insisted on their taking the box and going, because this was an educational, aesthetic entertainment for the children.

Praskovya Fyodorovna came in looking self-satisfied, but with a trace of guilt. She sat down, asked about his health, merely, as he saw, for the sake of asking, and not to find out, knowing that there was nothing to find out, and started to say what she had to say: She would not have gone on any account, but the box had been taken, and Hélène, and their daughter, and Petrishchev (the examining magistrate, their daughter's fiancé) were going, and it was impossible to let them go by themselves; and it really would have been so much more pleasant for her to stay at home with him. She just wished that he would follow the doctor's instructions in her absence.

"Yes, and Fyodor Petrovich [the fiancé] wanted to come in. May he? And Liza."

"Let them come in."

The daughter came in. She was all dressed up, with her young body exposed. His body caused him to suffer so much; but she flaunted hers. She was strong, healthy, obviously in love, and angered by the illness, suffering, and death which interfered with her happiness.

Fyodor Petrovich also came in, wearing a dress coat, with his hair fixed *à la Capoul,* with a long sinewy neck tightly enclosed in a white collar, with an enormous white chest and close-fitting narrow black pants over powerful thighs, with one white glove drawn over his hand, and with an opera hat.

After him there unobtrusively crept in the little high school student in a brand-new uniform; the poor thing was wearing gloves and had terrible dark blue circles under his eyes, the meaning of which Ivan Ilyich knew.

He had always felt sorry for his son. And terrible was his frightened and compassionate glance. It seemed to Ivan Ilyich that, aside from Gerasim, Vasya was the only one who understood and pitied him.

They all sat down and again asked about his health. A silence followed. Then Liza asked her mother about the opera glasses. Mother and daughter exchanged words about whose fault it was for having mislaid them. It was an unpleasant incident.

Fyodor Petrovich asked Ivan Ilyich whether he had seen Sarah Bernhardt. At first Ivan Ilyich didn't understand what it was that he was asking him, but then he said: "No. And have you seen her already?"

"Yes, in *Adrienne Lecouvreur*."

Praskovya Fyodorovna said that she was particularly good in that role. Her daughter disagreed. There followed a discussion of the grace and realism of her acting—that type of discussion which always turns out to be one and the same.

In the middle of the discussion Fyodor Petrovich looked at Ivan Ilyich and grew silent. The others looked at him too, and grew silent. With glittering eyes Ivan Ilyich was staring straight ahead, obviously angry with them. It was necessary to remedy this, but it was impossible to remedy it in any way. It was necessary to break the silence somehow. Nobody dared, and all became terrified by the thought that suddenly the lie dictated by propriety would somehow be disturbed and that the truth would become obvious to all. Liza was the first to make up her mind. She interrupted the silence. She wanted to conceal what all were experiencing, but she gave it away.

"Well, *if* we're *going,* then it's time we got started," she said, having glanced at her watch, a present from her father; and she gave the young man a barely perceptible smile, which meant something only to the two of them, and got up, her dress rustling.

All got up, said good-by, and left.

When they went out, it seemed to Ivan Ilyich that he felt better. The lie was gone—it had left with them—but the pain remained. That same constant pain, that same constant fear made him feel that his condition was neither better nor worse. But it was steadily growing worse.

Again minute followed minute, and hour followed hour. Always the same, and never an end to it. And the inevitable end became more and more terrifying.

"Yes, send Gerasim in," he said in answer to Peter's question.

IX

His wife returned late at night. She entered on tiptoe, but he heard her. He opened his eyes and quickly closed them again. She wanted to send Gerasim away and to sit up with him herself. He opened his eyes and said: "No. Go."

"Are you suffering very much?"

"It doesn't matter."

"Take some opium."

He agreed and took some. She went away.

Until about three o'clock he was in an agonizing oblivion. It seemed to him that he with his pain was being shoved into some sort of narrow, black, and deep sack, and being shoved farther and farther into it, but that it was impossible to push him into it completely. And this terrible experience was accompanied by suffering. And he was both afraid and wanted to fall into the sack, both resisted and helped along. And then suddenly he broke through, and fell, and came to. The same Gerasim was still sitting at his feet on the bed, drowsing calmly and patiently. And Ivan Ilyich was lying with his emaciated, stockinged feet resting on Gerasim's shoulders; and there was the same candle with the shade, and the same incessant pain.

"Go away, Gerasim," he whispered.

"It's all right, sir. I'll sit a while."

"No, go."

He put his feet down, and lay sidewise on his arm, and began to feel sorry for himself. He waited only until Gerasim went into the next room, and then no longer restrained himself, and burst into tears, like a child. He cried because of his helplessness, because of his terrible loneliness, because of the cruelty of men, because of the cruelty of God, because of the absence of God.

"Why have You done all this? Why did You bring me to this? Why, why are You torturing me so terribly?"

He both didn't expect any answer and cried because there was no answer and could be none. The pain rose again, but he didn't stir, didn't call anyone. He said to himself: "Well, do it again; strike me! But why? What have I done to You? Why?

Then he grew silent, and not only stopped crying, but also breathing, and became all attention—it was as though he were listening not to a voice which spoke with sounds, but to the voice of his soul, to the procession of thoughts which rose within him.

"What do you want?" was the first clear idea capable of being expressed in words which he heard.

"What do you want? What do you want?" he repeated to himself. "What? Not to suffer. To live," he answered.

And he again abandoned himself wholly to a concentration so intense that even his pain didn't distract him.

"To live? To live how?" asked the voice of his soul.

"Why to live as I used to live before: well, pleasantly."

"As you lived before, well and pleasantly?" asked the voice. And in his mind he began to review the best moments of his pleasant life. But, strange to say, all these best moments of his pleasant life now seemed to be completely different from what they had seemed to be before. All of them—except the first recollections of childhood. There, in his childhood, there had been something so really pleasant, something with which it would be possible to live if it returned. But the man who had experienced those pleasant sensations was no more—it was like a recollection of somebody else.

As soon as there began that which had resulted in the present man, in Ivan Ilyich, then everything which had once seemed to be a joy melted before his eyes and changed into something insignificant and frequently foul.

And the farther away from childhood and the closer to the present one came, the more insignificant and doubtful were the joys. This began with law school. Something truly good had still existed then—then there had been gaiety; then there had been friendship; then there had been hopes. But in the higher grades these good moments were now rarer. Then, at the time of his first position, with the governor, there again appeared some good moments—these were the recollections of his love for a woman. Then all of this got mixed up, and there was still less of what was good. Farther on there was still less of what was good, and the farther one went, the less there was.

His marriage . . . so accidental, and the disenchantment, and the odor from his wife's mouth, and the sensuality, and the hypocrisy! And that deadly work, and those worries about money; and so a year passed, and two, and ten, and twenty— and it was always the same. "And the farther I went, the deadlier it became. It was as though I were steadily going downhill while imagining that I was going uphill. That's the way it was. In the public opinion I was going uphill, while I was actually leaving life behind at the same pace. And now it's all finished—so die!

"But what does this all mean? Why? It can't be. It can't be that life is so senseless and so ugly! And if it really has been so ugly and senseless, then why should one die and die suffering? Something is wrong.

"Maybe I didn't live as I should have," it suddenly occurred to him. "But how can that be, since I did everything properly?" he said to himself and immediately dismissed this sole solution of the whole enigma of life and death as something completely impossible.

"What do you want now? To live? To live how? To live as you live in court when the bailiff announces: 'The judges are coming!'"

"The judges are coming; the judges are coming," he repeated to himself. "Here they are: the judges! But I'm not guilty!" he shrieked in anger. "Why am I on trial?" And he stopped crying and, turning his face to the wall, began to think of only one and the same thing: Why, why all this terror?

But no matter how much he thought, he found no answer. And when the thought occurred to him, and it occurred to him often, that all this was due to the fact that he had not lived as he should have, he immediately recalled the complete correctness of his life and dismissed this strange thought.

X

Two more weeks passed. Ivan Ilyich no longer got up from his sofa. He didn't want to lie in bed, and lay on the sofa. And lying almost all the time with his face to the wall, he continued to suffer in loneliness the same unresolved agonies, and in loneliness continued to think the same unresolved thought. "What is this? Can it be true that this is death?" And the inner voice answered him: "Yes, it's true." "Why these torments?" And the voice answered: "Why for no reason at all." There was nothing beyond or in addition to this.

From the very beginning of his illness, from the first time that Ivan Ilyich had gone to see the doctor, his life had been divided into two opposite, alternating moods—now there was despair and the expectation of an incomprehensible and terrible death, and now hope and an absorbing attention to the functions of his body. Now before his eyes there was nothing but his kidney or appendix, which had neglected to fulfill its obligations for a while, and now there was nothing but an incomprehensible, terrible death, from which it was impossible to save oneself by any means.

These two moods had alternated from the very beginning of his illness; but the farther his illness progressed, the more dubious and fantastic did his ideas about his kidney become, and the more real did his consciousness of approaching death become.

All he had to do was to remember what he had been three months before and what he was now, to remember how steadily he had been going downhill—and all possibility of hope was destroyed.

During the last stage of that loneliness in which he found himself, lying with his face turned to the back of the sofa, of that loneliness in the midst of a populous city and his numerous acquaintances and his family—a loneliness than which none more complete could exist anywhere, either at the bottom of the sea or in the earth—during the last stage of this terrible loneliness Ivan Ilyich lived only in his memories of the past. One after another there arose before him pictures of his past. This process of recollection always began with what was most recent and went back to what was most remote, to his childhood, and there it stopped. If Ivan Ilyich thought of the stewed prunes which he had been offered that day, he recalled the raw, wrinkled French prunes of his childhood, their particular taste, and the abundance of saliva when he reached the stone; and along with this recollection of the taste there arose a whole series of memories of that time: his nurse, his brother, his toys. "I shouldn't think of this—it's too painful," Ivan Ilyich would say to himself, and would again come back to the present. A button on the back of the sofa and wrinkles in the morocco. "The morocco is expensive, not durable; there was a quarrel because of it. But it was a different kind of morocco and a different kind of quarrel when we tore father's portfolio, and were punished, and mama brought us patties." And again his thoughts stopped at his childhood, and again it was painful for Ivan Ilyich, and he tried to drive away these thoughts and to think of something else.

And now again, together with this procession of memories, another procession of memories passed through his mind, of how his illness had intensified and grown. Again it was the same—the farther back he went, the more there was of life. There had been both more of the good in life and more of life itself. Both one and the other had blended together. "Just as my suffering keeps getting worse and worse, so my whole life kept getting worse and worse," he thought. There was one bright point back there, at the beginning of life, and then everything grew blacker and blacker, and everything went faster and faster. "Inversely proportional to the square of the distance from death," thought Ivan Ilyich. And this image of a stone falling downward with increasing velocity became fixed in his mind. Life, a series of increasing sufferings, falls more and more rapidly toward its end, a most terrible suffering. "I am falling. . . ." He trembled, stirred, wanted to resist; but he knew that it was impossible to resist; and again he stared at the back of the sofa with eyes that were weary from looking, but that could not help but look at what was in front of him; and he waited—waited for that terrible fall, jolt, and destruction. "It's impossible to resist," he said to himself. "But if I could only understand why it's so. But this is impossible. One might be able to explain it, if it could be said that I had not lived as I should have. But one certainly couldn't say that this was the case," he said to himself as he recalled the complete lawfulness, correctness, and propriety of his life. "It's certainly impossible to assume this," he said to himself, his lips smiling ironically as though someone could see this smile of his and be deceived by it. "There is no explanation! Torment, death. . . . Why?"

XI

Two weeks went by in this way. During these weeks there occurred an event which had been desired by Ivan Ilyich and his wife: Petrishchev made a formal proposal. This happened one evening. The following day Praskovya Fyodorovna entered her husband's room, wondering how to inform him of Fyodor Petrovich's proposal; but that very night Ivan Ilyich had taken a new turn for the worse. Praskovya Fyodorovna found him on the same sofa, but in a new position. He was lying on his back, groaning, and looking straight ahead with a fixed stare.

She began to speak of the medicine. His stare shifted to her. She didn't finish saying what she had begun—such malice, especially toward her, was expressed in this stare.

"For Christ's sake, let me die in peace," he said.

She wanted to go away, but just then the daughter came in and went up to greet him. He looked at his daughter in the same way as at his wife, and in reply to her questions about his health he told her dryly that he would soon free them all of himself. Both grew silent, sat a while, and went out.

"How are we to blame?" Liza asked her mother. "It's as though we had done something. I'm sorry for papa, but why torture us?"

The doctor arrived at the usual hour. Ivan Ilyich answered him "yes, no" without shifting his angry stare from him; and, towards the end, said: "Look, you yourself know that nothing will help me; so leave me alone."

"We can ease your suffering," said the doctor.

"You can't do that either. Leave me alone."

The doctor went into the drawing room and informed Praskovya Fyodorovna that the situation was very bad and that there was only one thing, opium, that could ease the suffering, which must be terrible.

The doctor said that his physical suffering was terrible, and that was true; but more terrible than his physical suffering was his spiritual suffering, and in this lay his chief agony.

His spiritual suffering stemmed from the fact that during that night, as he had looked at Gerasim's sleepy, good-natured face with its prominent cheekbones, a thought had suddenly occurred to him: "But what if my whole life, my conscious life, was not really right?"

It had occurred to him that what had formerly seemed to him to be an utter impossibility, namely, that he had not lived his life as he should have—that this might be true. It had occurred to him that those barely perceptible, timid impulses of his to struggle against that which was regarded as good by persons in the highest positions, the barely perceptible, timid impulses which he had immediately fought back—that these might have been right, while everything else might have been wrong. And his work, and his manner of living, and his family, and his social and official interests—all of this might have been wrong. He had tried to defend all of this to himself. And suddenly he had felt the complete weakness of everything which he was defending. And there had been no sense in defending it.

"And if this is so," he had said to himself, "and I'm leaving life with the consciousness that I've ruined everything which was given me and that it's impossible to set things aright, what then?" He had lain back and begun to review his life from an entirely different point of view. In the morning, when he had seen the footman, then his wife, then his daughter, then the doctor—every movement of theirs, every word of theirs had confirmed for him the terrible truth which had been revealed to him during the night. In them he had seen himself, all that he had been living by, and had clearly seen that it was all wrong, that it was all a terrible, huge deception concealing both life and death. This consciousness had increased, multiplied tenfold his physical suffering. He groaned, and tossed about, and tore at his clothes. It seemed to him that his clothes stifled and weighed him down. And for this he hated them all.

He was given a big dose of opium and he fell into unconsciousness, but at dinner time the same thing began again. He drove all away from himself, and tossed about from one spot to another.

His wife came to him and said: "*Jean,* darling, do this for me [for me?]. It can't do any harm, and it often helps. After all, it's nothing much. Even healthy people often. . . ."

He opened his eyes wide. "What? Take communion? What for? It isn't necessary! Still. . . ."

She began to cry. "Will you, my dear? I'll send for our priest —he's such a nice man."

"Fine, very good," he said.

When the priest came and heard his confession, he felt more kindly, felt as if he were somewhat relieved of his doubts and, consequently, of his suffering, and experienced a moment of hope. Again he began to think of his appendix and the possibility of curing it. He took communion with tears in his eyes.

After communion, when he was put down on the sofa, he felt better for a moment, and again there appeared the hope that he would live. He began to think of the operation which had been suggested to him. "I want to live, to live," he said to himself. His wife came to congratulate him; she said the customary words, and added: "You feel better now, don't you?"

Without looking at her, he said: "Yes."

Her clothes, her figure, the expression on her face, the sound of her voice—everything told him one and the same thing: "It's not the right thing. Everything by which you lived and are living is a lie, a fraud which conceals life and death from you." The moment he thought this, his hatred welled up, and with his hatred came the agonizing physical suffering, and with the suffering, a consciousness of inescapable, approaching ruin. Something new happened—there were boring and stabbing pains, and his breathing was constricted.

When he said "Yes," there was a horrible expression on his face. Having said this "Yes," looking straight into her face, he turned face downward with a rapidity unusual for someone in his weak condition, and screamed: "Go away, go away, leave me alone!"

XII

From this moment on there began that screaming which didn't stop for three days and which was so terrible that one couldn't hear it, even through two closed doors, without feeling horror. The moment he answered his wife, he understood that he was lost, that there was no return, that the end had come, the final end, while his doubt had still not been resolved and still remained a doubt.

"Oo! Oo-o! Oo!" he screamed with various intonations. He had begun to scream: "I don't want to!" and continued screaming the sound "oo."

For three whole days, in the course of which time didn't exist for him, he thrashed about in that black sack into which an invisible, invincible force was trying to shove him completely. He struggled as a prisoner condemned to death struggles in the hands of a hangman, even though he knows he can't escape; and with every minute he felt that, in spite of all the efforts of the struggle, he was coming closer and closer to what terrified him.

He felt that his suffering resulted from his being shoved into that black hole, and still more from his not being able to crawl into it completely. And what prevented him from crawling through was his assertion that his life had been a good one. This justification of his life clutched at him, and wouldn't let him get in, and tormented him more than anything else.

Suddenly some sort of force pushed him in the chest and in the side, caused his breathing to become even more constricted; and he tumbled into the hole, and there, at the end of the hole, was a light. What happened to him was what used to happen in a railroad car when he thought he was riding forward but was actually riding backward, and suddenly discovered the real direction.

"Yes, it was all wrong," he said to himself, "but that doesn't matter. It's possible, it's possible to do the right thing." He asked himself: "What is the right thing?"—and suddenly grew quiet.

This happened at the end of the third day, an hour before his death. It was then that the little high school student stole quietly into his father's room and went up to his bed. The dying man was screaming desperately and thrashing about with his arms. His hand fell on the head of the little student. The little student caught it, pressed it to his lips, and started to cry.

Just then Ivan Ilyich tumbled in and saw the light, and it was revealed to him that his life had not been what it should have been, but that it was still possible to rectify this. He asked himself: "What is the right thing?"—and grew quiet, listening. At this point he felt that someone was kissing his hand. He opened his eyes and glanced at his son. He felt sorry for him. His wife came up to him. He glanced at her. She was looking at him in despair, her mouth wide open and the undried tears on her nose and cheek. He felt sorry for her.

"Yes, I'm torturing them," he thought. "They're sorry, but they'll be better off when I'm dead." He wanted to say this, but he didn't have the strength to utter it. "But why talk? I must act," he thought. With his eyes he directed his wife's attention to the son and said: "Take him away . . . am sorry . . . and for you too. . . ." He wanted to add *prosti,* but said *propusti;*[7] and now too weak to correct himself, he waved his hand, knowing that the One Who should understand, would understand.

And suddenly it became clear to him that what had been tormenting him and would not come out—that it was suddenly coming out all at once, from two sides, from ten sides, from all sides. He felt sorry for them; he had to spare them the anguish, to free them and himself from this suffering. "How good and how simple," he thought. "And the pain?" he asked himself. "Where has it gone? Well, pain, where are you?"

He waited for a sign of it.

"Yes, there it is. Well, so what? Let the pain go on."

"And death? Where is it?"

He sought his former customary fear of death, and could not find it. "Where is it? What death?" There was no fear, because there was also no death.

Instead of death there was light.

"So that's what it is!" he suddenly said aloud. "What joy!"

For him all this took place in one moment, and the significance of this moment never changed. But for those who were present his agony lasted two hours more. Something kept gurgling in his chest; his emaciated body kept twitching. Then the gurgling and the death rattle grew less and less frequent.

"It's ended!" said someone standing over him.

He heard these words and repeated them in his mind. "Death is ended," he said to himself. "It is no more."

He drew in a breath, stopped in the middle of a sigh, stretched, and died.

---

[7] The first word means *forgive me,* the second, *let me pass.*

THE POWER OF DARKNESS
or
"When the Claw Is Caught,
the Whole Bird Is Lost"

But I say to you that every man who looks at a woman with lust has already committed adultery with her in his heart.

And if your right eye leads you astray, tear it out and fling it away from yourself, for it is better that one of your members perish than that your whole body be flung into hell.

MATTHEW, V, 28, 29

Characters

(The names in parentheses are those by which the characters are also referred to in the course of the play.)

PETER IGNATICH a rich peasant, forty-two years old, married for the second time, sickly.

ANISYA MIKHAILOVNA (Anisyushka) his wife, thirty-two years old, a sharp dresser.

AKULINA (Akul) Peter's daughter by his first marriage, sixteen years old, hard of hearing, simple-minded.

ANYUTKA (Anna Petrovna) Peter and Anisya's daughter, ten years old.

NIKITA (Nikishka, Nikitka, Nikitushka) their hired man, twenty-five years old, a sharp dresser.

71

AKIM Nikita's father, fifty years old, a homely and God-fearing
  peasant.

MATRYONA Akim's wife, fifty years old.

MARINA (Marinka, Marinushka, Marishka) an orphan, twenty-two
  years old.

FRIEND AND NEIGHBOR OF ANISYA (Mavra)

MARTHA Peter's sister.

PEOPLE

MITRICH an old hired man, an ex-soldier.

NEIGHBOR

BRIDEGROOM'S FATHER (Ivan, Matchmaker) a gloomy peasant.

FIRST GIRL

SECOND GIRL

MARINA'S HUSBAND (Semyon Matveyevich)

CONSTABLE

DRIVER

BEST MAN

BRIDEGROOM'S MOTHER

AKULINA'S BRIDEGROOM

ELDER

GUESTS, PEASANT WOMEN, GIRLS, PEOPLE AT THE WEDDING

ACT I

*The action takes place in autumn in a large village. The stage
represents the inside of Peter's spacious hut. Peter is seated on
a bench, mending a horse collar. Anisya and Akulina are spinning and singing in two-part harmony.*

PETER (*looking out the window*) The horses have gotten
out again. Before you know it, they'll kill the colt. Nikita! Hey,
Nikita! He's gone deaf! (*Listens. To the women.*) Stop singing;
I can't hear anything!

NIKITA'S VOICE (*from the yard*) What do you want?

PETER Drive the horses in!

NIKITA'S VOICE I will. Just give me a chance to.

PETER (*shaking his head*) Eh, these hired men! If I were

well, I'd never keep one. They're only a nuisance. (*Gets up and then sits down again.*) Nikita! You can't get an answer. Why don't one of you go out? Akul, go and drive them in.

AKULINA   The horses?

PETER   Well, what else?

AKULINA   Right away. (*Exit.*)

PETER   The fellow is a real loafer, no good as a farmer. Won't lift a finger unless he has too.

ANISYA   And you're so lively yourself, aren't you? From the oven[1] to the bench, that's as far as you ever get. All you can do is hound other people.

PETER   If I didn't hound all of you, we wouldn't even have a house left in a year's time. Eh, what people!

ANISYA   You shove a dozen jobs off on a person, and then swear at him. It's easy enough to give orders when you're lying on the oven.

PETER (*sighing*)   Eh, if I weren't plagued by this sickness, I wouldn't keep him even a day.

AKULINA'S VOICE (*off-stage*)   Pse, pse, pse . . . . (*Sounds of a colt neighing and horses running in through the gate. The gate creaks.*)

PETER   Bragging—that's what he's good at. I really wouldn't keep him.

ANISYA (*mimicking*)   I won't keep him. If you got a move on yourself, then you could talk.

AKULINA (*enters*)   I had the hardest time driving them in. The roan always——

PETER   And where's Nikita?

AKULINA   Nikita? He's standing in the street.

PETER   Why's he standing there?

AKULINA   Why's he standing there? He's just standing around the corner—jawing.

PETER   You can't get any sense out of her. Well, who's he jawing with?

---

[1] Russian ovens had a place on top for sleeping.

AKULINA (*not having caught what he said*)   What? (*Peter waves his hand at Akulina; she sits down to her spinning.*)

ANYUTKA (*runs in. To her mother*)   Nikitka's mother and father have come to see him. They're taking him back home to stay, so help me God.

ANISYA   Are you lying?

ANYUTKA   It's true! May I drop dead if it isn't! (*Laughs.*) I'm walking by, and Nikita says to me: "Good-by now, Anna Petrovna," says he. "You'll have to come to my wedding and have a good time. I," says he, "am leaving you people." And he laughs.

ANISYA (*to her husband*)   He certainly doesn't stand in any great need of you. See, he's decided to leave on his own. And you're talking of getting rid of him.

PETER   So let him go. Think I can't find somebody else?

ANISYA   And what about the money he got in advance?

(*Anyutka goes up to the door, listens to what they're saying, and then leaves.*)

PETER (*frowning*)   If need be, he can work off the money in the summer.

ANISYA   You're glad to let him go, aren't you—you won't have to feed him. And in winter I can do the work all by myself, like some kind of a gelding. The girl isn't too eager to work, and you'll be lying on the oven. I know you.

PETER   You don't know anything, so what's the sense of wagging your tongue for nothing?

ANISYA   The yard is full of livestock. You didn't sell the cow and you're keeping all the sheep through the winter; there's no keeping up with the feeding and watering of them—and you want to let the hired man go. But I'm not going to do a man's work! I'm going to lie down on the oven just like you. Let everything go to pot. Do what you want to do.

PETER (*to Akulina*)   Why don't you go and see about the feed? It's time.

AKULINA The feed? Well, all right. (*Puts on a caftan and takes a rope.*)

ANISYA I won't work for you. I've had enough already. I won't. Go and work yourself.

PETER Oh, stop it. What are you having a fit about? You're as crazy as a sheep.

ANISYA And you're a mad dog! There's no getting any work or joy out of you. All you do is nag. A shaky dog, that's what you are.

PETER (*spits and puts on his coat*) You go to hell! The Lord forgive me! I've got to go out and see what's going on. (*Exit.*)

ANISYA (*shouting after him*) You rotten, long-nosed devil!

AKULINA Why are you bawling out father?

ANISYA Beat it, you fool. Shut up.

AKULINA (*walking up to the door*) I know why you're bawling him out. You're a fool yourself, you bitch. And I'm not afraid of you.

ANISYA What's that? (*Jumps up and looks around for something to hit her with.*) Look out, or I'll let you have it with the poker.

AKULINA (*having opened the door*) You're a bitch, a devil, that's what you are! Devil, bitch, bitch, devil! (*She runs out.*)

ANISYA (*deep in thought*) "Come to the wedding," says he. What's this they're up to? Going to marry him off? Look out, Nikita. If that's what you're thinking of doing, I'll make sure . . . . I can't live without him. I won't let him go.

NIKITA (*enters, looking about him. Seeing that Anisya is alone, he quickly goes up to her. In a whisper*) Well, dear, it's a mess. My father has come, wants to take me away—tells me I've got to go home. "We're definitely getting you married and you're going to live at home," says he.

ANISYA Well, get married. What do I care?

NIKITA You don't say! Here I'm trying to figure out how to size up this business a little better, and look at her—tells me to get married. Why? Or have you forgotten?

ANISYA   Go ahead and get married. A lot I care . . . .

NIKITA   What are you snorting about? See, she won't even let me pat her. Why, what's the matter with you?

ANISYA   And as for your wanting to leave me . . . . And if you want to leave me, well, I don't need you. That's what I've got to say to you.

NIKITA   Oh, stop it, Anisya. Do you think I want to forget you? Never. So I definitely won't leave you. Now I'm figuring it like this—even if I'm married off, I'll still come back to you; if only he doesn't take me back home.

ANISYA   Much use you'll be to me when you're married.

NIKITA   But what else can I do, dear? After all, there's just no way of getting out of what a person's father wants him to do.

ANISYA   You're blaming it on your father, but it's really your idea. You've been screwing with that piece of yours, with Marinka, a long time. It's she who put you up to it. It wasn't for nothing that she came running here the other day.

NIKITA   Marinka?! A lot I care about her! There are more than a few of that sort chasing me.

ANISYA   Then why did your father come? You told him to! You've been deceiving me! (*Cries.*)

NIKITA   Anisya, how can you say a thing like that? Why, I never even dreamed of such a thing. I knew absolutely nothing about it. My old man thought it all up himself.

ANISYA   And if you don't want to do it yourself, do you think somebody is going to drag you into it with a lasso?

NIKITA   I figure I just can't buck my father. But I don't want to get married.

ANISYA   Just don't give in.

NIKITA   There was one such fellow who wouldn't give in, and so the authorities gave him a real flogging. It's very simple. I don't want any of that either. They say it tickles.

ANISYA   Stop your joking. You listen here, Nikita, if you marry Marina, there's no telling what I'll do to myself . . . . I'll kill myself! I've sinned, broken God's law, and it's too late to turn back now. And if you should leave, I'll——

NIKITA   Why should I leave? If I wanted to leave, I'd have left long ago. The other day Ivan Semyonych was really after me with a coachman's job . . . . And what a life that is! But I didn't go. That's the attitude I take because everybody likes me here. If you didn't love me, then it would be a different matter.

ANISYA   Just keep this in mind. The old man is going to die any day now, and I'm thinking we can cover up all our sins. I've been thinking I'll marry you and you'll be the master here.

NIKITA   Eh, what's the use of making plans? What do I care? I work just as hard as I would if I were doing it for myself. My master likes me and his woman, of course, loves me. And as for all these women loving me, why that's no fault of mine—it's very simple.

ANISYA   Will you go on loving me?

NIKITA (*embraces her*)   Here's how! Just as you've always been in my heart——

(*Matryona enters and crosses herself before the icons for a long time. Nikita and Anisya move apart.*)

MATRYONA   And I didn't see what I saw, didn't hear what I heard. You've been having a little fun with the young woman—so what? Even a calf, you know—even it has fun. Why not have a little fun? After all, you're young. But, son, the master is asking for you outside.

NIKITA   I just came in to get the axe.

MATRYONA   I know, I know, dear, what kind of axe you came for. That kind of axe is mostly found around women.

NIKITA (*bending down and picking up the axe*)   Well, mother, do you really want to get me married off? I figure it's completely pointless. And besides, I don't want to get married.

MATRYONA   Eh, my dear, why marry you off? Just go on living as you are now. It's all the old man's idea. Run along, dear; we can settle everything without your help.

NIKITA   It's a queer business, that's for sure. Now they want to marry me off, and now they don't. I can't figure it out at all. (*Exit.*)

ANISYA   Well, how about it, Auntie[2] Matryona? Do you really want to marry him off?

MATRYONA   How can we afford to marry him off, my dear? You know we've got no means. My old man is just talking through his hat: "We're going to get him married, we're going to get him married." But he doesn't understand the first thing about it all. Horses don't stray away from oats, you know; let well enough alone—and that's just the situation here. Can't I see (*winks*) how things are shaping up here?

ANISYA   Why should I try to hide it from you, Auntie Matryona? You know everything. I've sinned; I've fallen in love with your son.

MATRYONA   Well now, isn't this a surprise. And Auntie Matryona didn't even know about it. Eh, my girl, Auntie Matryona has been around. Let me tell you, my dear: Auntie Matryona can see a yard under ground. I know everything, my dear! I know why young women need sleeping powders. I brought some. (*Unties the knot in her handkerchief and takes out the powders, which are wrapped in a piece of paper.*) I know about things that are needed, but I know nothing about things that aren't needed. That's the way it is with me. Auntie Matryona was once young herself. I had to know how to get along with my own fool too, you know. I know all the hundred and one dodges. I can see, my dear, that your old man is fading away, fading away. There's no strength to him. Stick a pitchfork into him and you won't draw blood. Just see if you don't bury him in the spring. You should take somebody on to help around the place. And isn't my son as good a man as any? No worse than others. So what have I got to gain by taking him away from a good thing? Am I my own boy's enemy?

ANISYA   If only he wouldn't leave us.

MATRYONA   He won't leave, my dear. It's all nonsense. You know my old man. He isn't at all sharp; but sometimes he gets

---

[2] They aren't related. *Auntie, grandfather,* etc. are often used merely as forms of address.

an idea into his noggin, and it gets stuck there—you just can't knock it out.

ANISYA   But how did all this get started?

MATRYONA   Well, you see, my dear, the boy, as you know yourself, has a weakness for women; and he's really good-looking, there's no denying. Well, he worked, as you know, on the railroad; and there they had an orphan girl working as a cook. Well, so this girl started to chase after him.

ANISYA   Marinka?

MATRYONA   The same, damn her. Well, I don't know whether anything really happened or not, but my old man heard about it. He heard it from others, or she herself blabbed to him!

ANISYA   She's really bold, that piece of trash!

MATRYONA   So this blockhead of mine gets on his high horse: "We're going to get him married, we're going to get him married so as to cover up the sin," says he. "We'll take the boy home and get him married," says he. I tried to talk him out of it in every which way. It was absolutely no use! Well, I thought, fine. I'll try a different tack. These fools, my dear, always have to be managed just right. You pretend you agree with them. But when the right moment comes, you at once switch things your own way. A woman, you know, comes flying down from the oven with a hundred and one ideas; so how's he to figure out what's up? "Why, it's a good idea, old man," says I. "Only we've got to think it over. Let's go visit our son," says I, "and we can talk it over with Peter Ignatich. Let's hear what he has to say." So we came.

ANISYA   O-oh, Auntie, but what's going to happen? What if his father just orders him to get married?

MATRYONA   Orders him? He can shove his orders you-know-where. Now don't you worry; it won't happen. I'll sift and strain the whole matter with your old man right away, and everything will go down the drain. I came with him just to take care of this one thing. Here my son is living happily, is looking forward to happiness, and am I going to try to marry him off to a slut? What, am I a fool maybe?

ANISYA   She even came to see him here—Marinka, that is.
Would you believe it, Auntie, when I was told that he was going
to get married, I felt as though somebody had stuck a knife into
my heart. I thought he loved her.

MATRYONA   Not at all, my dear! What, is he a fool maybe?
Catch him being in love with a homeless slut! Nikishka, you
know, is also a smart fellow. He knows whom to be in love with.
And don't you worry, my dear. We won't ever take him away.
And we won't marry him off. Just give us enough money, and
he can go on living here.

ANISYA   I think I'll die if Nikita goes away.

MATRYONA   That's the way it is with you young people. It's
no laughing matter! You're a healthy young woman, and to
have to live with such a worthless rag——

ANISYA   Believe me, Auntie, I hate, I really hate that long-
nosed dog of mine. I can't stand the sight of him.

MATRYONA   Yes, that's the way it goes. Just take a look
here. (*In a whisper, looking around.*) You know, I went to see
that old man about the powders; he gave me two kinds of drugs.
Just take a look here. "This," says he, "is a sleeping powder.
Give him a dose," says he, "and it'll make him sleep so soundly
that he won't wake up no matter what you do. And this," says
he, "is such a drug that if," says he, "you give it in a drink, it
can't be smelled; but it's very strong. It's to be given seven
times," says he, "a pinch each time. Give it seven times. And
freedom," says he, "will soon be hers."

ANISYA   O-o-oh . . . . What's this you're saying?

MATRYONA   "No tell-tale signs whatsoever," says he. He
charged a ruble. "I can't do it for less," says he. Because, you
know, it's really hard to get them. I paid him with my own
money, my dear. I thought: "I'll bring them to Mikhailovna,
and she can take them or not."

ANISYA   O-oh! But couldn't something bad come of them?

MATRYONA   Why what bad thing could come of them, my
dear? It would be different if your man were healthy, but the

truth of the matter is that he's barely alive. He's not long for this world, you know. Things like this happen a lot.

ANISYA   Oh, oh, poor me! I'm afraid, Auntie, that it might be sinful. No, how can you suggest a thing like that?

MATRYONA   I can take them back, you know.

ANISYA   And are these supposed to be dissolved in water, just like the others?

MATRYONA   "Better in tea," says he. "You can't notice a thing," says he. "Absolutely no smell to them—nothing." He's a real smart man.

ANISYA (*taking the powders*)   Oh, oh, poor me! Would I be willing to do such things if my life weren't so hard?

MATRYONA   And don't forget the ruble. I promised the old man I'd bring it to him. He's very worried about it.

ANISYA   Of course. (*Goes to the chest and hides the powders.*)

MATRYONA   And keep them well-hidden, my dear, so that no one will find them. And if, God forbid, anyone should come across them, then say they're for cockroaches . . . . (*Takes the ruble.*) They're also good for cockroaches—— (*Akim enters and she abruptly stops speaking. Akim crosses himself before the icons.*)

PETER (*enters and sits down*)   So what do you say, Uncle Akim?

AKIM   It would be better, Ignatich, it would seem to be better, whachama-call-it, better . . . . Because I'm afraid of whachama-call-it, some mischief, you know. I'd like him to whachama-call-it, to get down to business, you know; I'd like the lad to get down to business. But if you, you know, whachama-call-it, then we could also whachama-call-it. It would seem to be better——

PETER   All right, all right. Sit down and we'll talk it over. (*Akim sits down.*) Well, what's the story? Do you want to marry him off?

MATRYONA   As far as the marrying is concerned, we can

wait a while, Peter Ignatich. You know yourself, Ignatich, how poor we are. How can we afford to marry him off? We haven't got enough to fill our own stomachs. How can we afford to marry him off?

PETER   Decide what's best.

MATRYONA   Besides, there's no need to hurry about marrying him off. This is the kind of thing you don't rush. He's not like a ripe raspberry that'll fall off if you don't pick it.

PETER   Well, it would be a good thing to get him married.

AKIM   I'd like him to, you know, whachama-call-it . . . . Because I, you know, whachama-call-it, got a job in town—got a job—a good-paying one, you know——

MATRYONA   Some job! Cleaning privies. When he came home the other day, I just puked and puked. Phew!

AKIM   That's right; at first it does absolutely whachama-call-it, knock you over—you know, that smell—but when you get used to it, it's not bad—just like swill. And of course it's whachama-call-it, good-paying . . . . And as for the smell being, you know, whachama-call-it, it's not for the likes of us to be choosey. Besides, you can change your clothes. I wanted Nikitka home, you know. Let him look after things, you know. Let him look after things at home, and I'll whachama-call-it, earn something in town.

PETER   If you want your son home, that's all right. But what about the advance I gave him?

AKIM   That's so, that's so, Ignatich. You've, you know, whachama-call-it, hit the nail on the head. Because when he hired out, he sold himself. So let him serve out his time, you know. But this would be just so that he could whachama-call-it, get married. Let him off for a while in that case, you know.

PETER   Why not, that can be arranged.

MATRYONA   But we don't agree on this. I'll lay everything before you, Peter Ignatich, as I would before God. You judge between my old man and me. He started to harp on this business of marrying the boy off. But you just ask him whom he's going to marry the boy to. If it were a decent girl, would I be my child's enemy? But this is a girl with a fault——

AKIM   Now this is unjust. You're unjustly whachama-call-it, blackening the girl's name. Unjustly. Because she, this here girl, has been wronged by my son—wronged, you know. The girl, you know.

PETER   Just how has she been wronged?

AKIM   Why it seems that she, you know, whachama-call-it—with my son Nikitka. With Nikitka, you know, she whachama-call-it.

MATRYONA   Now you just keep quiet a while. I can say it better. Let me tell it. As you yourself know, our boy worked on the railroad before he came to your house. And there this girl began to chase after him. She's just stupid, you know. Name is Marinka, and she worked as a cook for their gang. So now she, this same girl, is accusing our son, saying that he, Nikita, betrayed her.

PETER   This doesn't sound good.

MATRYONA   But she's a good-for-nothing—runs around. Nothing but a slut.

AKIM   There you go again, old woman, not telling, you know, the whachama-call-it. You're not telling the whachama-call-it at all; you're not telling the whachama-call-it at all, you know——

MATRYONA   Whachama-call-it, whachama-call-it, whachama-call-it— that's all you get out of this he-man of mine; and he doesn't know himself what he means by whachama-call-it. Don't take my word on the girl, Peter Ignatich; ask others about her. Everybody will tell you the same thing. She's nothing but a homeless half-wit.

PETER (*to Akim*)   Well, Uncle Akim, if that's the way things are, then there's no point to having him marry her. You know, even a daughter-in-law isn't like a bast shoe that you can just take off of your foot.

AKIM (*excitedly*)   It's not true, old woman, you know, what you said about the girl—whachama-call-it, it's not true. Because the girl is whachama-call-it, very good—a very good girl, you know. I'm sorry—sorry, you know, for this girl.

MATRYONA   He's just like Maremyana the holy woman who grieves for the whole world while everybody at home goes hungry. You're sorry for the girl, but you're not sorry for your son. Tie her around your neck and carry her around with you. Stop talking such nonsense.

AKIM   No, it's not nonsense.

MATRYONA   Don't you interrupt. Let me finish.

AKIM (*interrupting*)   No, it's not nonsense. You know, you're always twisting everything to suit yourself, whether you're talking about the girl or yourself. You're always twisting everything to suit yourself, to make everything come out the way it's best for you; but God, you know, will whachama-call-it, will twist everything back to suit Himself. That's what'll happen in this case.

MATRYONA   Eh, what's the sense of wasting breath on you?

AKIM   She's a hard-working girl, decent, and, you know, whachama-call-it, in the neighborhood she—you know. And she'd also be a whachama-call-it, a help, you know, to us in our poverty. And the wedding wouldn't cost much. But the most important thing is that this girl was wronged. She's a, you know, a whachama-call-it, an orphan; that's what she is, this girl. And she was wronged.

MATRYONA   They all tell the same story——

ANISYA   Uncle Akim, you pay more attention to what us women have to say. We can tell you a thing or two!

AKIM   But what about God, God? Isn't she a human being, this girl? You know, she's also a human being before whachama-call-it, before God. And what do you think?

MATRYONA   Ah, he's starting to harp on——

PETER   Well now, Uncle Akim, you can't believe these girls either, you know. But the lad's alive, and he's here, you know. Have him come in and ask him straight out if it's true. He won't ruin his soul. Call the lad! (*Anisya gets up.*) Tell him his father wants to see him. (*Anisya exit.*)

MATRYONA You've settled this well, my dear. Let the lad speak for himself. Nowadays they don't make people get married against their will either, you know. The lad should be asked too. There's no chance that he'll want to marry her and disgrace himself. To my way of thinking, he should live with you and serve his master. And there's no reason for taking him away for the summer; we can hire somebody. Just give us ten rubles and let him stay with you.

PETER Now first let him have his say; we have to do this properly. Let's finish one thing before going on to the next.

AKIM I've, you know, been saying all this, Peter Ignatich, because, you know, whachama-call-it, such things happen. You intend to, you know, make things come out the way it's best for yourself, and you whachama-call-it, forget about God completely. You think it's better this way. You twist things to suit yourself, but what happens? It turns out that you've gotten yourself into a mess, you know. You were figuring how to make things come out best, but, without God, they come out much worse.

PETER Of course! You have to remember God.

AKIM What happens? Things turn out worse. But if you do things according to the law, and according to God's way, somehow it always whachama-call-it, makes your heart feel glad. You feel you like to do it, you know. So that's why I was thinking to myself, you know, that I'll get him married, you know, and save the lad from sin, you know. He'll be home, you know, whachama-call-it, like he should be according to the law, and I'll be, you know, whachama-call-it, busy in town. The job suits me well. The pay is good. It'll all be according to God's way, you know, and it'll be whachama-call-it, better when it's like that. Besides, she's an orphan, you know. Let me give you an example of what I've been driving at. Last summer they got some wood from the steward, also in an underhanded way. They wanted to cheat the steward, and they did cheat him. But you know, whachama-call-it, they didn't cheat God, and what a whachama-call-it——

(*Enter Nikita and Anyutka.*)

NIKITA   Did you want me? (*Sits down and takes out his tobacco.*)

PETER (*quietly and reproachfully*)   What's the matter with you? Don't you know how to behave? Your father wants to talk to you, and you sit down and start fooling around with your tobacco. You come over here! Get up!

(*Nikita goes over to the table and carelessly leans on it with his elbows, smiling.*)

AKIM   It seems that there's a complaint—a complaint, you know—you know, whachama-call-it, sort of against you, Ni-kishka.

NIKITA   A complaint? From who?

AKIM   The complaint? The complaint is from the girl, from the orphan, you know. It's from her, you know, that there's a complaint against you—from that same Marina, you know.

NIKITA (*chuckling*)   That's really strange. Just what kind of a complaint is it? Who told you this? Maybe she herself?

AKIM   I'm the one who's whachama-call-it, asking the questions now; and you, you know, whachama-call-it, must give the answers. Did you get mixed up with the girl, you know? That is, did you get mixed up with her, you know?

NIKITA   I don't even know what in the world you're talking about.

AKIM   You know, foolishness. Was there any whachama-call-it, foolishness, you know, between you two? Foolishness, you know.

NIKITA   There was nothing much. I was bored, so I kidded around with the cook and played the accordion while she danced. What other kind of foolishness should there be?

PETER Don't you stall, Nikita. Answer your father's questions seriously.

AKIM (*solemnly*) Nikita, you can hide it from men, but you can't hide it from God. Nikita, you know, whachama-call-it, think of that and don't you dare to lie! She's an orphan, you know, and it's easy to wrong her. An orphan, you know. Explain it a little better.

NIKITA Well, there's nothing more to say. I told you absolutely everything, and that's why there's nothing more to say. (*Getting excited.*) She's likely to say anything. She'll say anything she has a mind to behind my back. Why didn't she tattle on Fedka Mikishkin? What's this? You mean you can't even kid around a little nowadays? Let her talk all she wants to.

AKIM Oh, Nikishka, watch out! A lie will always come out. Was there anything or not?

NIKITA (*aside*) Boy, he's really being a pain in the neck. (*To Akim.*) I tell you, I don't know anything. There was nothing going on between her and me. (*Angrily.*) So help me God, may I drop dead on this spot if I'm lying. (*Crosses himself.*) I know absolutely nothing. (*Silence. Nikita continues, even more excitedly.*) Where did you ever get the idea of making me marry her? Why it's really and truly disgraceful. Nowadays nobody has a right to force a person to marry against his will. It's very simple. And I've sworn that I don't know anything more.

MATRYONA (*to her husband*) There now, what did I tell you, you stupid blockhead? They feed you a lot of gossip, and you just believe it all. All you've done is to disgrace the lad for nothing. It'd be better if he stayed at his master's, as he's been doing up to now. And the master will give us ten rubles to help us get along. When the right time comes, we'll marry the lad off.

PETER Well, how about it, Uncle Akim?

AKIM (*clicking his tongue. To his son*) Watch out, Nikita. The tears of someone who's been wronged don't just whachama-call-it, disappear; they always whachama-call-it, plague the guilty man. Watch out that this doesn't happen to you.

NIKITA   Now why should I watch out? You'd better watch out yourself. (*Sits down.*)

ANYUTKA   I'll go and tell mama. (*Runs out.*)

MATRYONA (to Peter)   Well, that's the way it always is, Peter Ignatich. When this fool of mine gets something into his head, you can't knock it out at all. We've just given you a lot of trouble for nothing. Just let the lad stay with you as he has up to now. Keep the lad—he's your servant.

PETER   So what do you say, Uncle Akim?

AKIM   Well, I whachama-call-it, wasn't forcing the lad. Just so long as there isn't any whachama-call-it. I wanted, you know, whachama-call-it——

MATRYONA   You don't know what you're babbling about yourself. Let the lad stay on as he has up to now. He himself doesn't want to leave. And what do we need him for? We can get along without him.

PETER   One thing, Uncle Akim, if you're going to take him away for the summer, I won't be needing him for the winter. If he stays, then it's for the whole year.

MATRYONA   Oh, he'll hire out for the whole year. If we need any help at home in the busy season, we'll hire somebody. And let the lad stay here. And now give us ten rubles.

PETER   So what do you say? For another year?

AKIM (*sighs*)   Well, all right—I really—obviously whachama-call-it, if that's the way, you know—obviously—I really whachama-call-it.

MATRYONA   For another year, starting from St. Dmitri's Day. We know you'll pay decent wages, and in the meantime let us have ten rubles. Give us a helping hand. (*Gets up and bows.*)

(*Anisya and Anyutka enter. Anyutka sits down to one side.*)

PETER   Well now, if that's the case, then it's settled. Let's go to the tavern and have a drink on it. Come on, Uncle Akim, let's go and have a drink.

AKIM   I don't drink; that is, I don't drink liquor.

PETER   Well then, you can have some tea.

AKIM   I'll admit I've got a weakness for tea. I've really got a weakness for tea.

PETER   And the women can have some tea too. And you, Nikita, get to work: drive in the sheep and pick up the straw.

NIKITA   All right. (*All leave, except for Nikita. It's growing dark. Nikita lights a cigarette.*) Boy, they really got after me, harping on my telling them about the fun I had with the girls. It'd take a long time to tell all that. "Marry her," says he. If I married them all, I'd have a lot of wives. A lot I need to get married when I'm doing as well as any married man; there are plenty that wish they were in my shoes. It's funny how it was as though someone suddenly gave me the idea to swear by the icon. Right then and there I put an end to the whole business. They say it's dangerous to swear to a lie. But that's just nonsense —nothing but talk. It's very simple.

AKULINA (*enters in a caftan, puts down a rope, takes off the caftan, and goes into the storeroom*)   You could at least light a lamp.

NIKITA   Why? To look at you? I can see you without a light.

AKULINA   Oh, get lost!

ANYUTKA (*runs in. In a whisper to Nikita*)   Nikita, come out quickly. There's somebody asking for you outside, so help me God.

NIKITA   Who?

ANYUTKA   Marinka, from the railroad. She's waiting around the corner.

NIKITA   You're lying.

ANYUTKA   So help me God, I'm not.

NIKITA   What does she want?

ANYUTKA   She wants you to come out. "All I want is a word with Nikita," says she. I asked her what it was she wanted, but she wouldn't tell me. Just asked: "Is it true that he's leaving you?" And I said: "It's not so. His father wanted to take him away and get him married; but he wouldn't do it, and he's staying on with us for another year." And then she said: "For God's sake, have him come out to me. I just have to have a word with him," she said. She's been waiting for you a long time now. Go on out to her.

NIKITA   Oh, to hell with her. Why should I?

ANYUTKA   She says that if you don't come out, she's coming into the house herself to see you. So help me God, she says she's coming in.

NIKITA   Don't worry. She'll wait around a while and then go.

ANYUTKA   "Could they be wanting to marry him to Akulina?" she says.

AKULINA   (*enters from the storeroom and goes up to Nikita while on her way to get a distaff*)   Marry who to Akulina?

ANYUTKA   Nikita.

AKULINA   Much chance of that! Why, who's saying this?

NIKITA   Why, obviously, people are saying it. (*Looks at her and laughs.*) How about it, Akulina? Will you marry me?

AKULINA   Marry you? Maybe a while ago I might have married you, but now I won't.

NIKITA   Why won't you now?

AKULINA   Because you won't love me.

NIKITA   Why won't I?

AKULINA   Because you won't be allowed to. (*Laughs.*)

NIKITA   Who won't allow me?

AKULINA   My stepmother. She's always swearing, always watching you.

NIKITA (*laughing*)   Is that so? You really notice things.

AKULINA   Who, me? What's so hard to notice? Do you think I'm blind? She's been giving father a real blowing up today, the fat-faced witch. (*Exit to the storeroom.*)

ANYUTKA   Nikita! Look! (*She looks out the window.*) She's coming. So help me God, it's her. I'm leaving. (*Exit.*)

MARINA (*enters*)   What are you doing to me?

NIKITA   What am I doing to you? I'm not doing anything.

MARINA   Do you want to get rid of me?

NIKITA (*angrily getting up*)   Now what's the point of coming here?

MARINA   Oh, Nikita!

NIKITA   You're really some character. What did you come for?

MARINA   Nikita!

NIKITA   Well, what about Nikita? He's right here. What do you want? I'm telling you—get out of here.

MARINA   So, I see, you want to get rid of me, to forget me.

NIKITA   What's there to remember? You don't know yourself. You were standing around the corner; you sent Anyutka for me; I didn't come out to see you. That means I don't want you. It's very simple. Now go away.

MARINA   You don't want me! Now you don't want me. I believed you when you said you'd always love me. And after you've ruined me, then you say you don't want me.

NIKITA   You're just wasting your time with this talk. It's all a lot of nonsense. You've even been telling tales to my father. Do me a favor and get out of here.

MARINA   You know yourself that I haven't loved anyone but you. And I wouldn't feel hurt if you didn't actually want to marry me. I haven't done you any dirt. Why don't you love me anymore? Why?

NIKITA   There's no sense to our wasting time talking about nothing. Get out of here. Oh, these stupid women!

MARINA   It's not because you tricked me, promised to marry me, that I feel hurt; it's because you don't love me anymore. And it's really not because you don't love me anymore, but because you've dropped me for someone else—and I know who that someone else is.

NIKITA (*maliciously advancing upon her*)   Eh, what's the point of talking with a woman like you. You won't listen to reason. Get out, I tell you, or, so help me God, I'll——

MARINA   You'll what? What will you do, beat me? Go ahead, beat me! Why are you turning your face away? Oh, Nikita!

NIKITA   Obviously, this isn't any good—people are going to be coming in. And why waste time with this kind of talk?

MARINA   So then, this is the end. It's all over and done with. You're telling me to forget it all! Well, remember this, Nikita.

I protected my honor as the most precious thing I had. You ruined me for nothing—you tricked me. You had no pity for an orphan (*crying*); you got rid of me. You've killed me, but I won't hold a grudge against you. God be with you! If you find someone better, you'll forget me; if someone worse, you'll remember me. You'll remember me, Nikita. If that's the way things are, then good-by. And I loved you so much. Good-by for the last time. (*Wants to embrace him, and grasps his head.*)

NIKITA (*tearing himself away*)   Eh, what's the sense of talking with you. If you don't want to go, I will, and you can stay.

MARINA (*crying out*)   You beast! (*In the doorway.*) God won't give you any happiness! (*Exit, crying.*)

AKULINA (*coming out of the storeroom*)   You're a real bastard, Nikita.

NIKITA   What do you mean?

AKULINA   How she cried! (*Cries.*)

NIKITA   What are you talking about?

AKULINA   What am I talking about? You've wro-o-onged her. And you'll wrong me the same way . . . you bastard. (*Goes into the storeroom.*)

NIKITA (*after a silence*)   It's a real mess. I love these women like sugar. But after you've sinned with them, it's a mess!

Curtain

ACT II

The stage represents a street and Peter's hut. On the audience's left is the two-part hut and the vestibule, with a porch in the middle; on the right are the gate and a part of the yard. Anisya is beating hemp in the yard. Six months have passed since Act I.

ANISYA (*stops working and listens*)   He's growling again. Must have climbed down from the oven. (*Akulina enters, with pails on a yoke.*) He's calling. Go and see what he wants. Just listen to him howl!

AKULINA   Why can't you go?

ANISYA   Go, I tell you! (*Akulina goes into the hut.*) He's worn me out. Won't tell me where the money is, and that's the end of it. He was in the vestibule the other day, so he must have hidden it there; and now I don't know where it is. Thank God, he's afraid to let it get too far away from him. It's still in the house. If I could only find it. And he didn't have it on him yesterday. And now I don't know where it is. He's worn me to a frazzle. (*Akulina comes out, tying her kerchief on her head.*) Where are you going?

AKULINA   Where? Why he told me to get Auntie Martha. "Go and get my sister," says he. "I'm going to die," says he, "and I have to tell her something."

ANISYA (*to herself*)   He's getting his sister here. Oh, poor me! O-oh! He probably wants to give it to her. What should I do? Oh! (*To Akulina.*) Don't go! Where are you going?

AKULINA   To get Auntie.

ANISYA   Don't go, I tell you. I'll go myself, and you take the wash down to the river. Otherwise you won't get it done by the evening.

AKULINA   But he told *me* to go.

ANISYA   Go where I tell you. I'm going for Martha myself, I told you. Take the shirts off of the fence.

AKULINA   The shirts? But I bet you won't go. He told me to.

ANISYA   I said I'd go and I will. Where's Anyutka?

AKULINA   Anyutka? She's tending the calves.

ANISYA   Send her here. I don't think they'll run off. (*Akulina picks up the wash and goes out.*) If I don't go, he'll give me hell; but if I go, he'll give his sister the money. All my work will be for nothing. I don't really know what to do. My head is splitting. (*Continues to work.*)

MATRYONA (*enters. Like a traveller, she carries a staff and bundle*)   God bless you, my dear.

ANISYA (*looks around, stops working, and claps her hands with joy*)   Why I wasn't expecting you, Auntie. God has sent me the very person I need right now.

MATRYONA   Well, what's up?

ANISYA   I'm simply going crazy. It's a mess!

MATRYONA   Well, they say he's still alive.

ANISYA   Don't even mention it. He's neither alive nor dead.

MATRYONA   He didn't give the money to anyone, did he?

ANISYA   He's just sent for Martha, his sister. Probably has something to do with the money.

MATRYONA   There's no doubt about it. But he hasn't given it to anybody in the meantime, has he?

ANISYA   No, I've been watching him like a hawk.

MATRYONA   But where is the money?

ANISYA   He won't say. And I can't find out in any way. He hides it first in one place and then in another. And having Akulina around is no help either. She may be a real idiot, but still she's always spying, watching. Oh, poor me! I'm worn out.

MATRYONA   Oh, my dear, if he slips the money past you, you'll regret it the rest of your life. They'll kick you off of the place without a thing. My dear, all your life you've suffered and suffered with someone you hate, and now you'll have to go begging as a widow.

ANISYA   Don't even mention it, Auntie. My heart is aching, and I don't know what to do, and there's nobody I can ask for advice. I talked to Nikita. But he's afraid, doesn't want to get mixed up in this business. All he did was to tell me yesterday that it's under the floor.

MATRYONA   Well, did you crawl under there?

ANISYA   I couldn't—he was around. I've noticed that sometimes he has it on himself, and sometimes he hides it.

MATRYONA   Remember, my girl, once you let a chance go by, you won't get another in a lifetime. (*In a whisper.*) Well, have you been giving him the strong tea?

ANISYA   O-oh! (*Wants to answer, but sees the Friend and keeps quiet. The Friend walks by the hut, listening to Peter calling from inside.*)

FRIEND (*to Anisya*)   Say, neighbor! Anisya, hey, Anisya! I think your man is calling.

ANISYA   That's just the way he coughs; it sounds like he's calling. He's in pretty bad shape.

FRIEND (*walks up to Matryona*)   Hello, granny. Where are you coming from?

MATRYONA   From the farm, my dear. I came to see my son. Brought him some shirts. One is naturally concerned about one's child, you know.

FRIEND   Well, that's the way it is. (*To Anisya.*) Well, neighbor, I wanted to bleach the linen, but I guess it's too early yet. Nobody else has started.

ANISYA   Why hurry?

MATRYONA   Well, has he had communion yet?

ANISYA   Of course. The priest was here yesterday.

FRIEND   My dear, I saw him myself yesterday, and I can't see what his soul is holding on to. He's gotten so thin. And, my dear, here the other day he was almost dead, and they put him under the icons. They were already mourning, and were getting ready to wash him.

ANISYA   He came to and got up. Now he's mogging around again.

MATRYONA   Well, are you going to give him extreme unction?

ANISYA   They say we should. If he's still alive tomorrow, we want to send for the priest.

FRIEND   Oh, I bet it's hard on you, Anisyushka. It's not for nothing that they say: "It's not the sick man who suffers, but the one who over him hovers."

ANISYA   It's really so hard. If there were only an end to it—either one way or the other.

FRIEND   Of course. It's no small matter to see him dying for a whole year. He's tied your hands.

MATRYONA   But a widow's life is no fun either. It's all right when she's young, but who feels sorry for her in her old age? It's no fun to be old. Look at me, for example. I've walked only a short distance, and I'm so tired, and my feet are numb. Where is my son?

ANISYA   Plowing. But why don't you come in? We'll get the samovar ready. The tea will make you feel better.

MATRYONA (*sits down*)   I'm really tired out, my dears. And as for extreme unction—you've got to make sure he gets it. People say it's good for the soul.

ANISYA   Well, we'll send for the priest tomorrow.

MATRYONA   That's good. It'll be better that way. And, you know, my girl, we had a wedding.

FRIEND   What's this? A wedding in the spring? [8]

MATRYONA   Well, it seems there's good sense in the saying that "even the night's too short for the poor man to get married." Semyon Matveyevich married Marinka.

ANISYA   So she's finally found happiness.

FRIEND   He's a widower. He must have married her because of the children.

MATRYONA   There are four. What decent girl would marry him? Well, he married her. And she's real happy about it. She couldn't afford to be choosey, you know.

FRIEND   You don't say! Was there talk about her? And is the peasant well-off?

MATRYONA   So far they're getting along all right.

FRIEND   Obviously no one would want to marry a man with children. Take our Mikhailo, for example. He's a fine man, my dear, but still . . . .

A PEASANT'S VOICE   Hey, Mavra, where the hell did you go? Go and drive the cow in. (*Exit Friend.*)

MATRYONA (*speaking in a normal voice while the friend is leaving*)   They married her off because she was you-know-what, my girl. Well, at least now my old fool won't be thinking of marrying Nikishka to her. (*Suddenly changes her voice to a whisper.*) She's gone! Well, I asked you, have you been giving him some of that tea?

---

[8] Because of the work in the fields, peasants didn't usually get married in the spring.

ANISYA   Don't even mention it. I wish he'd die without it. He's not dying anyway; all I've done is taken a sin on my soul. O-oh, poor me! And why did you give me those powders?

MATRYONA   What about the powders? Those are sleeping powders, my girl, and why shouldn't I give them to you? No harm can come of them.

ANISYA   I'm not talking about the sleeping powders, but about those others—the whitish powders.

MATRYONA   Well now, my dear, those are medicinal powders.

ANISYA (*sighing*)   I know, but I'm scared. He's worn me out.

MATRYONA   Well, did you use up a lot?

ANISYA   I gave them to him twice.

MATRYONA   They can't be noticed, can they?

ANISYA   I took a little sip of the tea myself. It's slightly bitter. But he drank the tea and said: "I can't even stand the taste of tea anymore." So I said: "Everything tastes bitter to a sick man." But I was real scared, Auntie.

MATRYONA   Just don't think about it. It's worse when you think about it.

ANISYA   I wish you hadn't given them to me and hadn't led me into sinning. I shiver every time I think of it. Now why did you give them to me?

MATRYONA   Why, what are you saying, my dear? How can you talk like this? Why are you trying to shove the blame off on me? Watch out, my girl, don't try to switch the blame from a guilty person to an innocent one. And if anything should go wrong, I won't be in the picture. I won't know a thing about it. I'll swear that I didn't give you any powders, and that I haven't seen any, and that I haven't ever heard of any such powders. Use your head, my girl. Why, just the other day we got to talking about you and were saying how much you're suffering, you poor dear. Your stepdaughter's a fool and your husband is rotting away—only a miracle can save him. What wouldn't one do when saddled with such a life?

ANISYA   Well, I won't deny that. With a life like mine I've got no choice but to do something like this, or to hang myself, or to strangle him. Can you call this life?

MATRYONA   That's just the point. There's no time to lose in gabbing. You've got to find the money somehow and give him the tea to drink.

ANISYA   O-oh, poor me! I don't know what to do now, and I'm so afraid. I wish he'd die by himself. I just don't want it on my soul.

MATRYONA (*maliciously*)   But why doesn't he let out where the money is? What does he think he can do, take it with him? Does he think nobody will get it? Is that right? God forbid that such a lot of money should be lost for nothing. Wouldn't that be a sin? Just why is he acting like this? Shouldn't he be watched?

ANISYA   I don't really know myself what I should do. He's worn me out.

MATRYONA   Why shouldn't you know? The thing is clear enough. If you make a slip now, you'll regret it the rest of your life. He'll give his sister the money, and you can go whistle.

ANISYA   O-oh, and he did send for her. I've got to go get her.

MATRYONA   Now you just hold off on going for a while. First, get the samovar ready. We'll give him some tea, and then we'll look for the money together. Don't worry, we'll find it.

ANISYA   O-oh! I hope we don't get into trouble.

MATRYONA   Have you got any better ideas? Why waste time? Are you going to come that close to getting the money, and then let it get away? Go and do as I tell you.

ANISYA   All right, I'll go and get the samovar ready.

MATRYONA   Go on, my dear, and do things the way they should be done, so as not to have any cause for regrets later. That's the girl! (*Anisya walks off; Matryona calls after her.*) One more thing, don't tell Nikitka about all these things. He's kind of foolish. God forbid that he should find out about the powders. God knows what he'd do. He's very soft-hearted. You know, it used to be that he wouldn't even kill a chicken. Don't tell him. He won't understand, and there'll be trouble. (*Stops in horror; Peter appears at the door.*)

PETER (*holding on to the wall, drags himself out onto the porch and calls in a weak voice*) Why can't I get an answer out of you? O-oh! Anisya, who's here? (*Falls down on a bench.*)

ANISYA (*coming out from around the corner*) What did you crawl out here for? Why didn't you stay put?

PETER Well, has the girl gone for Martha? I feel real bad. Oh, if I could only die soon!

ANISYA She's busy. I sent her down to the river. Give me time to get ready and I'll go myself.

PETER Send Anyutka. Where is she? Oh, I feel real bad! Oh, I'm dying!

ANISYA I did send for her.

PETER Oh! Well, where is she?

ANISYA I don't know where she is, damn her.

PETER Oh, I can't stand it. My insides are on fire. I feel as if an auger is being turned inside of me. Why did you leave me by myself, like a dog? Nobody around to even give me a drink . . . . Oh . . . send Anyutka to me!

ANISYA Here she is. Anyutka, go to your father. (*Anyutka runs in. Anisya walks off around the corner.*)

PETER Go . . . oh . . . to Aunt Martha. Tell her: "Father," tell her, "wants you to come—he needs you."

ANYUTKA All right.

PETER Wait. Tell her I need her right away. Tell her I'm dying. O-oh . . . .

ANYUTKA Just let me get my kerchief and then I'll be right off. (*Exit running.*)

MATRYONA (*winking*) Well, my girl, remember what you're to do. Go into the hut and hunt everywhere. Search like a dog searches for fleas. Turn everything upside down, and I'll search him.

ANISYA (*to Matryona*) I'll do it right away. I always feel braver when you're around. (*Walks up to the porch. To Peter.*)

Should I get the samovar ready for you? Auntie Matryona has come to see her son; so you can have some tea with her.

PETER   All right. Get it ready.

(*Anisya goes into the vestibule. Matryona goes up to the porch and bows.*)

PETER   Hello.

MATRYONA   How are you, benefactor? How are you, my dear? It's plain that you're still sick. My old man feels so bad about you too. "Go and see how he is," says he. He sends his best. (*Bows again.*)

PETER   I'm dying.

MATRYONA   As I look at you, Ignatich, I can see that suffering is not off in the woods, but keeps close to people. I can see you've wasted away, wasted away completely, you poor thing. It's plain that sickness doesn't make one look good.

PETER   My hour has come.

MATRYONA   Well, Peter Ignatich, it's God's will. You've had communion and God grant that you receive extreme unction. You have a smart wife, thank God, and you'll be buried and have prayers said for you in proper fashion. And then too, in the meantime my son will look after the place.

PETER   There's no one I can give an order to! The woman isn't reliable, fools around—oh yes, I know all about it . . . I know . . . . The girl is stupid, and also young. I've built up this place, but there's no one to take care of it. It's a real shame. (*Whimpers.*)

MATRYONA   Well now, if there's money or anything, you can tell——

PETER (*to Anisya in the vestibule*)   Well, has Anyutka gone?

MATRYONA (*aside*)   What do you know, he didn't forget about it.

ANISYA (*from the vestibule*)   She went right off. Why don't you come back in the house? I'll help you.

PETER   Let me sit here for the last time. It's stuffy in there.

I feel awful . . . . Oh, my heart's all on fire . . . . If I could just die . . . .

MATRYONA If God doesn't take away the soul, it won't fly away by itself. It's God's will that rules life and death, Peter Ignatich. And you can't know when you'll die, either. It could be that you'll get well again after all. There was this case in our village when a man was almost dead——

PETER No. I've got a feeling I'm going to die today. I've got that feeling. (*Leans back and closes his eyes.*)

ANISYA (*entering*) Well how about it, are you coming in or not? I'm tired of waiting for you. Peter! Hey, Peter!

MATRYONA (*stepping away and beckoning to Anisya*) Well?

ANISYA (*coming down from the porch toward Matryona*) It's not there.

MATRYONA But did you look everywhere? Under the floor?

ANISYA It's not there, either. Maybe in the barn. He dragged himself out there yesterday.

MATRYONA Look for it, look for it real hard. Turn everything upside down. You know, I can tell he's going to die today: his nails are blue, and his face has turned the color of the earth. Well, is the samovar ready?

ANISYA Just about.

(*Nikita comes in from the other side. If possible, he rides up to the gate on a horse. He doesn't see Peter.*)

NIKITA (*to his mother*) Hello, mother. Is everyone at home all right?

MATRYONA Thank God we're alive while there's still some bread to eat.

NIKITA Well, how's the master?

MATRYONA Sh, he's sitting over there. (*Points to the porch.*)

NIKITA Well, so what? He can go on sitting for all I care.

PETER (*opening his eyes*) Nikita, oh Nikita, come over here. (*Nikita goes over to him. Anisya and Matryona talk in whispers.*) Why did you come back so soon?

NIKITA   I've finished the plowing.

PETER   Did you plow the strip beyond the bridge?

NIKITA   That's too far away.

PETER   Too far away? It's even farther from the house. Now you'll have to make a special trip out there. You could have killed two birds with one stone. (*Anisya, without showing herself, is listening.*)

MATRYONA (*walking up to them*)   Oh, son, you ought to do better by your master. Your master is sick; he's depending on you; you ought to work real hard for him, like you would for your own father. That's what I told you.

PETER   Well, you better whachama-call-it—oh—get the potatoes out. The women can—oh—sort them out.

ANISYA (*to herself*)   Sure, try to get me out of the way. He wants to send everybody away again; he must have the money on him now. He wants to hide it some place.

PETER   Otherwise—oh—they'll be rotten when the time comes to set them out. Oh, I've got no strength left. (*Gets up.*)

MATRYONA (*runs up on the porch and supports Peter*)   Want me to help you into the house?

PETER   Yes. (*Stops.*) Nikita!

NIKITA (*angrily*)   What else do you want?

PETER   I won't see you again . . . . I'm going to die today . . . . Forgive me, for Christ's sake, forgive me if I've sinned against you. I sinned in word and deed when . . . . There were all sorts of things. Forgive me.

NIKITA   There's nothing to forgive. I'm a sinner too.

MATRYONA   Oh, son, show more feeling.

PETER   Forgive me, for Christ's sake. (*Cries.*)

NIKITA (*snuffling*)   God will forgive you, Uncle Peter. Why, there's no reason for me to feel offended by you. You've done me no wrong. You should forgive me. I may have sinned more against you. (*Cries. Peter goes off whimpering. Matryona supports him.*)

ANISYA   Oh, poor me! There's something behind his words. You can see he's thought of something. (*Goes over to Nikita.*)

Why did you say the money is under the floor? It's not there.

NIKITA (*crying, doesn't answer*) I've never been wronged by him. Been treated well. And see what I've done!

ANISYA Now stop this. Where's the money?

NIKITA (*angrily*) Who knows? Look for it yourself.

ANISYA How come you're so full of pity?

NIKITA I'm sorry for him. I'm really and truly sorry for him. Did you see how he cried? E-eh!

ANISYA Aren't you the softhearted one! And he's certainly a fine one to feel sorry for. He's always treated you like dirt, and just now he gave orders to have you thrown off the place. You'd do better to feel sorry for me.

NIKITA And why should I feel sorry for you?

ANISYA He'll hide the money and die——

NIKITA Don't worry, he won't hide it——

ANISYA Oh, Nikitushka! He's sent for his sister, you know; wants to give it to her. We'll be in a real fix. How'll we live if he gives her the money? You might at least be of some help in this. Didn't you say he dragged himself out to the barn yesterday?

NIKITA I saw him coming out of it. But who knows where he hid the money?

ANISYA Oh, poor me! I'll go out and look for it there.

(*Matryona comes out of the hut and goes down the steps to Anisya and Nikita.*)

MATRYONA (*in a whisper*) Don't go anywhere. He's got the money on him. I felt it. It's on a string around his neck.

ANISYA Oh, poor me!

MATRYONA If you miss your chance now, you might as well go whistle. His sister'll be here, and then you can kiss it good-by.

ANISYA That's right. If she comes, he'll give it to her. What are we going to do? Oh, poor me!

MATRYONA What are we going to do? Now look here, the samovar has come to a boil, so you go fix some tea and serve it to him; (*in a whisper*) and pour out the rest of the powder in the paper and give it to him. When he finishes the cup, take the money. Don't worry, he won't tell anybody.

ANISYA   Oh, I'm scared!

MATRYONA   Don't waste time talking about it. Do it right away, and I'll head off his sister if need be. Now don't mess it up. Take the money and bring it here, and Nikita'll hide it.

ANISYA   Oh, poor me. How can I come up to him and . . . and——

MATRYONA   I tell you, don't waste time talking. Do just as I say. Nikita!

NIKITA   What do you want?

MATRYONA   You stay here. Sit here on the mound,[4] just in case you're needed.

NIKITA (*waving his hand*)   God knows what these women are up to. They're going to get me into a real fix. Oh, the hell with them. I've got to go and get the potatoes out.

MATRYONA (*holding him back by the arm*)   Stay here, I tell you.

(*Anyutka enters.*)

ANISYA   Well, what's the story?

ANYUTKA   She was in her daughter's garden. She'll come right away.

ANISYA   What'll we do if she comes?

MATRYONA (*to Anisya*)   You'll have plenty of time. Do as I tell you.

ANISYA   I don't really know what to do; I haven't the faintest idea. I'm all mixed up. Anyutka! Darling, go out to the calves. They've run off. (*Anyutka exit.*) Oh, I won't get up the nerve to do it.

MATRYONA   Why don't you get going? The samovar must be boiling over by now.

ANISYA   Oh, poor me! (*Exit.*)

---

[4] A low mound of earth banked along the walls of a hut.

MATRYONA (*going up to her son*) That's the way it goes, son. (*Sits down on the mound, next to him.*) Your interests have to be considered too. They can't just be left to take care of themselves.

NIKITA What kind of interests?

MATRYONA Why, just how you're going to get along in the world.

NIKITA How I'm going to get along? Others get along, and I'll do the same.

MATRYONA The old man'll probably die today, don't you think?

NIKITA If he does, the kingdom of heaven be his. What's it to me?

MATRYONA (*keeps glancing at the porch while speaking*) Eh, son! A being has to think about living. And you need a lot of sense for this too, my dear. You know, I've been to all kinds of places, looking after your interests. I've worn myself down to the bone, tending to your interests. So remember, don't forget about me later on.

NIKITA What's this you've been tending to?

MATRYONA To your interests, to your future. If they're not tended to in good time, nothing will come of them. Do you know Ivan Moseich? I also go to see him now and then. I dropped in on him the other day. You see, I also tended to a certain matter of his. I was there a while, and we got to talking. "Ivan Moseich," says I, "how would a certain matter be decided? Suppose," says I, "there's a widower, and suppose he's taken a second wife, and suppose that all the children there are is a daughter by the first wife and one by the second. What happens," says I, "when this man dies? Can another man," says I, "step in and marry this widow? Can this man," says I, "marry off the daughters and take over the place?" "He can," says Ivan Moseich, "only," says he, "it takes a lot of doing in a case like this. If you've got the money," says he, "this matter can be arranged; but if you haven't," says he, "forget it."

NIKITA (*laughing*)   Well, that goes without saying. Just give
them the money. Everybody wants money.

MATRYONA   Well, my dear, so I told him all about the matter. "In the first place," says he, "your son must register himself
in that village. For this you need money—to treat the old men
to drinks. Then they'll sign. Everything," says he, "has to be
done sensibly." Look here. (*Takes a paper out of her kerchief.*)
Here's the paper he's written up. Read it; you've got learning,
you know. (*Nikita reads it; Matryona listens.*)

NIKITA   The paper is obviously a judgment. There's nothing
special about it.

MATRYONA   Now you listen to what Ivan Moseich said should
be done. "Above all, Auntie," says he, "make sure that the
money doesn't get away. If she doesn't get her hands on the
money," says he, "she won't be able to get married again. Money
is the main thing in this matter," says he. So watch out. Things
will soon come to a head, son.

NIKITA   What do I care? It's her money, so let her do the
worrying.

MATRYONA   What kind of talk is that, son? Can a woman
think these things out properly? Suppose she does get the
money. How can she think things out properly? You know what
a woman's like. But you, after all, are a man. So you'd know
how to hide it and all such things. After all, you've got more
sense in case anything happens.

NIKITA   Eh, you women have got no brains whatsoever.

MATRYONA   What do you mean by "no brains"? You just
grab the money, and the woman will be in your hands. Then if
she should start kicking up her heels or something of the kind,
you can pull in the reins on her.

NIKITA   You can all go to hell. I'm leaving.

(*A pale Anisya runs out of the hut and around the corner toward Matryona.*)

ANISYA   He did have it on him. Here it is. (*Shows it under
her apron.*)

MATRYONA   Give it to Nikita! He'll hide it. Nikita, take it and hide it somewhere.

NIKITA   Well, all right. Give it to me.

ANISYA   O-oh, poor me. But maybe I better hide it myself. (*Starts toward the gate.*)

MATRYONA (*grabs her by the arm*)   Where are you going? They'll miss you. There's his sister coming. Give it to him. He knows what to do with it. What a fool!

ANISYA (*stops, undecided*)   Oh, poor me!

NIKITA   Come on, why don't you give it to me? I'll hide it some place.

ANISYA   Where you going to hide it?

NIKITA   What's the matter? You scared? (*Laughs. Akulina enters with the wash.*)

ANISYA   O-oh, poor me! (*Gives up the money.*) Be careful, Nikita.

NIKITA   What are you scared of? I'll hide it so well that I won't even be able to find it myself. (*Exit.*)

ANISYA (*transfixed in fright*)   O-oh! What if he——

MATRYONA   Well, is he dead?

ANISYA   Yes, I think so. He didn't stir when I took it off of him.

MATRYONA   Get into the house. There's Akulina coming.

ANISYA   Here I've sinned, and he's taking the money——

MATRYONA   Stop this! Get into the house. There's Martha coming too.

ANISYA   Well, I put myself in his hands. Not much I can do now. (*Exit. Martha enters from one side and Akulina from the other.*)

MARTHA (*to Akulina*)   I'd have come long ago, but I was at my daughter's. Well, how's the old man? Is he going to die?

AKULINA (*putting down the wash*)   I don't know. I was down at the river.

MARTHA (*pointing to Matryona*)   Who's she?

MATRYONA   Why, I'm from Zuevo; I'm Nikita's mother, from Zuevo, my dear. How are you? He's wasted away; your dear brother has wasted away. He came out. "Send for my dear sister," says he, "because," says he—— Oh, no! Don't tell me he's dead!

(*Anisya runs out of the house with a shriek. She takes hold of a post and begins to wail.*)

ANISYA   O-o-oh, and who-o-o have you left me to? And, o-o-oh, who-o-o have you a-ban-doned me for? O-o-oh! I'm a poor widow. You have closed your eyes forever and ever——

(*The Friend enters. She and Matryona support Anisya under her arms. Akulina and Martha go into the hut. People gather.*)

A VOICE AMONG THE PEOPLE   Send for the old women. The body has to be laid out.

MATRYONA (*rolling up her sleeves*)   Is there any water in the kettle? If not, then I think there's some in the samovar. It wasn't emptied. I can be of some help too.

Curtain

ACT III

The inside of Peter's hut. Winter. Nine months have passed since Act II. Anisya, in everyday clothes, is sitting at the loom, weaving. Anyutka is on the oven. Mitrich, the old hired man, enters slowly.

MITRICH (*taking off his coat*)   Oh Lord have mercy! Well, isn't the master back yet?
ANISYA   What did you say?
MITRICH   Nikita isn't back from town yet?
ANISYA   No.
MITRICH   Looks like he's on a spree. Oh Lord!
ANISYA   Have you cleaned up the threshing-floor?
MITRICH   Of course. I fixed everything up proper and covered it with straw. I don't like to do things just so-so. Oh Lord!

Merciful St. Nicholas! (*Picking the calluses on his hands.*) It's really time he was back.

ANISYA   Why should he hurry? He's got money, so I suppose he's having a good time with the girl——

MITRICH   He's got money, so why shouldn't he have a good time? And why did Akulina go to town?

ANISYA   Why don't you ask her why the hell she went there?

MITRICH   Why would a body go to town? In town there's lots of everything if you've only got the money. Oh Lord!

ANYUTKA   Oh mother, I heard it with my own ears. "I'll buy you a little shawl," says he. So help me God, says he: "I'll buy you a little shawl." "You can pick it out yourself," says he. And you should see how she decked herself out—she put on a sleeveless velveteen jacket and a French kerchief.

ANISYA   It's a fact that a girl's modesty lasts only as far as the door. Once she goes through it, that's the end. The shameless bitch!

MITRICH   Oh well, what's there to be ashamed of? You've got the money, so have a good time. Oh Lord! It's too early for supper yet, isn't it? (*Anisya is silent.*) I'll go get warm in the meantime. (*Climbs up on the oven.*) Oh Lord! Holy Mother of God! St. Nicholas, Servant of God!

FRIEND (*enters*)   Looks like your man hasn't come back yet, has he?

ANISYA   No.

FRIEND   It's time he should have. Maybe he's dropped in at the tavern. My sister was saying there are a lot of sledges from town there.

ANISYA   Anyutka! Hey, Anyutka!

ANYUTKA   What do you want?

ANISYA   Run down to the tavern, dear, and see if he maybe got drunk and stopped off there.

ANYUTKA (*jumping down from the oven and putting on her coat*)   I'll do it right away.

FRIEND   He took Akulina with him, did he?

ANISYA   Why else would he go? It's because of her that he found business to attend to. "I've got to go to the bank," says he. "The interest is ready." But its just her leading him astray.

FRIEND (*shaking her head*)   Looks bad, that's for sure.

(*Silence.*)

ANYUTKA (*at the door*)   And what do I say if he's there?

ANISYA   Just see if he's there.

ANYUTKA   All right, I'll be back soon. (*Exit.*)

(*There is a long silence.*)

MITRICH (*bellowing*)   Oh Lord! Merciful St. Nicholas!

FRIEND (*shuddering*)   Oh, he scared me! Who's that?

ANISYA   Why, Mitrich, the hired man.

FRIEND   Oh, he scared me out of my wits! I'd forgotten all about him. My dear, what's this I hear about somebody wanting to marry Akulina?

ANISYA (*coming out from behind the loom and going toward the table*)   There was a feeler from Dedlovo, but I think the rumor has spread even there. There was a feeler, and then nothing more—the matter was dropped. Who'd want her?

FRIEND   And what about the Lizunovs from Zuevo?

ANISYA   They made a move, but that didn't come to anything either. He won't even talk with any prospects.

FRIEND   But you should marry her off.

ANISYA   You're telling me! My dear, I'd like to get her out of the house, but I can't manage it. He doesn't want to let her go. And she doesn't want to go herself, either. You see, he hasn't had enough of a good time with his beauty yet.

FRIEND   E-e-eh, how sinful. It's unnatural. After all, he's her stepfather.

ANISYA   Eh, my dear. They've done such a good job of cheating and tricking me that it's even hard to imagine. And like a fool I didn't notice anything, didn't give it a thought, and so I married him. I didn't suspect a blessed thing, but they already had an understanding.

FRIEND   O-oh, what a shocking thing!

ANISYA   As time went by, I could see they were trying to hide something from me. Oh, my dear, I'm so sick of it, so sick of life. I wish I didn't love him so.

FRIEND   That goes without saying.

ANISYA   And it hurts me so, my dear, to put up with such insults from him. Oh, it really hurts me.

FRIEND   And is it true what they say? That he's even started to knock you around?

ANISYA   There's a lot of that sort of thing. It used to be that **he** was peaceful when he was drunk. He used to drink before, it's true; but, still, he loved me. Now when he gets loaded, he rushes at me and wants to trample me underfoot. The other day he grabbed me by the hair, and it was all I could do to get away from him. And the girl is worse than a viper; I've never seen the likes of such a shrew.

FRIEND   O-o-oh! I can see how you're suffering, my dear! How can you stand it? You took in a beggar, and now he's humiliating you like this. Aren't you going to take him in hand?

ANISYA   Oh, my dear! What can I do about my feeling for him? My dead husband was certainly strict, but I could still twist him the way I wanted to. But I can't do that with this one, my dear. As soon as I see him, my heart melts. I just can't stand up to him. I'm as meek as a lamb when he's around.

FRIEND   O-oh, my dear! It looks pretty much like you've been bewitched. They say Matryona does such things. It must be she.

ANISYA   That's what I've been thinking too, my dear. Sometimes I feel so hurt, it seems like I'd like to tear him to pieces. But as soon as I see him—no, I can't feel mad.

FRIEND   It's pretty plain that you're bewitched. It doesn't take long to ruin a person by witchcraft, my dear. As I look at you, I can see that something fishy has been going on.

ANISYA   My legs are as thin as sticks. But just look at that fool, at that Akulina. She was a filthy mess, but just look at her now. Where did it all come from? Why, he's decked her out.

She's togged herself out, struts like a pouter pigeon. She may be a fool, but she's got the idea that she's the mistress here. "The house is mine," says she. "It was me that father wanted him to marry." And, my God, can she be mean! When she gets mad, she really raises hell.

FRIEND   O-oh, my dear. I can see what a life you lead. And here people even envy you. "She's rich," they say. But it sure is true, my dear, that you can be unhappy even if you've got money.

ANISYA   What's there to envy? All the money will be gone with the wind anyway. It's a crime how he's wasting it.

FRIEND   But, my dear, how come you let him have it so easily? The money is yours.

ANISYA   Oh, if you only knew the whole story. You see, there was a little mistake I made.

FRIEND   My dear, if I were in your place, I'd go straight to some big official. The money is yours. How can he waste it? He has no right to do that.

ANISYA   Who pays attention to that nowadays?

FRIEND   Eh, my dear, I can see you've grown pretty weak.

ANISYA   I have, my dear—weak, very weak. He's worn me out. And I just don't know what to do. O-oh, poor me!

FRIEND   I think somebody's coming. (*Listens. The door opens, and Akim enters.*)

AKIM (*crosses himself, knocks the snow from his bast shoes, and takes off his coat*)   Peace be upon this house. Is everybody well? Hello, Auntie.

ANISYA   Hello, father. Have you come from the farm? Come right in and take off your things.

AKIM   Thought that I'd whachama-call-it, you know, come down to whachama-call-it, to see my son—come down to see my son. I started late; had dinner, you know, and started out. But it was snowing so hard; it was whachama-call-it, hard—hard to walk. So I'm whachama-call-it, late, you know. And is my son home? Is my son at home?

ANISYA   No, he's not here. He's in town.

AKIM (*sitting down on a bench*)   I've got a little business with him, that is, whachama-call-it, a little business. I was telling him, you know, the other day about whachama-call-it; you know, I was telling him about what I need. My horse died; you know, my horse. Somehow I've whachama-call-it, got to get one —any kind of horse, but a horse. So I've whachama-call-it, come, you know.

ANISYA   Nikita was telling me about it. You can talk with him when he gets back. (*Gets up and walks toward the oven.*) Have some supper, and he'll be along. Mitrich, come and have supper. Hey, Mitrich.

MITRICH (*bellowing as he wakes up*)   What?

ANISYA   Time for supper.

MITRICH   Oh Lord! Merciful St. Nicholas!

ANISYA   Come and eat supper.

FRIEND   I'll be going now. Good-by. (*Exit.*)

MITRICH (*climbing down*)   I fell asleep before I even knew it. Oh Lord! St. Nicholas, Servant of God! Hello, Uncle Akim.

AKIM   Well, Mitrich! What are you doing here, you know, whachama-call-it?

MITRICH   Why, I'm working and living at Nikita's, at your son's.

AKIM   You don't say! So you're whachama-call-it, working for my son. You don't say!

MITRICH   I was staying with a merchant in town, but I went broke, drinking. So I came back to the village. I've got no place to stay, so I hired out. (*Yawning*) Oh Lord!

AKIM   Well, whachama-call-it, but whachama-call-it, what's Nikishka doing? Does he, you know, have a lot of extra work that he hired, you know, whachama-call-it, that he hired a man?

ANISYA   What extra work? He used to manage everything himself before, but nowadays he's got something else on his mind; so he got a hired man.

MITRICH   He's got money, so why not——

AKIM That's whachama-call-it, wrong. Now that's completely whachama-call-it, wrong. That's wrong. That's spoiling oneself, you know.

ANISYA Well, he's already spoiled, so spoiled that there's trouble.

AKIM That's just what happens: whachama-call-it, you try to figure out how to make everything come out the way it's a little better for yourself but it whachama-call-it, you know, comes out worse. A lot of money will spoil a man; it'll spoil him.

MITRICH Too much of anything is bad. If you've got too much money, you can't help but get spoiled. You should have seen the spree I went on when I had the money. Drank three weeks without stopping. Didn't stop till I'd sold the shirt off of my back. When I didn't have anything left, well, then I stopped. Now I've sworn off. The hell with drinking.

AKIM And your old woman, you know, where is she?

MITRICH My old woman, brother, is just where she belongs. She hangs around taverns in town. She's a fine-looking one too: one eye torn out, the other black, and her mug twisted. And she's never sober, damn her.

AKIM O-oh! How come?

MITRICH So what else can a soldier's wife do? She's doing just what she ought to be doing.

(*Silence.*)

AKIM (*to Anisya*) Why did Nikita go to town? Did he whachama-call-it, take something in to sell? You know, did he take something in?

ANISYA (*setting the table and serving the food*) He didn't take anything. He went to get some money—went to the bank to get some money.

AKIM (*eating*) Well now, are you planning to use it, the whachama-call-it, the money, for something else—the money, you know?

ANISYA No, we don't touch the capital. There was just

twenty or thirty rubles in interest; so we have to take that out.

AKIM Have to take it out? Why should you take out the whachama-call-it, the money? Today, you know, whachama-call-it, you take some out; tomorrow, you know, you take some out; so you end up by whachama-call-it, taking it all out, you know.

ANISYA This is the interest. But the money hasn't been touched.

AKIM Hasn't been touched? What do you mean that whachama-call-it, that it hasn't been touched? You take it out, but it hasn't been whachama-call-it, hasn't been touched. Well now, put some whachama-call-it, some flour, you know, into a whachama-call-it, a bin, or into a whachama-call-it, a barn, and then take the flour from there—well, can you say that it whachama-call-it, that it hasn't been touched? There's something wrong here, you know. They're cheating you. You better look into this, or they'll swindle you. How can the money be untouched? Here you're whachama-call-it, taking it out, and it's supposed to be untouched.

ANISYA I don't really know anything about it. That was what Ivan Moseich told us to do at the time. "Put the money in the bank," says he, "and the money'll be safer and you'll get interest."

MITRICH (*finished eating*) That's so. I lived at a merchant's house, and that's the way they do it. They put in the money, and just lay around on the oven and get the interest.

AKIM What you're saying doesn't whachama-call-it, make sense. How can you whachama-call-it, get money—whachama-call-it, get money? And where, you know, whachama-call-it, do they get the whachama-call-it, the money, from? The money, you know.

ANISYA They get it from a bank.

MITRICH What's that? These women are no good at explaining things. Now look here, I'll explain it all to you. Pay attention. Let's suppose you have money; and let's suppose it's spring, my land is idle, and I don't have any seed—or maybe I have to pay the taxes. So then I, you know, come to you.

"Akim," I say, "give me ten rubles. I'll get the crops in, give you back the money by October, and, what's more, I'll harvest a desyatina[5] for you because of the favor you've done me." Let's suppose you see that I can be skinned—I have a horse maybe, or a cow. So you say: "Give me two-three rubles for the favor, and we'll call it quits." The noose is around my neck; I can't get along without the money. "All right," I say and I take the ten rubles. In the fall I sell some of my crop, bring you the money I borrowed, and you skin me to the tune of three rubles.

AKIM   But this is, you know, whachama-call-it, the kind of crooked thing a peasant will whachama-call-it, will do when he whachama-call-it, forgets God, you know. This isn't right, you know.

MITRICH   Now just wait a minute. Shortly Anisya runs into the man who lent me the money, namely, you. Pay attention. So what's happened up to now? You've skinned me, you know. Well, let's suppose Anisya has some money that's just laying around. She has no place to put it and, being a woman, doesn't know how to put it to use. So she comes to you. "Can't I make some use of my money?" says she. "Of course you can," you say to her. And so you wait. In the spring I come to you again. "Give me another ten rubles," I say, "and I'll pay you back with a favor." And so you think it over. If my hide isn't completely gone, if you can skin me some more, then you give me Anisya's money. But let's suppose that I haven't got a thing, nothing for you to gobble up. Then you take my measure, you see that I can't be skinned, so presently you say: "God help you, brother." And you find somebody else; you pass out your money again, and you add Anisya's to it; and you skin him. Now this is just what a bank does. And that's how it works. Brother, it's a very smart business.

AKIM (*getting excited*)   What in the world do you call this? This is, you know, whachama-call-it, a filthy business. When a

---

[5] A desyatina is 2.7 acres.

peasant whachama-call-it, does this sort of thing, the others whachama-call-it, consider it a, you know, a sin. It's whachama-call-it, not according to God's law—not according to God's law, you know. This is a filthy business. How can educated people whachama-call-it——

MITRICH This, brother, is what they like to do best of all. Now pay attention. Take someone who's kind of stupid, or a woman, and can't put his money to use himself. Then such a person takes it to the bank; and they, damn them, snatch it up and then use this money to skin the people. It's a very smart business!

AKIM (*sighing*) Eh, I can see that there's whachama-call-it, trouble, if you haven't got whachama-call-it, money, but that the trouble is whachama-call-it, double, if you have got the money. How come? God has commanded you to work. But you, you know, whachama-call-it, put the money in the bank and then lay around sleeping; and the money is supposed to feed you while you're, you know, whachama-call-it, laying around doing nothing. This is a filthy business, you know; it's not according to God's law.

MITRICH Not according to God's law? Brother, people don't worry about such things nowadays. And they'll really clean you out. That's the way things are.

AKIM (*sighing*) Well, I guess that's whachama-call-it, that's the way things are nowadays. Now take the toilets that I've, you know, whachama-call-it, that I've seen in town. I mean, look at what's been done with them. They've been fixed up, fixed up, you know, decorated. They've been gotten up like a tavern. And it's pointless, all pointless. Oh, we've forgotten God. We've forgotten Him, you know. We've forgotten, forgotten God—God. Thank you, my dear, I've had enough, I'm full. (*They leave the table. Mitrich climbs up on the oven.*)

ANISYA (*taking away the dishes and eating*) If only his father would bring him to his senses, but I'm even ashamed to mention it.

AKIM What's that?

ANISYA Nothing, I was just talking to myself.

(*Anyutka enters.*)

AKIM   Ah, there's a smart girl. Always flying around!
You're cold, I bet.

ANYUTKA   I'm terribly cold. Why, hello, grandpa.

ANISYA   Well, how about it? Is he there?

ANYUTKA   No, but Andrian had just come there from town
and he said he saw them in town, in a tavern. He said father is
real drunk.

ANISYA   I guess you probably want something to eat. Here.

ANYUTKA (*walking toward the oven*)   It's really cold. Even
my hands are numb.

(*Akim takes off his shoes. Anisya washes the spoons.*)

ANISYA   Father!

AKIM   What is it?

ANISYA   Well, is Marishka getting along good?

AKIM   Not bad. She's getting along. She's a whachama-call-
it, a smart little woman, and peaceable. She's getting along. She,
you know, whachama-call-it, tries hard. Not bad. The little
woman is, you know, a good worker; and always whachama-call-
it, tries hard; and she's whachama-call-it, obedient. The little
woman isn't, you know, bad, you know.

ANISYA   Well now, we've heard talk from your village that a
relative of Marinkina's husband wanted to marry our Akulina.
Did you hear anything about it?

AKIM   Was it one of the Mironovs? Seems to me the women
were saying something about it. But I don't remember, you
know. I'm not, you know, sure about whachama-call-it. The old
women were saying something about it. But I've a bad memory,
a bad memory, you know. Well, the Mironovs are, you know,
whachama-call-it, good whachama-call-its, good peasants.

ANISYA   I just can't wait to get her married off as soon as
possible.

AKIM   Why's that?

ANYUTKA (*listening to the noise off-stage*)   They're back.

(*A drunk Nikita enters, carrying a sack, a bundle under his arm, and wrapped-up purchases. After opening the door, he stops.*)

ANISYA   Now keep out of their way. (*She continues to wash the spoons and doesn't look around when the door opens.*)

NIKITA   Anisya! Wife! Who's come? (*Anisya looks around and, turning away, keeps silent. Nikita continues in a threatening manner.*) Who's come? Maybe you've forgotten?

ANISYA   Stop showing off and come in.

NIKITA (*in a more threatening manner*)   Who's come?

ANISYA (*goes up to him and takes hold of his arm*)   Well, my husband has come. Come into the room.

NIKITA (*resisting*)   That's right, your husband. And what's your husband's name? Say it correctly.

ANISYA   Oh, come on—it's Nikita.

NIKITA   That's right! Pig—call me by my middle name.

ANISYA   Akimych. So there!

NIKITA (*still at the door*)   That's right. No, tell me what my last name is.

ANISYA (*laughing and pulling him by the arm*)   Chilikin. You're certainly mad.

NIKITA   That's right. (*Supporting himself by the door jamb.*) No, tell me what foot Chilikin puts out first when he steps into the room.

ANISYA   Now enough of this. You'll let the cold in.

NIKITA   Tell me, what foot does he put out first? You absolutely have to tell me.

ANISYA (*to herself*)   Now he's going to make a nuisance of himself. All right, the left foot. Now come on in.

NIKITA   That's right.

ANISYA   Take a look at who's in the room.

NIKITA   My father? So what? I don't hate my father. I can show my father proper respect. Hello, father. (*Bows to him and gives him his hand.*) My respects to you.

AKIM (*not answering him*)   It's the liquor, the liquor, you know. Just see what it does. It's a filthy business.

NIKITA   The liquor? You're talking about my having a
drink? I'm definitely guilty of this. I took a drink with a friend.
I was congratulating him.

ANISYA   Why don't you go and lie down?

NIKITA   Wife, where am I standing? Tell me!

ANISYA   Now that's enough. Go and lie down.

NIKITA   No, I'm going to have some tea with father. Get the
samovar ready. Akulina, why don't you come in?

AKULINA (*dressed up, walks in with her purchases. To Nikita*)   Why did you go and scatter everything? Where's the
yarn?

NIKITA   The yarn? The yarn is over there. Hey, Mitrich,
where the deuce are you? You sleeping? Go and take care of
the horse.

AKIM (*doesn't see Akulina; continues to look at his son*)
What's he doing? The old man is, you know, whachama-call-it,
dead tired, you know—been threshing; and here you're
whachama-call-it, showing off. "Take care of the horse." My
God, what a filthy business!

MITRICH (*comes down from the oven and puts on his felt
boots*)   Oh merciful Lord! The horse is outside, is it? You've
worn it out, I bet. Damn it, just look how he's lapped it up.
Loaded. Oh Lord! St. Nicholas, Servant of God! (*Puts on his
fur coat and goes out.*)

NIKITA (*sits down*)   Forgive me, father. I've been drinking,
that's true. But how can I help it? Even a chicken drinks. Isn't
that so? So forgive me. And as for Mitrich—he isn't offended;
he'll take care of the horse.

ANISYA   Do you really want me to get the samovar ready?

NIKITA   Get it ready. Father has come. I want to talk with
him, and we'll drink tea. (*To Akulina.*) Did you bring in all the
things we bought?

AKULINA   The things? I brought in my own; the rest is out
in the sledge. Here, take this; it doesn't belong to me. (*Throws
a parcel on the table and starts to put her purchases into a chest.
Anyutka watches Akulina putting away her things. Akim doesn't*

look at his son; he is putting his leg cloths and bast shoes on the oven.)

ANISYA (*leaving with the samovar*)   The chest is full as it is, and here he's bought more things.

NIKITA (*trying to look sober*)   Don't be angry with me, father. You think I'm drunk. I can do absolutely everything. It's all right to drink, as long as you don't lose your senses. I can talk with you right now, father, as if nothing had happened. I remember everything. Your horse died, and you need some money—I remember it all. I can take care of that. There's no problem about doing that for you. If you needed a real lot of money, then you might have to wait a little. But I can take care of this without any trouble. Here you are!

AKIM (*still busy with his leg cloths*)   Eh, young fellow, a whachama-call-it, you know, a spring path is not a whachama-call-it, a road——

NIKITA   What do you mean by that? You think there's no point to talking with someone who's drunk? Now don't you worry about that. We'll drink some tea together. And I can take care of everything; I can set everything absolutely right.

AKIM (*shaking his head*)   Eh, eh-he-he!

NIKITA   The money—here it is. (*Reaches into his pocket, gets his wallet, riffles through the bills, and pulls out a ten-ruble bill.*) Take this for the horse. Take it for the horse—I won't let my father down. I positively won't abandon you. Because you're my father. Here, take it. It's very simple. I don't begrudge you the money. (*Comes up to Akim and pushes the money into his hand. Akim doesn't take the money. Grabs Akim by the arm.*) Take it, I tell you. When I offer it, I don't begrudge it.

AKIM   I can't, you know, whachama-call-it, can't take it; and I can't whachama-call-it, talk with you, you know. Because you're not whachama-call-it, not yourself, you know.

NIKITA   I won't let you go. Take it. (*Pushes the money into Akim's hand.*)

ANISYA (*enters and stops*)   You better take it, or he won't give you any rest.

AKIM (*takes it, shaking his head*)   Eh, that liquor! It makes an animal out of a man, you know——

NIKITA   Now that's better. If you pay it back—fine; if not —so what? That's the way I do things. (*Sees Akulina.*) Akulina, show them your presents.

AKULINA   What?

NIKITA   Show them your presents.

AKULINA   The presents? What's the point of showing them? I've put them away already.

NIKITA   Get them out, I tell you. Anyutka would like to see them. I tell you, show them to Anyutka. Unwrap the little shawl. Give it to me.

AKIM   O-oh, it makes me sick to my stomach to look at this! (*Climbs up on the oven.*)

AKULINA (*gets her things and puts them on the table*) Well, here they are. What's there to look at?

ANYUTKA   Oh, how nice it is! It's just as nice as Stepanida's.

AKULINA   Stepanida's? Stepanida's doesn't even come close to this. (*Becoming animated and unwrapping the shawl.*) Just look at this—the quality . . . . It's French.

ANYUTKA   It's a real pretty print. Mashutka has one like it, only hers is lighter—on a sky-blue background. This one is real nice.

NIKITA   That's a fact.

(*Anisya angrily goes into the storeroom, returns with the samovar chimney and a tablecloth, and walks over to the table.*)

ANISYA   Get this stuff off. You've got it scattered all over the table.

NIKITA   Take a look at this!

ANISYA   What's there to look at? Do you think I haven't seen anything before? Take it away. (*Sweeps the shawl onto the floor.*)

AKULINA   What are you doing that for? Throw your own things on the floor. (*Picks it up.*)

NIKITA   Anisya, take a look at this!

ANISYA   What's there to look at?

NIKITA   You think I've forgotten you, but look at this. (*Shows her a parcel and then sits down on it.*) It's a present for you. Only you have to earn it. Wife, where am I sitting?

ANISYA   Stop your bullying. I'm not afraid of you. After all, whose money is it you're using to have a good time on and to buy presents for your fatty? Mine.

AKULINA   What do you mean "yours"? You wanted to steal it, but you didn't get a chance to. Get out of my way! (*Wants to pass by and pushes her.*)

ANISYA   What are you shoving for? I'll give you a shove.

AKULINA   You will, will you? All right, try it. (*Pushes against her.*)

NIKITA   Now, women, women! Stop it! (*Stands between them.*)

AKULINA   See how she keeps butting in! You'd think she'd keep quiet; you'd think she'd keep her mouth shut. You think nobody knows about you?

ANISYA   What do you know? Go ahead, go ahead and tell me what you know!

AKULINA   I know what you've done.

ANISYA   You slut, you're living with somebody else's husband.

AKULINA   And you killed yours.

ANISYA (*rushing at Akulina*)   You're lying.

NIKITA (*holding her back*)   Anisya, have you forgotten?

ANISYA   Why are you threatening me? I'm not afraid of you.

NIKITA   Get out! (*Turns Anisya around and starts pushing her out of the room.*)

ANISYA   Where will I go? I won't leave my own house.

NIKITA   Get out, I tell you. Don't you even dare to set foot in here again.

ANISYA   I won't go. (*Nikita pushes her. Anisya cries and screams, holding on to the door.*) What's he doing—throwing me out of my own house? What are you doing, you bastard? You think there's no law for the likes of you? Just you wait!

NIKITA   Well, well!

ANISYA   I'm going to the elder, to the constable.

NIKITA   Get out, I tell you. (*Pushes her out.*)

ANISYA (*from the other side of the door*)   I'll hang myself!

NIKITA   I doubt it.

ANYUTKA   O-o-oh! Dear, dear mama. (*Cries.*)

NIKITA   Who's afraid of her? What are you crying for? Don't worry, she'll be back. Go and look after the samovar. (*Anyutka exit.*)

AKULINA (*picking up her things and putting them away*) Just look at how the bitch messed things up! Just wait, I'll show her a thing or two. So help me, I will.

NIKITA   I've thrown her out. What more do you want?

AKULINA   She dirtied up my new shawl. So help me, if the bitch hadn't gotten out, I'd have torn her eyes out.

NIKITA   Stop blowing up. What are you blowing up for? You know I don't love her.

AKULINA   Love her? Who could love that fat-faced bitch? If you'd gotten rid of her earlier, there wouldn't have been any trouble. You should have sent her packing. Anyway, the house is mine, and so is the money. And she says she's the lady of the house, the lady of the house. What kind of a lady of the house was she to her husband? She's a murderer, that's what she is. And she'll do the same thing to you.

NIKITA   Oh, you just can't shut a woman's mouth. You don't know what you're talking about yourself.

AKULINA   Yes I do. I won't live in the same house with her. I'll chase her off the place. She can't live with me. Some lady of the house! She's no lady of the house; she's a jailbird.

NIKITA   Now stop it. You don't have to have anything to do with her. Don't listen to her. Listen to me. I'm the master here. And I do what I want. I don't love her anymore; I love you. I can love anybody I want to. I'm in charge here. And she'll do what she's told. That's where her place is, as far as I'm concerned. (*Points under his feet.*) Eh, I don't have an accordion here!

The bread is on the oven,
The kasha's on the shelf,
And we will live,
And have a good time;
And when death comes,
Then we will die.
The bread is on the oven,
The kasha's on the shelf——

MITRICH (*enters, takes his things off, and climbs up on the oven*)   Looks like the women have been fighting again. Going at it hot and heavy. Oh Lord! Merciful St. Nicholas!

AKIM (*sitting on the edge of the oven, gets his leg cloths and bast shoes and starts to put them on*)   Crawl over here, crawl over here into the corner.

MITRICH (*getting into the corner*)   They obviously just won't come to terms. Oh Lord!

NIKITA   Get the brandy. We'll have it with the tea.

ANYUTKA (*enters. To Akulina*)   Sis, the samovar is about to boil over.

NIKITA   And where's your mother?

ANYUTKA   She's out in the vestibule, crying.

NIKITA   Oh, that's right. Go tell her to bring the samovar in. (*Anyutka exit.*) And you get the dishes, Akulina.

AKULINA   The dishes? All right. (*Gets the dishes.*)

NIKITA (*getting the brandy, rolls, and herring*)   Now this is for myself. The yarn is for the wife. The kerosene is out in the vestibule. And here's the money. Just a minute. (*Takes the abacus.*) I'll figure it up right away. (*Adds.*) The wheat flour was eight grivenniks,[6] the lenten oil . . . . Ten rubles for father. Father, come and have some tea.

(*Silence. Akim sits on the oven, putting on his leg cloths.*)

ANISYA (*brings in the samovar*)   Where should I put it?

NIKITA   Put it on the table. Well, have you been to the

[6] A tenth of a ruble.

elder's? That's the way it goes: shoot off your mouth, and then you've got to eat crow. Now enough of this blowing up. Sit down and have a drink. (*Pours her a glass.*) And here's a present for you too. (*Gives her the parcel on which he had been sitting. Anisya takes it silently, shaking her head.*)

AKIM (*climbs down and puts on his fur coat. He goes up to the table and puts the money on it*)   Here's your money. Take it.

NIKITA (*not seeing the money*)   Why'd you put your coat on? Where you going?

AKIM   Why, it's time I was going, it's time I was going, you know. Forgive me, for Christ's sake. (*Takes his cap and belt.*)

NIKITA   Well, I'll be! Where you going at this time of night?

AKIM   I can't stay, you know, whachama-call-it, in your house; I whachama-call-it, can't, you know, stay; I can't stay. Forgive me.

NIKITA   But where are you rushing off to, without even having tea?

AKIM (*putting on his belt*)   I'm going because, you know, there's evil in your house; you know, whachama-call-it, there's evil in your house, Nikishka; whachama-call-it, there's evil. You know, you're leading a bad life, Nikishka, a bad life. I'm going.

NIKITA   Oh, come on now, stop this talk and sit down and have some tea.

ANISYA   Why we'll be put to shame, father. What are you insulted about?

AKIM   I'm not whachama-call-it, not insulted at all; I'm not insulted at all, you know. It's just that I whachama-call-it, that I see, you know, my son, you know, heading for ruin; my son is heading for ruin, you know.

NIKITA   What do you mean "ruin"? Prove it.

AKIM   Ruin, ruin, you're headed straight for ruin. What did I tell you last year?

NIKITA   So what was so important about what you told me?

AKIM   I talked to you about the whachama-call-it, the orphan, about your wronging an orphan. About wronging Marina, you know.

NIKITA   Why bring that up? That's just so much water over the dam. It's a thing of the past——

AKIM (*getting excited*)   A thing of the past? No, brother, it's not a thing of the past. One sin hooks onto another, you know, pulls it along. And you're bogged down in sin, Nikishka. I can see you're bogged down in sin. You're bogged down, sunk in it, you know.

NIKITA   Sit down and drink some tea, and stop this talk.

AKIM   I can't, you know, whachama-call-it, drink tea with you. Because this filthiness of yours, you know, whachama-call-it, makes me feel bad, makes me feel very bad. I can't whachama-call-it, drink tea with you.

NIKITA   Eh, stop wasting time and come to the table.

AKIM   Your wealth is whachama-call-it, like a snare for you. A snare, you know. Ah, Nikishka, your soul is an important thing!

NIKITA   What right have you got to criticize me in my own house? Why are you hounding me like this anyway? Do you think I'm just a little boy that you can pull by the hair? This sort of thing isn't done nowadays.

AKIM   That's right. I've heard that nowadays they even whachama-call-it, that they even pull their fathers' beards, you know. But this leads to ruin, to ruin, you know.

NIKITA (*angrily*)   We're getting along without any help from you. But here you had to come to us with your troubles.

AKIM   You're talking about the money? There's your money. I'll, you know, go and beg, but I won't whachama-call-it, won't take your money, you know.

NIKITA   Now stop that. Why are you getting mad, breaking up the party? (*Holds him back by the arm.*)

AKIM (*screams*)   Let me go. I'm not staying. I'd rather sleep out at the fence than in your filth. Phew! God forgive me. (*Exit.*)

NIKITA   Well, I'll be!

AKIM (*opening the door*)   Come to your senses, Nikita. Your soul is an important thing. (*Exit.*)

AKULINA (*picking up the cups*)   Well, should I start pouring?

(*All are silent.*)

MITRICH (*bellowing*)   Oh Lord, have mercy on me, sinner that I am!

(*All shudder.*)

NIKITA (*lying down on a bench*)   Oh, I feel bad, so bad, Akulina! Where's the accordion?

AKULINA   The accordion? Did you forget? You're having it fixed. I've poured the tea. Go ahead and drink it.

NIKITA   I don't want it. Put out the light . . . . Oh, I feel bad, I feel so bad! (*Cries.*)

Curtain

ACT IV

Scene 1

Autumn. Evening. The moon is shining. The farmyard. In the center is the vestibule; to the right, the winter part of the hut and the gate; to the left, the summer part of the hut and the cellar. Conversation and drunken shouts are heard from the winter part. The Neighbor comes out of the vestibule and beckons to the Friend.

NEIGHBOR   Why doesn't Akulina come out?

FRIEND   Why doesn't she come out? She'd really like to, but she doesn't feel up to it, you know. The matchmakers have come to look the bride over, but, my dear, she just lies out there in the summer part. And the poor dear won't show her face.

NEIGHBOR   Well, what's the matter?

FRIEND She says she's been bewitched and this has caused a stomach-ache.

NEIGHBOR You don't say!

FRIEND What else could it be? (*Whispers something in her ear.*)

NEIGHBOR Is that a fact? Why that's a sin. And the matchmakers will certainly find out about it.

FRIEND How'll they find out? They're all drunk. Besides, they're more interested in the dowry. Not bad. They're giving two fur coats, my dear, some six dresses, a French shawl, quite a bit of linen, and cash—two hundred rubles, they say.

NEIGHBOR Well, there's no pleasure in such money. It's such a disgraceful thing.

FRIEND Sh-sh! I think the matchmaker's coming. (*They stop talking and go into the vestibule. The Matchmaker—Bridegroom's Father—comes out of the vestibule alone, hiccuping.*)

BRIDEGROOM'S FATHER I'm sweating like a horse. My God, but it's hot. I've got to cool off a little. (*Stands, puffing.*) God alone knows what the story is. Something's not right here— something I don't like. Oh well, it's up to my old woman——

MATRYONA (*coming out of the vestibule*) Here I've been looking all over for the matchmaker—and there you are, my dear. Well, my dear, thank God everything's gone off properly. A body shouldn't brag while matchmaking. And I never did learn to brag. But you came to get a good deal and, you've got to admit, that, God willing, you'll be thankful to me all your life. The bride, you know, is a rare one. You won't find another such girl in the whole district.

BRIDEGROOM'S FATHER That's so, if only we don't get fooled about the money.

MATRYONA Don't you worry about the money. She's got all her parents left her. A hundred and fifty rubles isn't bad nowadays.

BRIDEGROOM'S FATHER We're satisfied, but we've got to think of our boy. We want to do the best we can by him.

MATRYONA I'm telling you the truth, matchmaker. If it

weren't for me, you'd never have found anyone like her. The Kormilins were interested in her, but I headed that off. And as far as the money is concerned, I'll tell you how it really was. When the old man was dying—the Kingdom of Heaven be his —he told the widow to take Nikita into the house, and so I know all about it from my son. The money, of course, was to go to Akulina. Now another man would have taken advantage of the situation, but Nikita is giving her absolutely everything that belongs to her. And it's not a small sum.

BRIDEGROOM'S FATHER   People are saying that she has more money coming to her. The young fellow's a pretty shrewd one, too.

MATRYONA   Eh, the poor fools. A piece of bread always looks big in somebody else's hands. She's getting everything that's coming to her. I'm telling you, stop fooling around and clinch the deal at once. What a girl—as sound as an apple.

BRIDEGROOM'S FATHER   That's so, but me and my wife have been bothered by one thing about the girl. Why hasn't she come out? We're thinking that maybe she's ailing.

MATRYONA   Eh! Her ailing? Why there isn't another like her in the whole district. The girl's real healthy—not a thing wrong with her. Why you saw her yourself the other day. And God, can she work. It's true she's a little hard of hearing, but, after all, one wormhole doesn't ruin a sound apple. And as for her not coming out, you know, that's because someone put the evil eye on her. She's been bewitched. And I know the bitch that did it. You see, she knew the matchmakers were coming, so she bewitched the girl. But I know how to cast the spell off. Tomorrow the girl will be up and around again. Don't you have no fears about the girl.

BRIDEGROOM'S FATHER   Well, all right. The matter is settled.

MATRYONA   Fine. Now don't you try to back out of it. And don't forget me. I went to a lot of trouble too. So don't you forget me——

A WOMAN'S VOICE (*from the vestibule*)   If we're going, let's go. Come on along, Ivan.

BRIDEGROOM'S FATHER I'm coming. (*Bridegroom's Father and Matryona leave. People crowd into the vestibule and drive away.*)

ANYUTKA (*running out of the vestibule and beckoning to Anisya* Mama!

ANISYA (*coming from the hut*) What is it?

ANYUTKA Mama, come over here, or they'll hear me. (*They walk over to the barn together.*)

ANISYA Well, what is it? Where's Akulina?

ANYUTKA She went into the barn. And she's carrying on something awful there. So help me God, she keeps saying: "I can't stand it." "I'm going to scream at the top of my lungs," says she. So help me God!

ANISYA She can wait. Let's see the guests off first.

ANYUTKA Oh, mama! It's so hard for her. And she's so angry. "There's no point to their drinking my health," says she. "I won't get married," says she. "I'm going to die," says she. Mama, I hope she doesn't die. I'm awfully scared.

ANISYA Don't worry, she won't die. And don't you go to her. Run along now. (*Anisya and Anyutka leave.*)

MITRICH (*alone, comes from the gate and starts to pick up the scattered hay*) Oh Lord, Merciful St. Nicholas! What a lot of liquor they've guzzled. And what a smell they've made. It stinks even out here in the yard. But no, I don't want any of it—the hell with it! Just look how they've scattered the hay around. They didn't eat it at all—just trampled it. See, there's a whole bundle of it. Oh, that smell! It's as if the liquor were right under my nose. The hell with it! (*Yawns.*) Time for bed. But I don't feel like going in. That smell is just floating around my nose. That damned liquor has a nice strong smell. (*The people can be heard departing.*) Well, they're gone. Oh Lord, Merciful St. Nicholas! They're just snaring each other, pulling the wool over each other's eyes. And it's all pointless.

NIKITA (*coming out*) Mitrich, why don't you go to sleep? I'll pick it up.

MITRICH   All right. Throw it to the sheep. Well, have you seen them off?

NIKITA   I have, but nothing's going right. I don't really know what to do.

MITRICH   What a lot of crap! What's the problem? That's what the foundling home is for. Anybody that wants can dump it there, and they'll pick it up. Give them as many as you want, and there'll be no questions asked. And they even pay money, if the woman wants to be a wet nurse. Nowadays these things are taken care of simply.

NIKITA   Watch out, Mitrich. If anything happens, don't say more than you have to.

MITRICH   It doesn't concern me. Do the best job you can in covering up. Boy, do you ever smell of liquor. I'm going in. (*Goes in, yawning.*) Oh Lord!

NIKITA (*After a long silence, sits down on a sledge*)   It's a bad business!

ANISYA (*coming out*)   Where are you?

NIKITA   Here.

ANISYA   What are you sitting around for? There's no time to waste. You have to take it out right away.

NIKITA   But what are we going to do?

ANISYA   I told you what. Now do it.

NIKITA   You ought to take it to the foundling home.

ANISYA   Take it yourself if that's what you want. You're ready enough to carry on your filthy business, but I can see you're chicken-hearted about straightening things out afterwards.

NIKITA   What am I supposed to do?

ANISYA   I told you: Go down in the cellar and dig a hole.

NIKITA   But can't you do it some other way?

ANISYA (*mocking him*)   Some other way? No, obviously we can't. You should have thought of that before. Go and do what I tell you!

NIKITA   Oh, it's a bad business, a bad business!

ANYUTKA (*running in*) Mama! Grandma's calling you. I think Sis had a baby. So help me God, I heard it crying.

ANISYA Stop lying, damn you. That's the kittens mewing there. Go into the house and go to sleep, or I'll give it to you.

ANYUTKA Mama dear, it's true; it really is——

ANISYA (*raising her hand*) I'll show you! Don't let me hear another word from you. (*Anyutka runs off. To Nikita.*) Go and do as you're told, or you'll regret it. (*Exit.*)

NIKITA (*after a long silence*) It's a bad business! Oh, these women! It's a mess! "You should have thought of that before," says she. When should I have thought of it? Well now, it was just last year that Anisya began to make up to me. Well, what was I supposed to do? Am I a monk? The master died and so I covered up the sin by marrying her, as is proper. I wasn't at fault here. Such things happen a lot. And then there were those powders. Was I the one who persuaded her to use them? Why if I had known, I would have killed her right there and then, the bitch! That's so, I would have killed her! She made me a partner in that filthy business, the slut! And I've hated her ever since then. When mother told me about it then, I began to hate her, to hate her; I couldn't stand the sight of her. Well, how could I go on living with her? And then this started. The girl was after me. So, why not? If I hadn't taken her up on it, it would have been someone else. And now look what's come of it! But again, it's not my fault at all. Oh, it's a bad business! (*Sits, deep in thought.*) Those women really have their nerve—look what they've thought up. But I won't go along with it.

MATRYONA (*enters hurriedly with a lantern and a spade*) What are you sitting for like a bump on a log? What did your wife tell you? Get everything ready.

NIKITA But what are you going to do?

MATRYONA Don't worry, we know what to do. You just take care of your end of the business.

NIKITA You're going to get me into a mess.

MATRYONA   What's this you're saying? Don't tell me you're thinking of backing out? You've gone so far, and now you want to back out.

NIKITA   But this is terrible. After all, it's a human being.

MATRYONA   A human being? Oh, come on now! What's there to it? It's barely alive. And what else can you do with it? If you go and take it to the foundling home, it'll die all the same; and the rumor will get around, right away they'll start gossiping, and we'll be stuck with the girl.

NIKITA   But if they find out?

MATRYONA   In your own house you can do the thing right. We'll fix it so that there won't be a trace. Just do as I tell you. After all, we're women, and we can't get along without a man's help. Here, take the spade, and go down and get things ready. I'll hold the lantern for you.

NIKITA   What should I get ready?

MATRYONA (*in a whisper*)   Dig a little hole. And then we'll bring it out and get rid of it quickly. There she is, calling again. Come on, get a move on. I'm going.

NIKITA   Well, is it dead?

MATRYONA   Of course it's dead. But you've got to move faster. People haven't gone to bed yet. They'll hear, they'll see —the scum want to know everything. And the constable has already come by this evening. Now here's what you do. (*Gives him the spade.*) Go down in the cellar. Dig a little hole in the corner there. The ground is soft. Then you can smooth it out again. Mother Earth won't tell anybody about it; it'll be as smooth as though a cow had licked it down. Go on, go on, dear.

NIKITA   You're going to get me into a mess. Oh, the hell with you all. So help me, I'm leaving. Do it yourselves as best you can.

Scene 2[7]

The set is the same as for Scene 1.

ANISYA (*from the door*)   Well, did he dig it?

MATRYONA   Why did you come away? Where did you put it?

ANISYA   I covered it with sacking. No one will hear it. Well, has he dug the hole yet?

MATRYONA   He doesn't want to!

ANISYA (*rushing out in a fury*)   He doesn't want to! Maybe he wants to feed lice in prison! I'm going to go right away and tell everything to the constable. We'll both get it in the neck. I'll tell him everything right away.

NIKITA (*frightened*)   What are you going to tell him?

ANISYA   What am I going to tell him? Everything! Who took the money? You did! (*Nikita is silent.*) And who gave him the poison? I did! But you knew about it, you knew, you knew! We had an understanding!

MATRYONA   Now stop it. What are you so stubborn for, Nikishka? Well, what else can we do? We'll have to do a little work. Go on, my dear.

ANISYA   My, what a sweet little fellow he is! He doesn't want to do it! You've made my life hell, and I've had it. You've walked all over me, and now it's my turn. Go on, I tell you, or I'll do as I said! Take the spade, here! Go on!

NIKITA   Take it easy. What are you nagging for? (*Takes the spade reluctantly.*) If I don't want to, I won't do it.

ANISYA   You won't do it? (*Begins to shout.*) H-e-y, everybody!

MATRYONA (*covering her mouth*)   What's the matter with you? Have you gone crazy? He'll do it. Go on, son. Go on, dear.

ANISYA   I'm going to start screaming for help right away.

[7] In response to criticism that Act IV was too horrific for stage presentation, Tolstoy wrote an alternate version of Scene 2. This is given on pp. 140-148.

NIKITA   Now stop it! Eh, what a pain in the neck. Why don't both of you get a move on? I might as well get it in the neck for one thing as another. (*Goes to the cellar.*)

MATRYONA   Yes, that's the way it goes, my dear. You've had fun, and now you have to pay the piper.

ANISYA (*still excited*)   He and that slut of his have been making fun of me. That's going to stop now! I won't be the only one mixed up in this. Let him be a murderer too. He'll find out how it feels.

MATRYONA   Oh, come on now, you're really boiling over. Don't you lose your temper, my girl, but do everything quietly and carefully—it's best that way. Go back to the girl, and he'll do what he's supposed to. (*Follows him with the lantern. Nikita goes down into the cellar.*)

ANISYA   I'll make him choke that damned bastard of his. (*Still excited.*) I'm worn out with having Peter's death on my conscience alone. Let him find out what it's like, too. I won't spare myself; I won't spare myself, I tell you!

NIKITA (*from the cellar*)   Give me some light!

MATRYONA (*adjusts the position of the lantern. To Anisya*) He's digging. Go and bring it out.

ANISYA   Watch him, or the scum will run off. I'll go and bring it out.

MATRYONA   Now don't forget to baptize it. If you don't, I will. Have you got a cross?

ANISYA   I'll find one. I know how to do it. (*Exit.*)[8]

MATRYONA (*to herself*)   Did she ever flare up! But, there's no denying, it's insulting for her. Well, glory be to God, we'll cover the matter up and that'll be the end of it. We'll get rid of the girl and nobody'll be the wiser about her sin. Then the lad can live in peace. They have plenty of everything in the house, glory be to God. And he won't forget me either. What would they be without Matryona? They wouldn't be able to

[8] Scene 1 is frequently and erroneously extended to this point.

figure out anything. (*Calling into the cellar.*) Is it ready yet, son?

NIKITA (*coming out of the cellar. His head is visible*) What's going on? Why don't you bring it? What are you so slow about? If we're going to do it, let's do it.

(*Matryona walks over to the vestibule and meets Anisya, who has come out with the baby, wrapped in rags.*)

MATRYONA Well, did you baptize it?

ANISYA Why of course. Took it away from her by force. She didn't want to give it up. (*Goes up to Nikita and tries to give the baby to him.*)

NIKITA (*doesn't take it*) You take it down yourself.

ANISYA Here, take it, I tell you. (*Throws the child to him.*)

NIKITA (*catching the child*) It's alive! Good God, it's moving. It's alive! What should I do with it?

ANISYA (*grabs the child out of his arms and throws it into the cellar*) Strangle it right away, and then it won't be alive! (*Pushes Nikita into the cellar.*) It's your business, so you take care of it.

MATRYONA (*sitting down on a step*) He's too soft-hearted. It's hard for him, poor thing. Well, there's no help for it! It's his sin too. (*Anisya stands at the cellar entrance. Matryona sits down on the porch steps, looks at her, and muses.*) E-e-h, he's certainly scared! Well, there's no help for it. Though it's really hard for him, there's nothing else that can be done. How you going to get rid of it? And just think how some people pray to have children! And what happens? God doesn't give them any —they just keep having still-born children. For example, there's the priest's wife. And here nobody wants it, but it's born alive. (*Looks towards the cellar.*) He must be finished. (*To Anisya.*) Well, how's it going?

ANISYA (*looking into the cellar*) He's covered it with a board; he's sitting on the board. I think he's finished.

MATRYONA   O-oh! I'd like to get along without sinning, but what are you going to do?

NIKITA (*comes out, trembling violently*)   It's still living! I can't do it! It's still living!

ANISYA   If it's still living, then where are you going? (*Tries to stop him.*)

NIKITA (*lunges at her*)   Get away! I'll kill you! (*Grabs her by the arm; she tears herself away; he runs after her with a spade. Matryona intercepts and stops him. Anisya runs up on the porch. Matryona tries to take the spade from him. Nikita threatens his mother with it.*) I'll kill you; I'll kill you too! Get away from me! (*Matryona runs off to Anisya on the porch. Nikita stops.*) I'll kill you. I'll kill both of you!

MATRYONA   He's acting like this because he's scared. Don't worry, he'll get over it.

NIKITA   What have they done? What have they done to me? Oh, how it whined . . . . How it crunched under me. What have they done to me? And it's living; so help me, it's still living! (*Stops talking and listens.*) It's whining . . . . Hear it whining! (*Runs to the cellar.*)

MATRYONA (*to Anisya*)   He's going back. I think he's going to bury it. Nikita, you'll need the lantern.

NIKITA (*doesn't answer. Listens at the cellar entrance*)   I can't hear it now. It was my imagination. (*Goes away from the cellar and stops.*) Oh, how its little bones crunched under me. (*Imitates the sound of crunching.*) What have they done to me? (*Listens again for a sound from the cellar.*) It's whining again. So help me, it's whining. What's that? Mother, oh mother! (*Goes up to her.*)

MATRYONA   What is it, son?

NIKITA   Mother dear, I can't go on with it. I can't do anything. Mother dear, take pity on me!

MATRYONA   Oh, but you've taken a fright, poor dear. Why, just look at you! Why don't you have a little drink to get your courage up?

NIKITA   Mother dear, it's obviously my punishment. What

have you done to me? Oh, how those little bones crunched, and how it whined! Mother dear, what have you done to me? (*Walks off and sits down on the sledge.*)

MATRYONA   Go on, dear, and have a drink. It is scary at night. But wait a little bit; it'll be morning, and, you know, a couple of days will go by, and you'll forget all about it. Wait a little bit, we'll marry the girl off, and we'll forget all about it. Now you go and have a drink, go and have a drink. And I'll take care of everything in the cellar myself.

NIKITA (*rousing himself*)   Is there some liquor left? Maybe the liquor will make me forget. (*Exit. Anisya, who has been standing near the vestibule all this time, steps silently aside.*)

MATRYONA   Go on, go on, my dear, and I'll take care of everything. I'll go down in the cellar myself and bury it. Now where did he throw the spade? (*Finds the spade and goes halfway down into the cellar.*) Anisya, why don't you come here and hold the lantern for me?

ANISYA   And why can't he do it?

MATRYONA   Why he's awfully scared. You really gave it to him good. Never mind, he'll pull out of it. Let him be; I'll do the work myself. Put the lantern over here, and then I can see. (*Matryona disappears into the cellar.*)

ANISYA (*addressing herself toward the door through which Nikita left.*)   Well, had your fun? You lorded it over everybody; now just wait and see how it feels to be on the receiving end. You'll come down a peg or two.

NIKITA (*running out of the vestibule toward the cellar*)   Mother, oh mother?

MATRYONA (*her head appears out of the cellar*)   What is it, son?

NIKITA (*listening*)   Don't bury it. It's alive. Can't you hear it? It's alive! Hear it? It's whining. There, you can hear it real clear——

MATRYONA   Now how can it whine? You've flattened it like a pancake. You've smashed the whole head.

NIKITA   Well, what's that? (*Stops up his ears.*) It's still whining! It's the end for me—the end! What have they done to me? Where can I go? (*Sits down on the steps.*)

Curtain

Variant Scene 2

The hut of Act I. Anyutka, undressed, is lying on a bench, covered with a caftan. Mitrich is sitting on the hanging bed and smoking.

MITRICH   Just see how they've smelled up the place, damn them. They really guzzled it down. Can't even get rid of it by smoking. It just stays in your nose. Oh Lord! Must be time to go to sleep. (*Goes up to the lamp and starts to put it out.*)

ANYUTKA (*jumping up and sitting*)   Grandpa dear, don't put it out!

MITRICH   Why not?

ANYUTKA   There's been so much noise outside. (*Listening.*) Do you hear that? They've gone to the barn again.

MITRICH   So what's that to you? They're not calling you, are they? Lie down and go to sleep. And I'll put the light out now. (*Starts to put it out.*)

ANYUTKA   Grandpa dear, don't put it out. Let it burn a little bit, or I'll be scared.

MITRICH (*laughing*)   Well, all right, all right. (*Sits down near her.*) What are you scared of?

ANYUTKA   How can I help being scared, grandpa? Sis was tossing around so, beating her head against the bin. (*In a whisper.*) You see, I know . . . . She's going to have a little baby . . . . Maybe it's already born . . . .

MITRICH   What a fidget you are, darn you. You have to know everything. Lay down and go to sleep. (*Anyutka lies down.*) That's the way. (*Covers her.*) That's the way. If you know too much, you'll get old too soon.

ANYUTKA   Are you going up on the oven?

MITRICH   And where else would I be going? What a silly

girl you are. You have to know everything. (*Covers her some more and gets up to go.*) Now lay like this and go to sleep. (*Walks towards the oven.*)

ANYUTKA   It cried once, but I can't hear it now.

MITRICH   Oh Lord, Merciful St. Nicholas! What is it you can't hear?

ANYUTKA   The little baby.

MITRICH   There isn't any baby, so that's why you can't hear it.

ANYUTKA   But I did hear it; so help me God, I did hear it. It had such a th-i-i-i-n voice.

MITRICH   You didn't hear anything. And if you did, then it was a bogy-man putting a girl just like you into a sack and taking her away.

ANYUTKA   What bogy-man?

MITRICH   Why just a bogy-man. (*Climbing up on the oven.*) Boy, the oven feels good today—nice and warm. Just fine! Oh Lord, Merciful St. Nicholas!

ANYUTKA   Grandpa, are you going to go to sleep?

MITRICH   What did you think I was going to do? Sing?

(*Silence.*)

ANYUTKA   Grandpa, say grandpa! They're digging. It's so, they're digging; they're digging in the cellar. Listen! So help me God, they're digging!

MITRICH   What'll you think of next? Digging at night. Who's digging? It's just a cow scratching herself, and here you're imagining that someone's digging. Now go to sleep, I tell you, or I'll put the light out right away.

ANYUTKA   Grandpa dear, don't put it out. I won't talk anymore. I really won't; so help me, I won't. I'm scared.

MITRICH   Scared? Don't be afraid of anything, and then you won't be scared. You're afraid, so you tell me you're scared. Of course you'll be scared if you're afraid. What a foolish girl!

(*Silence. A cricket is heard.*)

ANYUTKA (*whispering*)   Grandpa! Say grandpa! Are you asleep?

MITRICH   Well, what is it now?

ANYUTKA   What's this bogy-man like?

MITRICH   Well, I'll tell you. If he sees a girl like you, one who won't sleep, then he comes with a sack and whisks her into the sack. Then he sticks in his own head, raises her shirt, and starts to give her a real whipping.

ANYUTKA   What does he whip her with?

MITRICH   With a broom.

ANYUTKA   But he can't see in there, inside the sack.

MITRICH   Don't worry, he can.

ANYUTKA   But I'll bite him.

MITRICH   No you won't, my dear.

ANYUTKA   Grandpa, someone's coming! Who is it? Oh dear, who is it?

MITRICH   Let him come, whoever it is. What are you worrying about? It's probably your mother.

ANISYA (*enters*)   Anyutka! (*Anyutka pretends to be asleep.*) Mitrich!

MITRICH   What do you want?

ANISYA   How come you've got the light on? We'll sleep in the summer part.

MITRICH   Why I just finished cleaning up. I'll put it out.

ANISYA (*looking for something in the chest and grumbling*) When you need something, you just can't find it.

MITRICH   Well what are you looking for?

ANISYA   For the cross. It has to be baptized. God grant that it'll die! It'd be a real sin to let it die unbaptized.

MITRICH   Of course, it's obvious you have to do everything as is proper. Well, did you find it?

ANISYA   I found it. (*Exit.*)

MITRICH   Good, but if she hadn't found it, I'd have given her mine. Oh Lord!

ANYUTKA (*jumping up, trembling*)   O-oh, grandpa. Please don't go to sleep. I'm so scared!

MITRICH   Why what are you scared of?

ANYUTKA   The little baby will probably die, won't it? The grandmother baptized Aunt Arina's baby the same way—and then it died.

MITRICH   If it dies—they'll bury it.

ANYUTKA   But maybe it wouldn't die if Grandma Matryona weren't here. You know, I heard what grandma was saying; so help me God, I did.

MITRICH   What did you hear? Go to sleep, I tell you. Cover up head and all, and let's put an end to this nonsense.

ANYUTKA   If it'd live, I'd take real good care of it.

MITRICH (*bellowing*)   Oh Lord!

ANYUTKA   Where'll they put it?

MITRICH   They'll put it where it should go. That's nothing you have to worry about. Go to sleep, I tell you. If your mother comes back, she'll give it to you.

(*Silence.*)

ANYUTKA   Grandpa! And that little girl you were telling me about—did she get killed?

MITRICH   Oh, you mean that one. Oh, that little girl came out all right.

ANYUTKA   How did you say she was found, grandpa?

MITRICH   Why she was just found.

ANYUTKA   But where was she found? Tell me.

MITRICH   She was finally found in their house. We came into the village; the soldiers began to rummage through the houses; and sure enough, there was that very same little girl, laying on her belly. They wanted to kill her. But I felt so sorry for her that I took her in my arms, though I had to struggle with her. She became heavy—two hundred pounds; and she kept grabbing anything she could get her hands on, and you couldn't make her let go. So, I picked her up, and I patted her on the head, patted her on the head. And she was as rough as a hedgehog. I patted her and patted her, and she calmed down. I moistened a piece of hardtack and gave it to her. She got the idea all right. Ate it up. We didn't know what else to do with her, so we took her along. We took her along, fed her and fed her, and she got so used to us that we took her along on our campaign. And so she came with us. She was a nice little girl.

ANYUTKA   But she wasn't baptized, was she?

MITRICH   Why who knows? They said she wasn't completely baptized because her people were different from ours.

ANYUTKA   Was she a German?

MITRICH   How silly you are! A German! She wasn't a German, but an Asiatic. They're just like kikes, but they're not kikes either. They're Poles, but Asiatics. They're called Krudles, Krugles . . . . Oh, I've forgotten already. We called the little girl Sashka. Sashka . . . . She was a nice little girl. You know, I've forgotten everything, but I can see that little girl, damn her, as if I were looking at her right now. That's all I remember from all those years in the army. I remember how they used to flog me and also this little girl. She used to hang on my neck and I'd carry her around. You couldn't find a better little girl anywhere. We gave her away later on. The captain's wife adopted her. And she turned out fine. The soldiers were real sorry to give her up!

ANYUTKA   And, grandpa, I also remember how it was when father was dying. You weren't living with us yet. Well, he calls Nikita and then he says: "Forgive me, Nikita," says he. And he started to cry himself. (*Sighs.*) That was also so sad.

MITRICH   Yes, that's the way it is.

ANYUTKA   Grandpa, say grandpa. There's some kind of a noise in the cellar again. Oh, dear, dear. Oh, grandpa, they're going to do something to it. They'll kill it. And it's so little. O-oh! (*Covers her head and cries.*)

MITRICH (*listening*)   Yes, they're really up to some filthy business, damn them. These women are a real filthy lot! You can't say much good about the men, but these women are worse. They're like wild animals. They're not afraid of doing anything.

ANYUTKA (*rising*)   Grandpa, say grandpa!

MITRICH   Well, what is it now?

ANYUTKA   The other day a traveler stopped overnight. He said that if a child dies, its little soul goes straight to heaven. Is that true?

MITRICH   Who knows? I suppose it is. Why are you asking?

ANYUTKA   What if I died? (*Whimpering.*)

MITRICH   If you did, you wouldn't be considered a child.

ANYUTKA   Up to ten you're still a child and your soul can still go straight up to God. After that you turn bad.

MITRICH   You turn bad and how! How can you women help but turn bad? Who teaches you? What do you see? What do you hear? Nothing but evil. I may not have learned a lot, but still I know something. Not well, but still better than a village woman. What is a village woman? Just trash. There are millions and millions of you women in Russia, and you're all like blind moles—you don't know anything. How to ward off a cow's death by magic, all kinds of spells, and how to cure children by taking them to roosting hens—this is all you know.

ANYUTKA   Mama did take me to the roosting hens.

MITRICH   That's just how it is. How many millions of you women and girls there are, and you're all like wild animals. You grow up knowing nothing, and you die knowing nothing. You haven't seen anything; you haven't heard anything. Now take a man. He'll learn something—at least at the tavern, or maybe in prison, by accident, or in the army, as I have. But what about a woman? Far from knowing anything about God, she doesn't even really know what Friday it is. "Friday, Friday," she'll say; but you ask her what Friday it is, and she won't know. They just crawl around like blind pups, sticking their heads into manure. All they know is their stupid songs: ho-ho, ho-ho. But what this ho-ho is, they don't know themselves.

ANYUTKA   But I know half of the Our Father, grandpa.

MITRICH   You know a lot, don't you? And one can't even expect anything of you women either. Who teaches you? Just a drunk peasant when he gives you a lesson with the reins. That's all the teaching you get. And who in the world knows who's responsible for you? Non-coms are responsible for recruits, but nobody's responsible for you women. You're like a bunch of cattle that no one's tending—you just make a lot of trouble. You're a real stupid lot, a real senseless lot.

ANYUTKA   But what are we supposed to do?

MITRICH   Oh, forget it. Cover up and go to sleep. Oh Lord!

(*Silence. The sound of a cricket is heard.*)

ANYUTKA (*jumping up*)   Grandpa! Someone's shouting. Someone's in trouble! It's really so. Someone's shouting. Grandpa dear, he's coming here.

MITRICH   Cover up, I tell you.

NIKITA (*entering with Matryona*)   What have they done to me? What have they done to me?

MATRYONA   Have a little drink, my dear, have a little drink. (*Gets the liquor and puts it on the table.*) What's the matter?

NIKITA   Here, give it to me. Maybe it'll make me forget.

MATRYONA   Quiet! Can't you see they're not asleep yet? Here, drink it.

NIKITA   But why do it this way? Why did you have to think of this? You could have just taken it some place.

MATRYONA (*whispering*)   Sit a little, sit a little here; have another drink or a smoke. It'll make you forget.

NIKITA   Mother dear, it's obviously my punishment. How it whined, and how its little bones crunched . . . . (*Imitates the sound of crunching.*) I'm not a human being anymore.

MATRYONA   E-eh, what you're saying doesn't make any sense. It is scary at night. But wait till it's morning, a couple of days will go by, and you'll forget all about it. (*Goes up to Nikita and puts a hand on his shoulder.*)

NIKITA   Get away from me! What have you done to me?

MATRYONA   What in the world is the matter with you, son? (*Takes him by the arm.*)

NIKITA   Get away from me! I'll kill you! It's all the same to me now. I'll kill you!

MATRYONA   Oh dear, how scared you are! Why don't you just go to bed?

NIKITA   There's nowhere I can go. It's the end for me.

MATRYONA (*shaking her head*)   Oh dear, I better go and take care of things. He'll relax a while and get over it. (*Exit.*)

NIKITA (*sits with his face in his hands. Mitrich and Anyutka are very quiet*)   It's whining. So help me, it's whining. There, there—real plain. She's going to bury it; so help me, she's going to bury it! (*Rushes to the door.*) Mother, don't bury it! It's alive!

MATRYONA (*returning; in a whisper*)   For God's sake, what's the matter with you? What are you imagining? How can it be alive? Why, all its little bones are crushed.

NIKITA   Give me some more to drink. (*Drinks.*)

MATRYONA   Go on, son. You'll be able to sleep now. There's nothing to worry about.

NIKITA (*gets up and listens*)   It's still alive . . . there . . . it's whining. Can't you hear it? There!

MATRYONA (*in a whisper*)   Of course not!

NIKITA   It's the end for me, mother dear. What have you done to me? Where can I go now? (*Rushes out of the room, with Matryona following.*)

ANYUTKA   Grandpa dear, they've strangled it!

MITRICH (*angrily*)   Go to sleep, I tell you. Oh you, darn you! I'll give it to you with the broom! Go to sleep, I tell you.

ANYUTKA   Grandpa dear! Someone's grabbing me by the shoulders; someone's grabbing me, grabbing me with his paws. Grandpa dear, so help me God, I'm getting away from here right away. Grandpa dear, let me get up on the oven! For God's sake, let me up! He's grabbing me . . . grabbing me . . . . O-oh! (*Rushes to the oven.*)

MITRICH   Just see how they've scared the little girl. Damn those sluts. Well, come on up!

ANYUTKA (*climbing up*)   Now don't you go away.

MITRICH   Where should I go? Come on, get up here! Oh Lord; St. Nicholas, Servant of God; Blessed Mother of God!

How they've scared the little girl. (*Covers her.*) You're a silly little girl, a real silly little girl. They've really scared her, the sluts, damn them.

Curtain

ACT V

Scene 1

The threshing floor. In the foreground, the grainricks; on the left, the threshing area; on the right, the barn. The barn doors are open; there is straw in the doorway. The farmyard can be seen in the background, and singing and tambourines can be heard from there. Two girls are walking on the path by the barn, headed for the hut.

First Girl   See, we got here without getting our shoes dirty. But it's terrible if you take the road through the village! Muddy. (*They stop and wipe their feet on the straw. The first girl peers into the straw and sees something.*) Why what's this here?

Second Girl (*peering in*)   That's Mitrich, their hired man. Boy, is he plastered.

First Girl   But I thought he didn't drink.

Second Girl   Looks like he didn't until somebody gave him some liquor.

First Girl   See, it looks like he came to get some straw, and just fell asleep with the rope in his hands.

Second Girl (*listening*)   They're still singing the praises. It looks like they haven't done the blessings yet. They say Akulina didn't do any lamenting at all.[9]

---

[9] She is referring to the ritualistic festivities which preceded the church ceremony among some peasants. The future bride and groom were praised in song and blessed by relatives and friends. Also, the future bride lamented, among other things, the coming loss of her innocence.

FIRST GIRL   Mama said she's being married against her will. Her stepfather is forcing her; otherwise she'd never do it. You should just hear the things they've been saying about her!

MARINA (*appears and catches up with the girls*) Hello, girls!

GIRLS   Hello, Auntie!

MARINA   Going to the wedding party, my dears?

FIRST GIRL   No, it's almost over. We just came to take a look.

MARINA   Could you call my old man for me? He's Semyon of Zuevo. You know him, don't you?

FIRST GIRL   Of course. Isn't he a relative of the bridegroom?

MARINA   That's right. The bridegroom is a nephew of my husband.

SECOND GIRL   Why don't you go yourself? Since you're here, why don't you go to the wedding?

MARINA   I don't feel like it, my girl. Besides, I don't have the time. We have to be off. We didn't plan to come to the wedding. We were going to town with the oats, stopped to feed the horses, and then they invited my old man.

FIRST GIRL   Where did you stop? At Fyodorovich's?

MARINA   That's right. So I'll wait here, and you go call my old man for me, my dear. Call him, my dear. Tell him his woman Marina says it's time to be going on. The helpers are harnessing the horses.

FIRST GIRL   All right, I'll do it, if you won't go yourself.

(*The girls walk off along the path in the direction of the farmyard. Singing and tambourines are heard.*)

MARINA (*deep in thought*)   I suppose I could go, but I don't feel like it because I haven't seen him since he ditched me. It's been more than a year now. But I'd like to take a peek and see how he's getting along with his Anisya. People say they quarrel. She's a coarse, stubborn woman. I bet he's thought of me more than once. He wanted to have an easy life, so he took her instead of me. Oh well, it doesn't matter—I don't hold it against him.

I felt hurt at the time. Oh, it was so painful. But now I'm over it—forgot about it. But I'd still like to have a look at him—— (*Looks towards the farmyard and sees Nikita.*) Oh no! Why's he coming? Did the girls tell him? Why did he leave his guests? I'm going. (*Nikita approaches with bowed head, swinging his arms. He is mumbling.*) My goodness but he looks gloomy!

NIKITA (*sees Marina and recognizes her*) Marina! My dear Marinushka! What are you doing here?

MARINA I came for my old man.

NIKITA Why didn't you come to the wedding? You could have looked at me and laughed.

MARINA Why should I laugh at you? I came to get my husband.

NIKITA Eh, Marinushka. (*Tries to embrace her.*)

MARINA (*angrily moving away*) Stop it, Nikita. Things are no longer like they used to be. I came to get my husband. He's at your place, isn't he?

NIKITA So we should forget about the past? Is that the way you want it?

MARINA There's no point to remembering the past. What was is over and done with.

NIKITA And so it can't be like it used to be?

MARINA And it can't be like it used to be. But why did you leave the party? You're the host, and here you've left the wedding.

NIKITA (*sitting down on the straw*) Why did I leave? Eh, if you only knew! I feel bad, Marina, so bad I wish I were dead. I got up from the table and left, left the guests. I just didn't want to look at anybody.

MARINA (*coming nearer to him*) Why, what's wrong?

NIKITA There's something I just can't forget. Oh, I feel miserable, so miserable. And the thing that makes me feel most miserable, Marinushka, is that I'm all alone and have no one to share my sorrow with.

MARINA You can't live without sorrow, Nikita. I cried over mine—and it passed away.

NIKITA You're talking of what's over and done with. Eh, my dear, you've done your crying, and now my punishment has come.

MARINA But what's the matter?

NIKITA I'm disgusted with my whole life. I'm disgusted with myself. Eh, Marina, you didn't know how to keep me, and you ruined me and yourself too! What kind of a life is this?

MARINA (*standing by the barn, crying and trying to restrain herself*) I'm not complaining about my life, Nikita. May God grant everybody such a life like mine. I'm not complaining. I told everything to my old man before he married me, and he forgave me. And he doesn't throw it up to me. I can't complain about my life. The old man is quiet and loving to me, and I wash and dress his children. And he takes good care of me. So why should I complain? Seems this is the way God wanted it to be. But what's wrong with your life? You're rich——

NIKITA My life! If it weren't for the fact that I don't want to upset the wedding, I'd just take a rope—this one here—(*picks a rope up from the straw*) and I'd just throw it over this here beam. Then I'd make a nice little noose, and I'd climb up on the beam, and I'd stick my head into the noose. That's the kind of life I've got!

MARINA Stop talking like that! How can you even think of such a thing?

NIKITA You think I'm joking? Think I'm drunk? No, I'm not drunk. I can't even get drunk nowadays. And my misery, my misery has done me in. It's done me in so completely that I don't take any pleasure in anything! Eh, Marinushka, I only lived when we whiled away those nights down at the railroad. Remember those nights?

MARINA Don't reopen old wounds, Nikita. I'm married and so are you. My sin is forgiven, so don't stir up the past——

NIKITA But what will I do with my heart? What can I do?

MARINA What can you do? You have a wife; don't lust after other women, but take care of your own. You loved Anisya; go on loving her.

NIKITA   Eh, that Anisya is bitter wormwood for me. She's gotten me into one big mess.

MARINA   No matter what she's like—she's still your wife. But what's the use of talking about it? You better go back to your guests and send my husband out to me.

NIKITA   Eh, if you only knew everything—— But what's the use of talking?

MARINA'S HUSBAND (*enters from the yard, red-faced and drunk. Anyutka is with him*)   Marina! Wife! Old woman! Are you out here?

NIKITA   Here's your husband coming. He's calling you. Go on.

MARINA   But what are you going to do?

NIKITA   Me? I'll lay down here for a while. (*Lies down in the straw.*)

MARINA'S HUSBAND   Now where could she be?

ANYUTKA   Why there she is, Uncle, near the barn.

MARINA'S HUSBAND   What are you standing there for? Come on to the wedding! The hosts ask you to come and honor them. They'll be going to the church soon, and then we can go on.

MARINA (*walking toward her husband*)   Why, I don't feel like it.

MARINA'S HUSBAND   Come on, I tell you. You can have a little drink. You can congratulate that rascal Petrunka. The hosts will be insulted if you don't come. We'll have plenty of time to tend to our business. (*Marina's husband embraces her and goes off with her, staggering.*)

NIKITA (*gets up and sits down on the straw*)   Eh, I've seen her, and now I feel even more miserable. The only life I ever really had was with her. I've ruined my life for nothing; brought ruination down on my head. (*Lies down.*) Where can I go? Oh, I wish the earth would just swallow me up!

ANYUTKA (*sees Nikita and runs to him*)   Father, say father! They're looking for you. Everybody, even godfather, has blessed them already. So help me God, they've blessed them. And they're getting angry at you.

NIKITA (*to himself*)   Where can I go?

ANYUTKA   What are you doing here? What are you talking about?

NIKITA   I'm not talking about anything. What are you bothering me for?

ANYUTKA   Father, come on, let's go. (*Nikita is silent. Anyutka pulls him by the hand.*) Father, go and bless them! They're getting angry and swearing, they really are.

NIKITA (*pulling his hand away*)   Leave me alone!

ANYUTKA   Oh, come on!

NIKITA (*threatening her with the rope*)   Beat it, I tell you, or I'll give it to you.

ANYUTKA   Well, I'll send mama out to you. (*Runs off.*)

NIKITA (*rising*)   But how can I go? How can I pick up the icon? [10] How can I look into her eyes? (*Lies down again.*) Oh, if there were a hole in the ground, I'd vanish into it. People wouldn't see me, and I wouldn't see anybody. (*Rises again.*) I just won't go. Let them go to hell. I won't go. (*Takes off his boots. Picks up the rope, makes a noose in it, and sticks his head into the noose.*) This is the answer. (*Nikita sees his mother, takes off the rope, and again lies down in the straw.*)

MATRYONA (*hurriedly coming up to him*)   Nikita! Say Nikita! Well I'll be, he won't even answer. Nikita, what's the matter with you? Are you drunk? Come on, Nikitushka. Come on, come on, my dear. The people are tired of waiting for you.

NIKITA   Oh, what have you done to me? I'm not a human being anymore.

MATRYONA   Why, what's the matter with you. Come on, my dear, bless them as is proper, and that'll be the end of it. After all, everybody's waiting for you.

NIKITA   But how can I bless them?

MATRYONA   It's easy enough. Don't you know how?

NIKITA   I know, I know. But who am I going to bless? What have I done to her?

[10] The future bride and groom were blessed with an icon.

MATRYONA   What have you done? Why think of that? No-body knows about it—not a soul. And the girl is getting married of her own free will.

NIKITA   How is she getting married?

MATRYONA   Out of fear, of course. But, anyway, she's getting married. It can't be helped now. She should have thought of that before. She can't back out of it now. And the matchmakers have no cause for complaint either. They saw the girl twice, and they got the money for her. Everything is hushed up.

NIKITA   And what's in the cellar?

MATRYONA (*laughing*)   What's in the cellar? Mushrooms, cabbage, potatoes, I suppose. What's the use of thinking about the past?

NIKITA   I'd be glad not to think of it, but I can't. The moment I think of it, I can hear the whining. Oh, what have you done to me?

MATRYONA   Now why in the world are you making such a fuss?

NIKITA (*turning face downwards*)   Mother! Don't torture me. I'm sick of it all.

MATRYONA   But you have to come. The people are gossiping as it is; and now suddenly the father goes off, doesn't come back, and can't get up the nerve to bless the couple. They'll start putting things together right away. As soon as you back out, they'll start to suspect right away. Put on a good face and they'll receive you with grace. Jump out of the frying pan, and you'll end up in the fire. Above all else, young fellow, don't let on, don't be timid—or they'll learn the worst.

NIKITA   Eh, you've really gotten me into a mess!

MATRYONA   Now stop that! Let's go. Go and bless them. Do everything like you should, all in proper style, and that'll be the end of the matter.

NIKITA (*still lying face downwards*)   I just can't.

MATRYONA (*talking to herself*)   Now what's happened? Everything was going just fine, and suddenly this came over him.

He must be bewitched. Nikita, get up! Look, Anisya has left the guests and is coming.

ANISYA (*enters, dressed up, red-faced, and a little drunk*) Everything is going so well, mother, so well and respectable! And how pleased the guests are. Where is he?

MATRYONA Here he is, my dear, here. He's just laying in the straw. Won't go.

NIKITA (*looking at his wife*) See, she's also drunk! It makes me sick to look at her. How can I live with her? (*Turning face downwards*) I'll kill her one of these days. It's going to get worse.

ANISYA Look where he's hidden himself—in the straw. Don't tell me the liquor's gotten the best of you. (*Laughs.*) I'd like to lay here a little while with you, but there isn't time. Come on, let's go—I'll help you. Oh, how very well everything is going back at the house! It makes you feel good to see it. And you should hear the accordion! The women are singing so nicely. Everybody's drunk. It's so very respectable and nice!

NIKITA What's nice?

ANISYA The wedding, the gay wedding. All the people are saying that you rarely see such a wedding. Everything is so nice and respectable. Come on. We'll go together. I've had some to drink, but I can help you there. (*Takes him by the hand.*)

NIKITA (*pulling himself away in disgust*) Go on by yourself. I'll come along.

ANISYA What are you pouting about? We got rid of all our troubles, got rid of the trouble-maker—so now all we have to do is to live and be happy. Everything is so respectable, according to the law. I just can't tell you how glad I am. It's as if I were marrying you again. O-oh, and the guests are so pleased! They're all thanking us. And the guests are just so nice. And Ivan Moseich—and also the constable. They sang their praises too.

NIKITA Well, why don't you go and stay with them? Why did you come here?

ANISYA We have to go back. How'll it look for the hosts to

go off and leave their guests? And the guests are just so nice.

NIKITA (*getting up and picking the straw off of his clothing*) Go ahead, and I'll be right along.

MATRYONA   The night cuckoo has done a better job of cuckooing than the day cuckoo. He didn't listen to me, but he'll do what his wife wants him to right away. (*Matryona and Anisya start walking off.*) Well, you coming?

NIKITA   I'll be right along. You go ahead, and I'll be right along. I'll go, I'll bless them—— (*The women stop.*) Go on. I'll be right along. Go on! (*The women leave. Nikita, deep in thought, watches them go off. He sits down and takes off his boots.*) You just wait till I come! That's right! You'd do better to look for me on the beam. I'll fix the noose, jump from the beam, and then you can look for me. And the rope is here, thank God. (*Musing.*) I'd have gotten over it. I'd have gotten over it, if it had been any other kind of sorrow! But this thing's right in my heart, and I can't get rid of it in any way. (*Peering towards the farmyard.*) Don't tell me she's coming back! (*Mimicking Anisya.*) "Everything is going well, so well! I'll lay here a little while with you!" O-oh, you filthy slut! Well, you can embrace me, when they take me down from the beam. Might as well get it over with. (*Grabs the rope and pulls it. A drunken Mitrich sits up, holding on to the other end of the rope.*)

MITRICH   I won't let you have it. I won't let anybody have it. I'll bring it myself. I said I'd bring the straw—and I'll bring it! Is that you, Nikita? (*Laughing.*) Oh hell! Did you come for the straw?

NIKITA   Give me the rope!

MITRICH   No, you wait. The peasants sent me for the straw. I'll bring it . . . . (*Gets up on his feet, begins to pick up the straw, totters, tries to keep his balance, and finally falls down.*) The liquor is stronger. It's got the best of me.

NIKITA   Give me the rope.

MITRICH   I told you—I won't. Ah, Nikishka, you're as dumb as a pig's bellybutton. (*Laughs.*) I love you, but you're dumb. You think I'm drunk, don't you? But what the hell do I care about you? You think I need you . . . . Look at me! I'm a non-com! You fool, you can't even pronounce it: a non-commissioned officer of the first regiment of Her Majesty's Grenadiers. I've served czar and country faithfully and honestly. And who am I? You think I'm a soldier? No, I'm not a soldier, but the very lowest of men. I'm an orphan; I'm a stray. I swore off drinking, and now I've tied one on! Well, you think I'm afraid of you? Of course not! I'm not afraid of anybody. I got drunk—so I got drunk! Now I'll be guzzling for about the next two weeks; I'll paint the town red. I'll sell the shirt off of my back and pawn my passport before I stop drinking. And I'm not afraid of anybody. In the regiment they used to flog me to make me stop drinking. They'd whip me and whip me. "Well," they'd say, "are you going to stop?" "No," I'd say. Why should I be afraid of such crap? Here I am! As God made me, so I am. I swore off drinking; I didn't drink. Now I've started drinking, and I'll go on drinking. And I'm not afraid of anybody. Because I don't lie, but tell the truth. What's there to be afraid of—that crap? "Here," I said, "here I am." There was a priest told me that the devil is the worst sort of bragger. "The minute you begin to brag," he said, "you get scared. And when you start getting scared of people, right away the cloven-footed one—right away he grabs you and jams you where he wants to. And since I'm not afraid of people, I have an easy time of it! I'll spit in the horned one's beard—and at his pig mother! He can't do anything to me. "Go kiss my ass," I'll say to him.

NIKITA (*crossing himself*)   My God, and what was I about to do? (*Throws the rope away.*)

MITRICH   What's that?

NIKITA (*rising*)   You said one's not supposed to be afraid of people?

MITRICH   What's there to be afraid of—that crap? Just take a look at them in the bathhouse. They're all made of the same dough. One has a bigger belly, another a smaller one—that's all the difference between them. They're nothing to be afraid of, damn them.

MATRYONA (*stepping out of the farmyard and calling*) Well, are you coming?

NIKITA Oh! Well, it's better this way. I'm coming. (*Walks off towards the farmyard.*)

Curtain

Scene 2

The hut of Act I is full of people sitting at tables and standing. Akulina and the Bridegroom are in the front corner. On a table are icons and bread. The Best Man, the Bridegroom's Mother, and Matryona are present. Among the guests and other people are Marina, Marina's Husband, the Driver, and the Constable. The women are singing. Anisya is serving the liquor. The singing stops.

DRIVER If we're going to go, then let's get going. The church is quite a ways off.

BEST MAN Just wait a little bit so the stepfather can bless them. Now where is he?

ANISYA He's coming. He'll be here right away, friends. Why don't you all have another drink—go ahead!

BRIDEGROOM'S MOTHER What's keeping him so long? We've been waiting an awfully long time.

ANISYA He'll come. He'll be here right away. He'll be here in two shakes of a lamb's tail. Come on, have another drink, friends. (*Serves them.*) He'll be here right away. In the meantime, sing another song, my beauties.

DRIVER But they've already sung all the songs they know while waiting for him.

(*The women sing. Nikita and Akim enter in the middle of the song.*)

NIKITA (*holding Akim by the arm and pushing him ahead of himself*) Go on, father! I can't do it without your help.

AKIM   I don't like to, you know, whachama-call-it——

NIKITA (*to the women*)   That's enough. Quiet down. (*Surveys everybody in the room.*) Marina, are you here?

BRIDEGROOM'S MOTHER   Go on, and take the icon and bless them.

NIKITA   Wait, wait a little. (*Looks around.*) Akulina, are you here?

BRIDEGROOM'S MOTHER   What are you calling roll for? Where else should she be? Why is he acting so strange?

ANISYA   My God, why he's barefoot!

NIKITA   Father, are you here? Look at me. Orthodox people, you're all here, and so am I! Here I am! (*Falls on his knees.*)

ANISYA   Nikitushka, what's the matter with you? Oh, poor me!

BRIDEGROOM'S MOTHER   Would you look at that!

MATRYONA   I tell you, he's had too much of that French wine. Come to your senses. What's the matter with you? (*They try to raise him, but he pays no attention to anybody, just keeps looking straight ahead.*)

NIKITA   Orthodox people! I'm guilty, and I want to confess.

MATRYONA (*pulling him by the shoulder*)   What's the matter with you? Have you gone mad? Friends, he's gone out of his mind. We have to take him away.

NIKITA (*pushing her aside with his shoulder*)   Leave me alone! And you, father, listen to me. First of all, Marinka, look at me. (*Bows to the ground before her and then gets up.*) I'm guilty towards you. I promised to marry you, and I seduced you. I tricked you and then ditched you. Forgive me, for Christ's sake! (*Again bows to the ground before her.*)

ANISYA   What are you raving about? It's absolutely improper. Nobody asked you about this. Get up and stop disgracing yourself.

MATRYONA   O-oh, he's been bewitched. And how did this happen? He has a spell on him. Get up! What're you talking nonsense for? (*Pulls him.*)

NIKITA (*shaking his head*)   Don't touch me! Forgive me my sin against you, Marina. Forgive me, for Christ's sake.

(*Marina covers her face with her hands and keeps quiet.*)

ANISYA   Get up, I tell you, and stop disgracing yourself. Why dig up the past? Stop making a spectacle of yourself. It's disgraceful! Oh, poor me! What's the matter with him? He's gone completely out of his head.

NIKITA (*pushing away his wife and turning to Akulina*) Akulina, now I have something to say to you. Listen, Orthodox people. I'm a great sinner! Akulina, I'm guilty toward you. Your father didn't just die. He was poisoned.

ANISYA (*screaming*)   Oh, poor me! What's he talking about?

MATRYONA   He isn't himself. Take him away!

(*People walk towards him, getting ready to seize him.*)

AKIM (*pushing them away*)   Hold it! Now lads, you know, whachama-call-it, hold it!

NIKITA   Akulina, I poisoned him. Forgive me, for Christ's sake.

AKULINA (*jumping up*)   He's lying! I know who did it!

BRIDEGROOM'S MOTHER   Stop that! Sit still.

AKIM   Oh Lord! How sinful, how sinful.

CONSTABLE   Grab him! And send for the elder and the official witnesses. I have to draw up a statement. Get up, you, and come over here.

AKIM (*to the Constable*)   Now look, you know, whachama-call-it, bright-buttons, just whachama-call-it, you know, hold off. Let him whachama-call-it, have his say, you know.

CONSTABLE (*to Akim*)   Don't interfere, old man. I have to draw up a statement.

AKIM   What a queer whachama-call-it you are. Hold off, I tell you. Stop whachama-call-it, talking, you know, about the batement. Here we've got whachama-call-it, God's business going on—a man is making his confession, you know—and you want to be drawing up a whachama-call-it, a batement.

CONSTABLE   Send for the elder!

AKIM   Let him first tend to God's business, you know; then, you know, you can whachama-call-it, tend to yours, you know.

NIKITA   There is another great sin I committed against you, Akulina: I seduced you. Forgive me, for Christ's sake! (*Bows to the ground before her.*)

AKULINA (*leaving the table*)   Let me go. I'm not going to get married. He was forcing me to, but now I won't.

CONSTABLE   Repeat what you just said.

NIKITA   Wait a minute, constable. Let me finish what I have to say.

AKIM (*ecstatic*)   Go on and talk, child. Tell everything and you'll feel better. Confess to God, and don't be afraid of the people. Think of God, think of God! He's here!

NIKITA   I poisoned the father, and, dog that I am, also ruined the daughter. I had the power over her, and I ruined her and her little baby.

AKULINA   That's true, that's true.

NIKITA   I smothered her little baby with a board in the cellar. I sat on it—smothering it—and its little bones crunched. (*Cries.*) And then I buried it in the ground. I did it—I alone.

AKULINA   He's lying. I told him to do it.

NIKITA   Don't protect me. I'm not afraid of anybody now. Forgive me, Orthodox people. (*Bows to the ground.*)

(*Silence.*)

CONSTABLE   Tie him up. Looks like your wedding is broken up.

(*People advance with belts.*)

NIKITA   Wait a minute. There'll be time enough for that . . . . (*Bows to the ground before his father.*) Father dear, you forgive me too, great sinner that I am! You told me, when I first started this sinful, filthy life—you told me: "When the claw is caught, the whole bird is lost." But I, dog that I am, didn't listen to you; and things turned out the way you said they would. Forgive me, for Christ's sake.

AKIM (*ecstatic*) God will forgive you, my child. (*Embraces him.*) You didn't pity yourself, but He'll pity you. Think of God, think of God! He's here!

ELDER (*entering*) There are enough official witnesses here.

CONSTABLE We'll do the questioning right away.

(*Nikita is tied up.*)

AKULIN (*takes her place by his side*) I'll tell the truth. Question me too.

NIKITA (*tied up*) There's no point to questioning her. I did it all myself. It was my plan and my work. Take me where you want to. I won't say another word.

Curtain

THE FRUITS OF
ENLIGHTENMENT

A Comedy in Four Acts

Characters

(The names in parentheses are those by which the characters are also referred to in the course of the play.)

Leonid Fyodorovich Zvezdintsev an ex-lieutenant of the Horse Guards, owner of 24,000 desyatinas[1] in various provinces. A robust man, about sixty years old. A mild pleasant gentleman. Believes in spiritualism and loves to amaze others with his stories.

Anna Pavlovna Zvezdintsev (Annette) his wife, a plump lady who tries to look young. Concerned about worldly proprieties, despises her husband, and blindly trusts her doctor. An irritable lady.

Betsy (Lizaveta Leonidovna) their daughter, a fashionable girl of about twenty with a free and somewhat masculine manner. Wears pince-nez. A flirt. Laughs a great deal. Speaks very rapidly and distinctly, compressing her lips like a foreigner.

Vasili Leonidych (Vovo) their son. A law-school graduate without any definite duties. A member of a bicycle club, a horse racing club, and a club for the encouragement of borzoi breeding. A young man enjoying excellent health and im-

---

[1] A *desyatina* is 2.7 acres.

perturbable self-confidence. Speaks loudly and abruptly. He is either entirely in earnest, almost gloomy, or noisily gay, laughing loudly.

PROFESSOR ALEKSEI VLADIMIROVICH KRUGOSVETLOV   a scientist, about fifty years old, with a calm, pleasantly self-confident manner and a kind of slow and singsong delivery. Likes to talk. He treats those who don't agree with him with a gentle contempt. He smokes a great deal. A lean, active man.

DOCTOR (Peter Petrovich)   about forty, a healthy, stout, red-faced man. Loud and coarse. Constantly chuckles with self-satisfaction.

MARYA KONSTANTINOVNA   a girl of about twenty, a conservatory graduate, and a teacher of music. Tufts of hair hang over her forehead. Wears exaggeratedly fashionable clothing. Flattering and easily confused.

PETRISHCHEV   about twenty-eight years old, a graduate in philology who is looking for a position. A member of the same clubs as Vasili Leonidych and also of the Society for the Promotion of Chintz and Calico Balls. Balding, quick in his movements and speech, and extremely polite.

BARONESS   a distinguished lady of about fifty, indolent. Speaks without intonation.

PRINCESS   a lady of fashion, a guest.

YOUNG PRINCESS   a fashionable young lady, grimaces, a guest.

COUNTESS   an ancient lady, moves about with difficulty, has false hair and teeth.

ANTON BORISOVICH GROSSMANN   a dark-complexioned man with Jewish features. Very active, nervous, speaks very loud.

STOUT LADY (Marya Vasilevna Tolbukhin)   very dignified, rich, and good-natured. She is acquainted with all remarkable people, past and present. Very stout, speaks very fast in her attempt to outtalk everybody else. Smokes.

BARON (COCO) KLINGEN   a graduate of St. Petersburg University, a Gentleman of the Bedchamber. Serves with an embassy. Very correct, and therefore calm and quietly gay.

A LADY

AN ELDERLY GENTLEMAN (who doesn't have any lines)

SERGEI IVANOVICH SAKHATOV   about fifty years old, a former assistant minister and an elegant gentleman. Has a broad European education. Has no special occupation, but is interested in everything. Holds himself with dignity and even somewhat severely.

FYODOR IVANYCH Leonid Fyodorovich's valet. Approaching sixty. A cultured man who is fond of culture. Makes too much use of his pince-nez and handkerchief, which he always unfolds slowly. Follows politics. An intelligent and kind man.

GRIGORI MIKHAILYCH a footman, about twenty-eight years old, handsome, dissipated, jealous, and bold.

YAKOV IVANYCH a butler, about forty, zealous, good-natured, lives only for his family interests in the village.

SEMYON (Syomka, Syoma) a butler's helper, a peasant of about twenty. A healthy, fresh country lad, blond, without a beard, calm, and smiling.

COACHMAN (Timofei) about thirty-five. A sharp dresser with a moustache. Coarse and determined.

OLD COOK (Pavel Petrovich) about forty-five. Shaggy, unshaven, bloated, yellowish, and trembling. Dressed in a ragged nankeen summer coat, dirty trousers, and torn boots. Speaks in a hoarse voice. Utters his words as though through a barrier of some sort.

WOMAN COOK (Lukerya) about thirty years old, a great talker, and a disgruntled person.

DOORMAN an ex-soldier.

TANYA (Tatyana Markovna) about nineteen years old, a maid. Energetic, strong, gay, and quickly passes from one mood to another. Squeals in moments of extreme delight.

FIRST PEASANT (Efim Antonych) about sixty, has been an elder, thinks that he knows how to handle gentlemen, and likes to hear himself talk.

SECOND PEASANT (Zakhar Trifonych) about forty-five, owner of a farm. Gruff and truthful. Doesn't like to say more than is necessary. Semyon's father.

THIRD PEASANT (Mitri Vlasevich Chilikin) about seventy. Wears bast shoes. Nervous, restless, and in a hurry. Timid, and covers up his timidity by talking.

FIRST FOOTMAN OF THE COUNTESS an elderly man of the old school. Has pride in his position.

SECOND FOOTMAN a huge, robust, and gruff man.

DELIVERY MAN   dressed in a blue coat. Has a fresh ruddy face.
Speaks firmly, impressively, and clearly.

The action takes place in the capital, in Zvezdintsev's house.

ACT I

*The entrance hall of a rich house in Moscow. There are three
doors: one leading to the outside, one to Leonid Fyodorovich's
study, and one into Vasili Leonidych's room. A staircase goes
up to the family rooms upstairs; back of it is a passage going
into the butler's pantry. Grigori, a young and handsome footman, is looking into the mirror and preening.*

GRIGORI   What a shame about my moustache! "A moustache
isn't appropriate for a footman," says she. And why not? Because she wants everybody to know that I'm just a footman. She's
afraid that I might outclass her darling son. There's not much
competition there! Even if I don't have a moustache, he still
has a long way to go—(*Looking into the mirror with a smile.*)
And what a lot of women are after me! But I don't like any of
them as much as that Tanya! She's just a simple maid, that's
right, but she's much better than any of these young ladies!
(*Smiles.*) And so sweet! (*Listens.*) Why, she's coming! (*Smiling.*) Just listen to that tapping of her heels—boy! (*Tanya
enters carrying a fur coat and shoes.*) My respects to Tatyana
Markovna!

TANYA   What, still looking at yourself? You think you're
pretty good-looking, don't you?

GRIGORI   Well, do you think I'm hard to look at?

TANYA   It's like this: You're not hard to look at; you're not
easy to look at; just half and half. What are all these coats doing
here?

GRIGORI   I'll take them away at once, madam. (*Takes down
a fur coat, drapes it on Tanya, and embraces her.*) Tanya,
what can I say to you——

TANYA   Oh, get lost! What're you bothering me for? (*Angrily tears herself away.*) I'm telling you, leave me alone!

GRIGORI (*looking around*)   Give me a kiss.

TANYA   Why in the world are you bothering me? I'll give you a kiss like this! (*Gets ready to swing at him. A bell is heard off-stage.*)

VASILI LEONIDYCH (*off-stage*)   Grigori!

TANYA   There he is—go on. Vasili Leonidych wants you.

GRIGORI   Let him wait. He's just opened his eyes. Listen, why don't you love me?

TANYA   What are you talking about? I don't love anybody.

GRIGORI   That's a lie. You love Syomka. And, boy, isn't he something—a clumsy butler's helper!

TANYA   Well, whatever he is, it's plain that you're jealous of him.

VASILI LEONIDYCH (*off-stage*)   Grigori!

GRIGORI   Don't be in such a hurry! What's there to be jealous of? Here you've just begun to get shaped up, and who are you getting tied up with? It would be a lot better if you were to love me. Tanya——

TANYA (*angrily and sternly*)   I tell you, don't get your hopes up.

VASILI LEONIDYCH (*off-stage*)   Grigori!!!

GRIGORI   Aren't you the high and mighty one.

VASILI LEONIDYCH (*off-stage. Flatly, persistently, and as loud as he can*)   Grigori! Grigori! Grigori! (*Tanya and Grigori laugh.*)

GRIGORI   You should see the kind of women who've loved me! (*Bell.*)

TANYA   Why don't you go to him and leave me alone?

GRIGORI   It's plain that you're dumb. After all, Semyon can't be compared to me.

TANYA   Semyon wants to get married and not to fool around.

(*The Delivery Man enters, carrying a large box with a dress.*)

DELIVERY MAN   Good morning!

GRIGORI   Hello. Who are you from?

DELIVERY MAN   From Bourdier, with a dress. And here's a note for the lady.

TANYA (*takes the note*)   Wait here. I'll take it in. (*Exit. Vasili Leonidych comes to the door in shirt-sleeves and slippers.*)

VASILI LEONIDYCH   Grigori!

GRIGORI   Right away!

VASILI LEONIDYCH   Grigori, do you hear me?

GRIGORI   I just came in.

VASILI   Get me some warm water and tea.

GRIGORI   Semyon will bring it in right away.

VASILI LEONIDYCH   And who's this? From Bourdier?

DELIVERY MAN   That's right, sir.

(*Vasili Leonidych and Grigori leave. The doorbell rings. Tanya runs in and opens the door.*)

TANYA (*to the Delivery Man*)   You're to wait.

DELIVERY MAN   That's what I've been doing.

(*Sakhatov enters.*)

TANYA   Excuse it, sir, the footman just went out. But please come in and let me help you. (*Helps him take off his fur coat.*)

SAKHATOV (*adjusting his clothes*)   Is Leonid Fyodorovich in? Is he up yet?

(*The doorbell.*)

TANYA   Certainly. He's been up a long time already.

DOCTOR (*enters. Looks around for the footman. Sees Sakhatov and addresses him with familiarity.*)   Ah, my respects!

SAKHATOV (*looking fixedly at him*)   You're the doctor, I believe?

DOCTOR   But I thought you were abroad. Did you come to see Leonid Fyodorovich?

SAKHATOV   That's right. And what are you doing here? Is somebody ill?

DOCTOR (*chuckling*)   Not exactly ill, but, you know, these ladies are a problem. She plays vint[2] until three every day and crams herself into a corset. And the lady is fat and flabby, and not exactly young, either.

SAKHATOV   Is that the way you present your diagnosis to Anna Pavlovna? I don't imagine she likes it.

DOCTOR (*laughing*)   Well, it's the truth. They pull all these stunts and then end up with digestive disorders, pressure on the liver, nerves—well, and the next thing you know, they're calling you and you're supposed to fix them up. They're a problem! (*Chuckling.*) And how about you? I gather you're also a spiritualist?

SAKHATOV   I? No, I'm not also a spiritualist . . . . Well, my respects! (*Wants to leave, but the Doctor stops him.*)

DOCTOR   You know, I can't reject it completely either when a man like Krugosvetlov is involved in it. How could I? He's a professor—has a European reputation. There must be something in it. I'd like to get a look at it sometime, but I've never got the time. There's always something else to do.

SAKHATOV   Yes, yes. My respects! (*Leaves after a slight bow.*)

DOCTOR (*to Tanya*)   Is she up?

TANYA   In her room. Please go up. (*The Doctor goes up.*)

FYODOR IVANYCH (*entering with a newspaper. To the Delivery Man*)   What are you doing here?

DELIVERY MAN   I'm from Bourdier, with a dress and a note. I was told to wait.

FYODOR IVANYCH   Ah, from Bourdier! (*To Tanya.*) Who just came in?

TANYA   Sakhatov—Sergei Ivanych—and the doctor too. They stood around talking in here. All about spiritanism.

---

[2] A card game.

FYODOR IVANYCH (*correcting her*)   About spiritualism.

TANYA   That's what I said: about spiritanism. And did you hear, Fyodor Ivanych, how well it went off last time? (*Laughing.*) There was rapping and things flew around.

FYODOR IVANYCH   And how do you know?

TANYA   Why, Lizaveta Leonidovna told me.

YAKOV (*running in with a glass of tea. To the Delivery Man*) Hello.

DELIVERY MAN (*sadly*)   Hello.

(*Yakov knocks on Vasili Leonidych's door.*)

GRIGORI (*opening the door*)   Let me have it.

YAKOV   You haven't brought back yesterday's glasses yet, and the tray is still in Vasili Leonidych's room. They'll hold me responsible for them, you know.

GRIGORI   The tray is filled with cigars.

YAKOV   Well, put them somewhere else. I'll have to answer for it, you know.

GRIGORI   I'll bring it, I'll bring it!

YAKOV   You keep saying you'll bring it, but you don't. It wasn't around the other day, and there wasn't anything to serve on.

GRIGORI   I tell you I'll bring it. What a nuisance!

YAKOV   It's easy enough for you to talk like that, and here this is the third time I've had to serve tea, and I have to get lunch ready too. I'm on the go from one end of the day to the other. Who's got more work in the house than me? And still I'm no good!

GRIGORI   Why, what more could be expected from you? See how good you are!

TANYA   You don't think much of anybody except yourself.

GRIGORI (*to Tanya*)   Who asked you? (*Goes back into the room.*)

YAKOV   Well, I'm not complaining. Tatyana Markovna, the lady didn't say anything about yesterday, did she?

TANYA   You mean about the lamp?

YAKOV God alone knows how it slipped out of my hands. I'd just begun to wipe it, wanted to get a better grip on it, and somehow it slipped out of my hands. Smashed into smithereens! That's just my luck! It's easy for him, for Grigori Mikhailych, to talk—all he's got to worry about is himself, but I've got a family. I've got to look after it and feed it too, you know. It's not the work that bothers me. So she didn't say anything? Well, thank God! How many spoons have you got, Fyodor Ivanych, one or two?

FYODOR IVANYCH One, one. (*Reads the newspaper.*)

(*The doorbell. Grigori, with the tray, and the Doorman enter.*)

DOORMAN (*to Grigori*) Tell the master that some peasants from the country are here.

GRIGORI (*pointing to Fyodor Ivanych*) Tell the valet. I haven't got the time. (*Exit.*)

TANYA Where are the peasants from?

DOORMAN From the Kursk village, I think.

TANYA (*squealing*) It's them. It's Semyon's father about the land. I'll go see them. (*Runs out.*)

DOORMAN Well, what do you want? Should I let them in or what? They say they've come about some land, that the master knows about it.

FYODOR IVANYCH Yes, it's about buying some land. That's right. But the master's got a guest right now. Tell you what: Tell them to wait a little.

DOORMAN Where should they wait?

FYODOR IVANYCH Let them wait outside. I'll send for them later.

(*The Doorman leaves. Tanya enters, followed by the three peasants. Grigori also comes in.*)

TANYA To the right. This way, this way!

FYODOR IVANYCH I didn't want them in here.

GRIGORI See, what did I tell you, you fidget?

TANYA   It won't do any harm, Fyodor Ivanych. They'll just stand here at the side.

FYODOR IVANYCH   They'll track up the place.

TANYA   They've wiped their feet. Besides, I'll clean up later. (*To the peasants.*) Stand right here.

(*The peasants advance into the room, carrying presents wrapped in kerchiefs: a cake, eggs, and towels. They look around for icons before which to cross themselves. They cross themselves before the staircase, bow to Fyodor Ivanych, and take a determined stand.*)

GRIGORI (*to Fyodor Ivanych*)   Fyodor Ivanych, here they've been saying that Pironet's shoes are the latest style, but this fellow has much better ones. (*Points to the Third Peasant.*)

FYODOR IVANYCH   All you can do is poke fun at people! (*Grigori leaves. Fyodor Ivanych gets up and goes over to the peasants.*) So you're the people from the Kursk village coming about the purchase of the land?

FIRST PEASANT   That's right. It originates, so to speak, in regard to the accomplishment of the sale of the land that we are here. Can't you tell him we're here?

FYODOR IVANYCH   Yes, yes, I know, I know. Just wait here, and I'll tell him right away. (*Exit.*)

(*The peasants look around, not knowing what to do with their presents.*)

FIRST PEASANT   How do you call that, you know, thing—I don't know it's name—on which the gifts are presented? We want to do this according to regulations. Couldn't you let us have a dish?

TANYA   Just wait a little bit. Give them to me and I'll put them over here for the time being. (*Puts them on the little sofa.*)

FIRST PEASANT   And what's the title, so to speak, of the honorable man who came up to talk to us?

TANYA   That's the vally.

FIRST PEASANT   The volly—that's simple enough. It means

that he's in the service too. (*To Tanya.*) And you, so to speak, are also in the service?

TANYA   I'm a maid. I'm also from Demen, you know. And I know you, and him, but I don't know him. (*Points to the Third Peasant.*)

THIRD PEASANT   You recognized them, but not me?

TANYA   You're Efim Antonych?

FIRST PEASANT   Denifitively.

TANYA   And you're Semyon's father, Zakhar Trifonych?

SECOND PEASANT   That's right.

THIRD PEASANT   And I'm Mitri Chilikin, you know. Recognize me now?

TANYA   Now I know you, too.

SECOND PEASANT   Whose daughter are you?

TANYA   Why Aksinya's—I'm the orphan of the soldier's wife.

FIRST AND THIRD PEASANTS (*astonished*)   Is that a fact?

SECOND PEASANT   There's truth in the saying: "Pay a little for a piglet, put him in the rye, and he'll grow up big and fine."

FIRST PEASANT   Denifitively. She resembles—looks like a mamzel.

THIRD PEASANT   That's so. Oh Lord!

VASILI LEONIDYCH (*off-stage, rings and then shouts*)   Grigori! Grigori!

FIRST PEASANT   Who's that getting so awfully excited, so to speak?

TANYA   That's the young master.

THIRD PEASANT   Oh Lord! He said we should wait outside for the time being.

(*Silence.*)

SECOND PEASANT   Are you the one Semyon's marrying?

TANYA   Did he write you about it? (*Covers her face with her apron.*)

SECOND PEASANT   Should be clear that he did. But he's making a mistake. I can see that the lad has become spoiled.

TANYA (*with animation*)   No, he's not at all spoiled. Should I send him to you?

SECOND PEASANT   Why send him now? Wait a little bit. There'll be plenty of time later!

(*Vasili Leonidych is shouting desperately: "Grigori, damn you!" He appears at the door in shirt-sleeves, putting on his pince-nez.*)

VASILI LEONIDYCH   Is everybody dead?

TANYA   He isn't here, Vasili Leonidych. I'll send him in right away. (*Walking towards the door.*)

VASILI LEONIDYCH   I thought I heard someone talking in here. What kind of scarecrows are these? Well?

TANYA   They're peasants from the Kursk village, Vasili Leonidych.

VASILI LEONIDYCH (*pointing to the Delivery Man*)   And who's this? Oh, yes, from Bourdier! (*The peasants bow. Vasili Leonidych doesn't pay any attention to them. Grigori meets Tanya at the door. Tanya remains.*) I told you—the other shoes. I can't wear these!

GRIGORI   But the others are in the same place too.

VASILI LEONIDYCH   Where in the same place?

GRIGORI   Why, in the same place.

VASILI LEONIDYCH   You're lying!

GRIGORI   Well, you'll see. (*Vasili Leonidych and Grigori leave.*)

THIRD PEASANT   But maybe it's not the right time now, you know. Maybe we better go to the lodging house and just wait there for the time being.

TANYA   No, it's all right. Wait here. I'll go get you some plates for the presents right away. (*Exit.*)

(*Sakhatov and Leonid Fyodorovich enter, followed by Fyodor Ivanych. The peasants take their presents and come to attention.*)

LEONID FYODOROVICH (*to the peasants*)   In a minute, in a

minute, just wait. (*Pointing to the Delivery Man.*) And who's this?

DELIVERY MAN   From Bourdier.

LEONID FYODOROVICH   Ah, from Bourdier!

SAKHATOV (*smiling*)   Well, I'm not denying it. But you'll have to admit that those of us who haven't seen all that you describe, who are uninitiated, find it hard to believe.

LEONID FYODOROVICH   You say you can't believe it. But we don't demand faith. We demand investigation. After all, I can't help but believe in this ring. And yet I received this ring from there.

SAKHATOV   What do you mean "from there"? From where?

LEONID FYODOROVICH   From the other world. Yes, that's right.

SAKHATOV (*smiling*)   Very interesting, very interesting!

LEONID FYODOROVICH   Granted you think I'm an impressionable person who imagines something that doesn't exist; but Aleksei Vladimirovich Krugosvetlov is not, I'd say, just anybody. He's a professor, but he acknowledges the same thing. And not just he. And what about Crookes? And Wallace? [3]

SAKHATOV   But I'm not denying it. All I'm saying is that it's very interesting. It would be interesting to know how Krugosvetlov explains it.

LEONID FYODOROVICH   He has his own theory! But why don't you come to see us this evening? He's definitely going to be here. First Grossmann will . . . you know, he's the famous mind reader.

SAKHATOV   Yes, I've heard of him, but I never had the chance to see him at work.

LEONID FYODOROVICH   Well, why don't you come? First there'll be Grossmann, and then Kapchich and our mediumistic séance. (*To Fyodor Ivanych.*) Has the messenger come back yet from Kapchich?

---

[3] Sir William Crookes, a physicist and chemist, and Alfred Russel Wallace, a naturalist, both accepted spiritualism.

FYODOR IVANYCH   Not yet.

SAKHATOV   Well, how'll I find out if he's going to be here?

LEONID FYODOROVICH   Just come, come all the same. If Kapchich doesn't come, we'll find our own medium. Marya Ignatevna is a medium—not as strong as Kapchich, but still . . . .

(*Tanya enters with the plates for the presents. She listens carefully to the conversation.*)

SAKHATOV (*smiling*)   Yes, yes. But here's one thing that bothers me: Why do the mediums always come from the so-called educated class? There's Kapchich and Marya Ignatevna, for example. Now if this is an actual power, then it should be found everywhere—among the people, among the peasants.

LEONID FYODOROVICH   That happens. That happens so often that we have a peasant in our house who has turned out to be a medium. The other day we called him in during a séance. We had him move a sofa, and then we forgot about him. Evidently he just fell asleep. And just imagine, our seance was over; Kapchich woke up; when suddenly we noticed medium-istic manifestations beginning in the other corner of the room, near the peasant. The table gave a start, and then began to move.

TANYA (*aside*)   That was when I was crawling out from under the table.

LEONID FYODOROVICH   Obviously, he's also a medium. That's not surprising, since he resembles Hume very much. Remember Hume? He was the naïve, blond fellow.

SAKHATOV (*shrugging his shoulders*)   Really! This is very interesting! Well, then you ought to test him.

LEONID FYODOROVICH   We are testing him. But he's not the only one. There's no end of mediums. We simply don't know them. Why just the other day a sickly old woman moved a stone wall.

SAKHATOV   Moved a stone wall?

LEONID FYODOROVICH   That's right. She was lying in bed and didn't have the slightest notion that she was a medium.

She leaned her arm against the wall, and the wall moved back.

SAKHATOV   And didn't cave in?

LEONID FYODOROVICH   And didn't cave in.

SAKHATOV   That's strange! Well, in that case, I'll come tonight.

LEONID FYODOROVICH   Please do. There'll definitely be a séance.

(*Sakhatov puts on his things. Leonid Fyodorovich sees him to the door.*)

DELIVERY MAN (*to Tanya*)   Tell the lady I'm here! What am I supposed to do, spend the night here?

TANYA   Just wait a little. She's going for a drive with her daughter; so she'll be out herself right away. (*Leaves.*)

LEONID FYODOROVICH (*goes up to the peasants, who bow and offer him the presents*)   There's no need of that!

FIRST PEASANT (*smiling*)   Well, this originates from our first duty. The commune wanted us to do this.

SECOND PEASANT   It's the proper thing.

THIRD PEASANT   Don't mention it. We're doing it because we're so satisfied . . . . Just as our parents, you know, served, you know, your parents, so we also want to serve you with all our hearts and not just . . . . (*Bows.*)

LEONID FYODOROVICH   Why, what are you doing? Just what is it you want?

FIRST PEASANT   We came to see Your Worship.

PETRISHCHEV (*dressed in an overcoat, quickly runs in*)   Is Vasili Leonidych up? (*Catches sight of Leonid Fyodorovich and bows to him with his head only.*)

LEONID FYODOROVICH   Did you want to see my son?

PETRISHCHEV   I? Yes, I want to see Vovo for a minute.

LEONID FYODOROVICH   Go on in. (*Petrishchev takes off his coat and quickly goes off to Vasili Leonidych's room. Leonid Fyodorovich addresses the peasants.*) Yes. Well, so what is it that you want?

SECOND PEASANT   Accept our presents.

FIRST PEASANT (*smiling*) The offerings from the village, you know.

THIRD PEASANT Don't mention it—it's nothing at all. We offer them as to a father. Don't mention it.

LEONID FYODOROVICH Well, all right . . . . Fyodor, take them.

FYODOR IVANYCH Well, give them to me. (*Takes the presents.*)

LEONID FYODOROVICH Now, what's your business?

FIRST PEASANT Why we came to see Your Worship.

LEONID FYODOROVICH That's obvious. But what is it that you want?

FIRST PEASANT Why, to make a motion in regard to the accomplishment of the sale of the land. It originates——

LEONID FYODOROVICH What's this? Are you buying land?

FIRST PEASANT Denifitively. That's right. It originates, you know, in regard to the purchase of the ownership of the land. So the commune has therefore, so to speak, empowered us to enter it, you know, as is proper, through the government bank, with the affixing of a stamp for the right amount.

LEONID FYODOROVICH In other words, you want to buy land through a bank. Is that it?

FIRST PEASANT That's right, just like you proposed to us last year. It originates, you know, from a total sum of 32,864 rubles for the purchase of the ownership of the land.

LEONID FYODOROVICH That's so, but how is the payment going to be made?

FIRST PEASANT Why the commune proposes, as was said last year, to spread out, you know, the reception of cash, according to the laws of the statutes, in totals of 4,000 rubles.

SECOND PEASANT That means that you'll get 4,000 now, and you wait for the rest.

THIRD PEASANT (*while unwrapping the bills*) You can be sure we'll mortgage ourselves before we'll do it in a slipshod manner—but, you know—after all—and it should be done, you know, whachama-call-it, properly.

LEONID FYODOROVICH   But I wrote you that I'd agree only if you got all the money together.

FIRST PEASANT   That would be denifitively pleasanter, but it's not in the possibilities, you know.

LEONID FYODOROVICH   I can't help that.

FIRST PEASANT   The commune has been, so to speak, relying on the proposition you made last year for spreading out the payment.

LEONID FYODOROVICH   That was last year; then I was willing, but now I can't———

SECOND PEASANT   But how come? You gave us hope, we even got the document, and we collected the money.

THIRD PEASANT   Have pity on us, father. We have little land —there isn't enough room for a chicken, you know, let alone for cattle. (*Bows.*) Don't sin, father! (*Bows.*)

LEONID FYODOROVICH   I admit it's true that last year I was willing to spread out the payment, but now something has happened—and so it's inconvenient for me now.

SECOND PEASANT   Without that land we'll starve to death.

FIRST PEASANT   Denifitively, without the land our residence will weaken and fall into ruin.

THIRD PEASANT (*bowing*)   Father, we have little land— there isn't enough room for a chicken, you know, let alone for cattle. Father, have pity on us! Take the money, father.

LEONID FYODOROVICH (*while looking through the document*) I understand your problem. I'd like to do you a favor. Just wait a little. I'll give you an answer in half an hour. Fyodor, tell the doorman I'm not seeing anyone.

FYODOR IVANYCH   Very well, sir.

(*Leonid Fyodorovich leaves. The peasants are dejected.*)

SECOND PEASANT   What a fix! He wants all the money. And where can we get it from?

FIRST PEASANT   If only he hadn't given us hope last year. And here we've been so denifitively counting on what he told us last year.

THIRD PEASANT   Oh Lord! I'd already unwrapped the money. (*Wraps the money.*) What do we do now?

FYODOR IVANYCH   Why what's your problem?

FIRST PEASANT   Our problem, honorable sir, is, so to speak, like this: Last year he proposed to spread out the payments. The commune agreed and empowered us. But now he, so to speak, proposes that we pay him the whole sum in full. But this deal is not at all suitable for us.

FYODOR IVANYCH   Have you got much money?

FIRST PEASANT   The whole sum we have in receipt is 4,000 rubles.

FYODOR IVANYCH   So what are you waiting for? Get to work and collect some more.

FIRST PEASANT   It was hard enough collecting this. We don't have the means for these considerations, sir.

SECOND PEASANT   You can't get blood out of a stone.

THIRD PEASANT   We'd really like to get it, but, you know, as it is, we had to use a fine tooth comb to get this sum together.

(*Vasili Leonidych and Petrishchev appear at the door, smoking cigarettes.*)

VASILI LEONIDYCH   But I've already said I'd try. I'll do my best. Well?

PETRISHCHEV   Remember, if you don't get it, it'll be a hell of a mess.

VASILI LEONIDYCH   But I already told you I'd try—and I will. Well?

PETRISHCHEV   Well, all right. I'm just telling you to be sure and get it. I'll wait. (*Leaves, closing the door.*)

VASILI LEONIDYCH (*waving his hand*)   Damn it! (*The peasants bow. Looks at the Delivery Man. To Fyodor Ivanych.*) Why don't you let this man from Bourdier go? He's practically moved in with us. Look at him, he's sleeping. Well?

FYODOR IVANYCH   Why he brought a note and was told to wait until Anna Pavlovna came out.

VASILI LEONIDYCH (*looking at the peasants and then staring at their money*) Why, what's this? Money? Who's it for? For us? (*To Fyodor Ivanych.*) Who in the world are they?

FYODOR IVANYCH They're peasants from the Kursk village. They've come to buy land.

VASILI LEONIDYCH Well, is it sold?

FYODOR IVANYCH Why no, they haven't come to any agreement yet. They're being stingy.

VASILI LEONIDYCH Oh? You've got to talk them into it. (*To the peasants.*) So you're buying land, eh?

FIRST PEASANT Denifitively. We are proposing to acquire the ownership of the possession of some land.

VASILI LEONIDYCH Don't be stingy. You know, I'll tell you how important land is for a peasant. Well? It's very important.

FIRST PEASANT Denifitively. Land is of first-rate importance for a peasant. That's right.

VASILI LEONIDYCH Well, now don't you be stingy. Now what is land? I'll tell you: You can sow rows of wheat on it, you know. You can harvest three hundred puds,[4] at a ruble a pud —that's three hundred rubles. Well? And if you plant mint, I tell you you can clean up a thousand rubles from a desyatina.

FIRST PEASANT Denifitively! That's true. You can raise all produces if you have the knowledge.

VASILI LEONIDYCH Then, by all means, sow mint. You see, I studied this. That's what's printed in books. I'll show you. Well?

FIRST PEASANT Denifitively. Regarding this subject, you know better about it from books. That's wisdom, you know.

VASILI LEONIDYCH So buy the land. Don't be stingy, but pass the money over. (*To Fyodor Ivanych.*) Where's papa?

FYODOR IVANYCH Home. He doesn't want to be disturbed.

VASILI LEONIDYCH Well, he's probably asking a spirit whether or not to sell the land. Well?

FYODOR IVANYCH That I can't say. I know that he was undecided when he went off.

[4] A *pud* is 36 pounds.

VASILI LEONIDYCH   What do you think, Fyodor Ivanych? Has he got any money? Well?

FYODOR IVANYCH   I don't really know. I doubt it. Why do you want to know? You got a big wad of it last week, you know.

VASILI LEONIDYCH   But I used that to pay for the dogs. And now, you know, we have a new club and Petrishchev has been elected to it. I've been borrowing money from Petrishchev, and now I have to pay for him and for myself. Well?

FYODOR IVANYCH   What kind of a club is it? A bicycle club?

VASILI LEONIDYCH   No. I'll tell you, this is a new club. Let me tell you, it's a very serious club. And do you know who's president of it? Well?

FYODOR IVANYCH   What's the purpose of this new club?

VASILI LEONIDYCH   It's a club for the encouragement of borzoi breeding. Well? And let me tell you, today is the first meeting and luncheon. And here I don't have any money! I'll go see him and give it a try. (*Exit.*)

FIRST PEASANT (*to Fyodor Ivanych*)   Honorable sir, who was that?

FYODOR IVANYCH (*smiling*)   The young master.

THIRD PEASANT   The heir, you know. Oh Lord! (*Puts the money away.*) I'd better put it away for the time being.

FIRST PEASANT   Why we were told that he's in the army, in the cavalry, so to speak.

FYODOR IVANYCH   No, being an only son, he's exempt from military service.

THIRD PEASANT   He's been left alone so he can take care of his parents, you know. That's proper.

SECOND PEASANT (*shaking his head*)   Nice care he'll take of them.

THIRD PEASANT   Oh Lord!

(*Vasili Leonidych enters. Leonid Fyodorovich comes to the door.*)

VASILI LEONIDYCH   That's the way it always is. It's really shocking. First they complain that I'm not doing anything, but then when I find an activity and get busy—when a serious club with noble aims is founded—then they begrudge me a lousy three hundred rubles!

LEONID FYODOROVICH   I told you I can't, and that's the end of it. I haven't got the money.

VASILI LEONIDYCH   But you sold the land, you know.

LEONID FYODOROVICH   In the first place, I didn't sell it; and in the second—leave me alone! You were told that I'm busy. (*Slams the door.*)

FYODOR IVANYCH   I told you this wasn't the time.

VASILI LEONIDYCH   Well, I'll tell you, this is some spot I'm in. Eh? I'll go see mama—it's my only hope. He's gone off his rocker with this spiritualism of his and forgotten everybody. (*Goes upstairs. Fyodor Ivanych sits down to read his paper. Betsy and Marya Konstantinovna come downstairs, followed by Grigori.*)

BETSY   Is the carriage ready?

GRIGORI   It's on the way.

BETSY (*to Marya Konstantinovna*)   Let's go, come on! I saw him—it's he.

MARYA KONSTANTINOVNA   Who?

BETSY   You know very well—Petrishchev.

MARYA KONSTANTINOVNA   Well, where is he?

BETSY   In Vovo's room. You'll see.

MARYA KONSTANTINOVNA   But suppose it isn't he?

(*The peasants and the Delivery Man bow.*)

BETSY (*to the Delivery Man*)   Ah, you're from Bourdier? With the dress?

DELIVERY MAN   That's right. Can I go now?

BETSY   Why, I don't know. Mama will have to decide that.

DELIVERY MAN   I wouldn't know. I was just told to bring it and get the money.

BETSY   Well, then wait.

MARYA KONSTANTINOVNA   Is that the costume for the charade?

BETSY   Yes, it's a charming costume. But mama won't accept it and doesn't want to pay for it.

MARYA KONSTANTINOVNA   Why not?

BETSY   You ask her. Five hundred rubles for Vovo's dogs isn't much, but a hundred rubles for a dress is too much. And I certainly can't play a scarecrow! (*Pointing to the peasants.*) And who in the world are they?

GRIGORI   Peasants. They've come to buy some land or other.

BETSY   And here I thought they were hunters. You're not hunters?

FIRST PEASANT   Not at all, ma'am. We are here in regard to the accomplishment of the sale of a deed of land. Came to see Leonid Fyodorovich.

BETSY   But how's that? Vovo was expecting hunters. Are you sure you're not hunters? (*The peasants are silent.*) How stupid they are! (*Walks over to the door.*) Vovo! (*Laughs.*)

MARYA KONSTANTINOVNA   But we just saw him upstairs.

BETSY   Who asked you to remember that? Vovo, are you in there?

PETRISHCHEV (*coming to the door*)   Vovo isn't here, but I'm ready to do all that's expected of him. Hello! Hello, Marya Konstantinovna! (*Firmly shakes Betsy's hand for a long time, and then repeats the process with Marya Konstantinovna.*)

SECOND PEASANT   Take a look at that—looks like he's pumping water.

BETSY   You can't replace him, but still you're better than nothing. (*Laughs.*) What's your business with Vovo?

PETRISHCHEV   Business? Fi-nancial business. That is, our business is "fie!" and at the same time "nancial"—besides being "financial."

BETSY   What does "nancial" mean?

PETRISHCHEV   That's the heart of the matter. The point is in the fact that it doesn't mean anything! [5]

---

[5] Petrishchev is trying to amuse the girls by making a defective charade.

BETSY Well, that didn't come off—didn't come off at all! (*Laughs.*)

PETRISHCHEV They can't be good all the time, you know. It's like a lottery. There's nothing, nothing—and then you hit the jackpot.

(*Fyodor Ivanych goes off to Leonid Fyodorovich's study.*)

BETSY Well, that didn't come off. But tell me, were you at the Mergasofs' yesterday?

PETRISHCHEV Not so much at *mère Gassof*'s as at *père Gassof*'s, and not really at *père Gassof*'s but at *fils Gassof*'s.

BETSY Can't you say anything without a *jeu de mots*? That's a disease. And were the gypsies there? [6] (*Laughs.*)

PETRISHCHEV (*sings*) "On her apron little cocks with golden combs . . . ."

BETSY How lucky you are! We had a boring time at Fofo's.

PETRISHCHEV (*continues singing*) "And she swore most solemnly, she would come and stay with me. . . ." How does the rest of it go? Marya Konstantinovna, how does the rest of it go?

MARYA KONSTANTINOVNA ". . . come and stay with me an hour . . . ."

PETRISHCHEV What's that? What's that, Marya Konstantinovna? (*Laughs.*)

BETSY *Cessez, vous devenez impossible!*

PETRISHCHEV *J'ai cessé, j'ai bébé, j'ai dédé . . . .*

BETSY I can see that there's only one way of getting away from your witticisms—and that's by making you sing. Let's go into Vovo's room; he has a guitar. Come on, Marya Konstantinovna, let's go! (*Betsy, Marya Konstantinovna, and Petrishchev go into Vasili Leonidych's room.*)

FIRST PEASANT Who are they?

[6] Betsy is referring to gypsy entertainers. Petrishchev answers her in the affirmative by singing a snatch of a gypsy song.

GRIGORI   One is the daughter, and the other a mamzel who teaches music.

FIRST PEASANT   So she promotes into science. And how neat she is—a regular portrait.

SECOND PEASANT   Why don't they marry them off? They're old enough, aren't they?

GRIGORI   You expect them to marry at fifteen, like yours do?

FIRST PEASANT   And the man is a musicianist, so to speak?

GRIGORI (*mocking him*)   A musicianist! You don't understand a thing!

FIRST PEASANT   Denifitively. We're stupid, you know, ignorant.

THIRD PEASANT   Oh Lord!

(*From Vasili Leonidych's room are heard gypsy songs with a guitar accompaniment. Semyon enters, with Tanya following. Tanya watches the reunion of father and son.*)

GRIGORI (*to Semyon*)   What are you doing here?

SEMYON   I was sent to Mr. Kapchich's.

GRIGORI   Well, what's the story?

SEMYON   He said he can't make it at all.

GRIGORI   All right, I'll let him know. (*Exit.*)

SEMYON (*to his father*)   Hello, father. My respects to you, Uncle Efim and Uncle Mitri! Is everybody all right at home?

SECOND PEASANT   Hello, Semyon.

FIRST PEASANT   Hello, lad.

THIRD PEASANT   Hello, young fellow. Getting along all right?

SEMYON (*smiling*)   Well, father, why don't we go and have some tea?

SECOND PEASANT   Wait'll we get through here. Can't you see we're busy now?

SEMYON   Well, all right. I'll be waiting for you out at the porch. (*Starts to leave.*)

TANYA (*running after him*)   How come you didn't say anything about us?

SEMYON   How can I say anything with the others around?

Wait a little bit. We'll go have some tea and then I'll tell him. (*Exit.*)

(*Fyodor Ivanych enters and sits down near the window with his paper.*)

FIRST PEASANT   Well, honorable sir, how is our affair coming along?

FYODOR IVANYCH   Wait a little. He'll be out right away. He's just finishing up.

TANYA (*to Fyodor Ivanych*)   What makes you think he's finishing up, Fyodor Ivanych?

FYODOR IVANYCH   Why, because when he finishes with the questions, he reads the questions and answers aloud.

TANYA   Is it really true that you can talk with spirits by means of a saucer?

FYODOR IVANYCH   Some think it is.

TANYA   Well now, if they told him to sign something, would he do it?

FYODOR IVANYCH   Of course he would.

TANYA   But they don't talk with words, do they?

FYODOR IVANYCH   No, they use letters. He notices what letters they point out.

TANYA   Now what would happen if, during a séance . . . ?

LEONID FYODOROVICH (*entering*)   No, my friends, I can't. I'd like to very much, but I just can't. If you had all the money, it would be a different matter.

FIRST PEASANT   Denifitively, it would be best that way. But we are not well-to-do, and it's absolutely impossible.

LEONID FYODOROVICH   I can't, I just can't. Here's your document back. I can't sign it.

THIRD PEASANT   Father, take pity on us, have mercy on us.

SECOND PEASANT   What'll we do? You're wronging us.

LEONID FYODOROVICH   I'm not wronging you, friends. Last summer I told you to go ahead if you wanted to do it. You didn't want to then, and now I can't.

THIRD PEASANT   Father, take pity on us. How are we going

to live? We have little land—there isn't enough room for a chicken, you know, let alone for cattle.

(*Leonid Fyodorovich walks off and stops in the doorway. Anna Pavlovna and the Doctor start to come downstairs. They are followed by Vasili Leonidych, who, in a happy and playful mood, is putting money into his wallet.*)

ANNA PAVLOVNA (*tightly laced and wearing a hat*)   So I should take them?

DOCTOR   Be sure to take them if the symptoms are repeated. But the main thing is, take better care of yourself. How can you expect thick syrup to pass through a thin capillary tube, especially if you squeeze the tube? Impossible, isn't it? It's the same thing with the biliary ducts. This is all very simple, you know.

ANNA PAVLOVNA   Well, fine, fine.

DOCTOR   You keep saying "fine," but you go on doing the same thing. And you absolutely must not keep on like this, madam. Well, good-by.

ANNA PAVLOVNA   Not good-by, but *au revoir*. I'll be expecting you this evening. I wouldn't risk it without you.

DOCTOR   Very well, very well. I'll drop in if I have the time. (*Exit.*)

ANNA PAVLOVNA (*seeing the peasants*)   What's this? What is this? Who are these people? (*The peasants bow.*)

FYODOR IVANYCH   They're peasants from the Kursk village. They've come to see Leonid Fyodorovich about buying some land.

ANNA PAVLOVNA   I can see that they're peasants. But who let them in here?

FYODOR IVANYCH   Leonid Fyodorovich said they could come in. He's just been talking with them about the sale of the land.

ANNA PAVLOVNA   What sale of land? There's no need to sell it. But the important thing is, why were these people off of the streets let into the house? Why were these people off of the streets let into the house? They've spent the night God knows where, and they should not be allowed in the house. (*Getting more and more excited.*) I wouldn't be surprised if every crease of their clothes is full of microbes: scarlet fever microbes, small-pox microbes, diphtheria microbes! Why they're from the Kursk province, where there's an epidemic of diphtheria! Doctor, doctor! Get the doctor back here!

(*Leonid Fyodorovich goes into his room, slamming the door. Grigori goes for the doctor.*)

VASILI LEONIDYCH (*blowing smoke into the peasants' faces*) Don't worry, mama. If you want me to, I'll fumigate these fellows so that all the microbes will drop dead. Well? (*Anna Pavlovna maintains absolute silence, waiting for the doctor to return. Vasili Leonidych to the peasants.*) Do you raise pigs? Now that's profitable.

FIRST PEASANT Denifitively. Now and then we raise pigs.

VASILI LEONIDYCH Pigs that go like this? (*Grunts like a piglet.*)

ANNA PAVLOVNA Vovo, Vovo, stop that!

VASILI LEONIDYCH Did I come close? Well?

FIRST PEASANT Denifitively. There is a similarity.

ANNA PAVLOVNA Vovo, I tell you, stop that!

SECOND PEASANT Why's he acting like that?

THIRD PEASANT I said we should have stayed at the lodging house for the time being.

DOCTOR (*entering with Grigori*) Well, what is it now? What's the matter?

ANNA PAVLOVNA Now here you tell me not to get excited, but how can I stay calm in this house? I haven't seen my sister for two months; I avoid every dubious visitor. And suddenly these people from the Kursk province—straight from the Kursk province where there's an epidemic of diphtheria—appear right smack in the middle of my house!

DOCTOR You mean these fellows here?

ANNA PAVLOVNA Why yes, straight from a diphtheria area!

DOCTOR Of course, if they're from a diphtheria area, then,

to be sure, it's not safe. But still, there's no reason to get very excited.

ANNA PAVLOVNA   But you yourself suggest caution.

DOCTOR   Well yes, that's right. But there's no reason to get very excited.

ANNA PAVLOVNA   What do you mean? There'll have to be a complete disinfection.

DOCTOR   No, why a complete disinfection? That's too expensive. That could run to some three hundred rubles, or even more. I'll fix you one that's cheap and effective. To a big bottle of water, add——

ANNA PAVLOVNA   Should it be boiled water?

DOCTOR   Doesn't matter. Boiled water is better . . . . So, to a bottle of water, add a tablespoon of salicylic acid. And then wash everything that they've even touched. And, of course, these fellows themselves must be sent away. That's all you have to do. Then you won't have to worry. And spray the air with two or three glasses of the same mixture, and you'll see how effective it'll be. You'll be absolutely safe.

ANNA PAVLOVNA   Where's Tanya? Call Tanya!

TANYA (*entering*)   What do you wish?

ANNA PAVLOVNA   Do you know that big bottle in my dressing room?

TANYA   You mean the one we used for disinfecting the laundress yesterday?

ANNA PAVLOVNA   Why of course, what other one could I mean? Now then, take this bottle, and first wash off the place where they're standing with soap; then with——

TANYA   Yes, ma'am, I know how to do it.

ANNA PAVLOVNA   And then take the atomizer . . . . On second thought, I'll come back and do it myself.

DOCTOR   Just do as I tell you, and then forget about it. Well then, good-by until this evening. (*Exit*.)

ANNA PAVLOVNA   And as for them, get them out of here, get them out of here. I don't want to see a trace of them. Get out of here, get out of here. Go on, what are you just standing there and looking for?

FIRST PEASANT   It's denifitively because of our stupidity. We were told——

GRIGORI (*leading the peasants out*)   All right, get out, get out!

SECOND PEASANT   Give me back the kerchief my present was wrapped in!

THIRD PEASANT   Oh Lord! I said we should have stayed at the lodging house for the time being. (*Grigori pushes him out.*)

DELIVERY MAN (*having made several attempts to say something*)   Will there be any answer?

ANNA PAVLOVNA   Ah, you're from Bourdier? (*Excitedly.*) There won't be any answer, none whatsoever, and take it back. I told her I didn't order any such costume and won't allow my daughter to wear it.

DELIVERY MAN   It's not my fault. I was just sent.

ANNA PAVLOVNA   Get out, get out. Take it back. I'll call there myself.

VASILI LEONIDYCH (*solemnly*)   Mr. Ambassador from Bourdier, get out!

DELIVERY MAN   You should have told me that long ago. Why'd you have me sitting here five hours?

VASILI LEONIDYCH   Envoy of Bourdier, get out!

ANNA PAVLOVNA   Please stop that! (*Delivery Man leaves.*) Betsy! Where is she? I'm eternally having to wait for her.

VASILI LEONIDYCH (*shouting at the top of his voice*)   Betsy! Petrishchev! Come on, quick! Quick! Quick! Well?

(*Betsy, Marya Konstantinovna, and Petrishchev enter.*)

ANNA PAVLOVNA   I'm eternally having to wait for you.

BETSY   On the contrary, I'm the one who's waiting for you.

(*Petrishchev bows with his head only and kisses Anna Pavlovna's hand.*)

ANNA PAVLOVNA   Hello. (*To Betsy.*) You're always talking back!

BETSY   If you're in a bad mood, mama, I'd rather stay home.

ANNA PAVLOVNA   Are we going or not?

BETSY   Well, let's go. What else can we do?

ANNA PAVLOVNA   Did you see the costume from Bourdier?

BETSY   I did, and I like it very much. I ordered the costume and I'll wear it when it's paid for.

ANNA PAVLOVNA   I won't pay for it, and I won't let you wear an indecent costume.

BETSY   What made it indecent all of a sudden? First it was decent, and now you're overcome by *pruderie*.

ANNA PAVLOVNA   It's not *pruderie*. The whole waist will have to be done over—then you can wear it.

BETSY   But mama, really, that can't be done.

ANNA PAVLOVNA   Well, go on and get your things on.

(*They sit down, and Grigori puts their overshoes on.*)

VASILI LEONIDYCH   Marya Konstantinovna! Do you notice how deserted the hall is?

MARYA KONSTANTINOVNA   What do you mean? (*Laughing in anticipation.*)

VASILI LEONIDYCH   Why it's because the man from Bourdier has gone. Well? That was good, wasn't it? (*Roars with laughter.*)

ANNA PAVLOVNA   Well, let's go. (*Goes out the door and immediately returns.*) Tanya!

TANYA   What do you wish?

ANNA PAVLOVNA   Don't let Fifi catch cold while I'm out. If she wants to go out, then be sure she has her little yellow coat on. She's not really well.

TANYA   Yes, ma'am.

(*Anna Pavlovna, Betsy, Marya Konstantinovna, and Grigori leave.*)

PETRISHCHEV. Well, did you get it?

VASILI LEONIDYCH Let me tell you, it wasn't easy. First I tried father—he started bellowing and threw me out. Then I tried mother—and I got it. It's here. (*Slaps his pocket.*) When I get my grippers on somebody, he doesn't get away—it's a dead man's grip I've got. Well? And today they're bringing my wolf-hounds, you know.

(*Petrishchev and Vasili Leonidych put on their coats and leave. Tanya follows them out.*)

FYODOR IVANYCH (*to himself*) Yes, nothing but these unpleasant scenes. And why can't they live in peace? And it's obvious that this younger generation doesn't amount to much. And then you've got this domination by women. Just now Leonid Fyodorovich wanted to put in a word for them, but he saw that she was having a fit and he slammed the door. He's a man of rare kindness! Yes, a man of rare kindness! What's this? Why, Tanya is bringing them in again.

TANYA (*enters, followed by the three peasants*) Come on in, come on in, friends. It's all right.

FYODOR IVANYCH Now why did you have to go and bring them in again?

TANYA But what else could I do, Fyodor Ivanych? Someone has to look after them. And I've got to wash up here anyway.

FYODOR IVANYCH But the deal won't go though. I can see that now.

FIRST PEASANT But how then, honorable sir, can be put our affair into motion? Intercede for us, your Honor, and we'll be able to present the commune's full gratitude as a reward for your trouble.

THIRD PEASANT Help us, little falcon. We can't get along on the land we've got. We have little land—there isn't enough room for a chicken, you know, let alone for cattle.

(*The peasants bow.*)

FYODOR IVANYCH   I really feel sorry for you, friends, but I don't know what can be done. I understand your situation real well, you know. But the fact is that he's refused. So what can be done? And the lady is also against it. It's pretty hopeless. Well, give me the document. I'll go and give it a try. I'll ask him. (*Exit. The three peasants sigh.*)

TANYA   Tell me, friends, what's holding the matter up?

FIRST PEASANT   If we could only get the signature by the affixing of his name.

TANYA   You just want the master to sign the document, is that it?

FIRST PEASANT   That's all, just to affix his name and to take the money. And that would be the end of it.

THIRD PEASANT   If he'd only write: "I want it to be, you know, just like the peasants, you know, want it to be." And that would be all. He'd take it, sign it, and it'd be over and done with.

TANYA   You just want him to sign it? You just want the master to sign the document? (*Thinking.*)

FIRST PEASANT   Denifitively. The deal depends only on that. He signs it, you know, and that's all there is to it.

TANYA   Why don't you just wait a little and see what Fyodor Ivanych has to say. If he can't convince him, I'll try a little trick.

FIRST PEASANT   You'll trick him?

TANYA   I'll try.

THIRD PEASANT   Oh, the girl wants to help us out. If you put this deal across, we promise, you know, to take care of you at the commune's expense for the rest of your life. That's a fact!

FIRST PEASANT   If this matter could be put into motion, we would denifitively be generous about money.

SECOND PEASANT   Why, of course!

TANYA   I won't promise for sure. Like they say: "Don't count your chickens before they're hatched." But then, "nothing . . . ."

FIRST PEASANT "Nothing ventured, nothing gained." That's denifitively so.

FYODOR IVANYCH (*entering*) No, friends, the deal is hopeless. He just won't agree. Here, take your document. You better go now.

FIRST PEASANT (*taking the document. To Tanya*) Well, we'll be relying on you, so to speak.

TANYA Just be patient for a little while. Go on out and wait in the street. I'll be right out and tell you something. (*The peasants leave.*) Dear Fyodor Ivanych, ask the master if he'll come out and see me. I have to tell him something.

FYODOR IVANYCH What are you up to?

TANYA It's important, Fyodor Ivanych. Please ask him. It's nothing bad, it really isn't.

FYODOR IVANYCH But what's this all about?

TANYA Well, it's a little secret. I'll tell you about it later. Just ask him.

FYODOR IVANYCH (*smiling*) I wish I knew what you were up to. Well, all right, I'll ask him, I'll ask him. (*Exit.*)

TANYA (*to herself*) I'll do it, I really will. After all, he himself said that Semyon has the power; and, after all, I know just how to do it. Nobody guessed then. And now I'll show Semyon how to do it. And if it doesn't work, nothing will be lost anyway. There's no sin in trying it.

LEONID FYODOROVICH (*enters smiling, followed by Fyodor Ivanych*) Ah, there's our petitioner. Well, what's this business of yours?

TANYA It's a little secret, Leonid Fyodorovich. Could I tell it to you alone?

LEONID FYODOROVICH What could it be? Fyodor, would you step out for a minute?

(*Fyodor Ivanych leaves.*)

TANYA Since I've lived and grown up in your house, Leonid Fyodorovich, and since I'm grateful to you for everything that you've done for me, I want to tell you what's going on, just as if you were my father. Semyon wants to marry me.

LEONID FYODOROVICH   Is that so?

TANYA   I want to tell you everything, absolutely everything. Being an orphan, there's no one I can turn to for advice.

LEONID FYODOROVICH   Well, why don't you marry him? He seems to be a nice fellow.

TANYA   That's so. He wouldn't make a bad husband. But there's one thing I'm worried about, and I wanted to ask you. There's something about him that I just don't understand— and I'm afraid it might be bad.

LEONID FYODOROVICH   What's that? Does he drink?

TANYA   No, God forbid! But since I know that there's such a thing as spiritanism—

LEONID FYODOROVICH   You do?

TANYA   Of course, sir! I understand it very well. Others, being ignorant, don't, of course, understand this——

LEONID FYODOROVICH   Well, what's the point you're driving at?

TANYA   Just this: I'm worried about Semyon. This happens to him.

LEONID FYODOROVICH   What happens to him?

TANYA   Why something like spirit—anism. Just ask the servants. The minute he dozes off at the table, the table gives a shake right away; and it begins to creak all over like this: tuk, tu-tuk! And all the servants have seen this.

LEONID FYODOROVICH   Why that's just what I was telling Sergei Ivanovich this morning. Well, does anything else happen?

TANYA   Why . . . . Now when was this? Oh yes, on Wednesday. We sat down to dinner. As soon as he sat down at the table, the spoon went jump right into his hand—all by itself.

LEONID FYODOROVICH   Ah, this is interesting! So it went jump into his hand? Well, had he dozed off?

TANYA   Now that I didn't notice. I think he had.

LEONID FYODOROVICH   Well, go on.

TANYA   Now that's the thing that worries me, the thing I

wanted to ask you about. Could some harm come of this? How could I spend my life with him when he has such a thing?

LEONID FYODOROVICH (*smiling*) No, don't be afraid; there's nothing bad here. All this means is that he's a *medium*—just a medium. I knew he was a medium even before you told me about this.

TANYA So that's it! And here I was scared of this!

LEONID FYODOROVICH No, don't be afraid. It's all right. (*To himself.*) This is working out fine. Kapchich can't make it, so we'll try this fellow out tonight. No, my dear, don't be afraid; he'll be both a good husband and also . . . . You see, this is a kind of power that everybody has. Only it's weaker in some and stronger in others.

TANYA Thank you very much, sir. I won't worry about it now. But before, I was afraid . . . . Just see how terrible our ignorance is!

LEONID FYODOROVICH No, no, don't be afraid. Fyodor! (*Fyodor Ivanych enters.*) I'm going out. Have everything ready for the séance by tonight.

FYODOR IVANYCH But Kapchich can't come.

LEONID FYODOROVICH That's all right. It doesn't matter. (*Puts on his overcoat.*) We'll have a trial séance with our own medium. (*Exit. Fyodor Ivanych goes out with him.*)

TANYA (*to herself*) He believed me, he believed me! (*Squeals with delight and jumps up and down.*) He really believed me! How wonderful! (*Squeals.*) Now I can put it across, if only Semyon doesn't lose his nerve.

FYODOR IVANYCH (*returning*) Well then, did you tell him your secret?

TANYA I did. And I'll tell you too, only later . . . . And I've got a request to make of you, Fyodor Ivanych.

FYDOR IVANYCH Well, what is it?

TANYA (*bashfully*) You've been like a second father to me, and I want to tell you absolutely everything.

FYODOR IVANYCH Now don't beat around the bush. Come to the point.

TANYA   You know what the point is? The point is that Semyon wants to marry me.

FYODOR IVANYCH   Is that so? I thought I noticed something.

TANYA   Why should I hide it? I'm an orphan, and you yourself know how it is here in the city—every man is after me. Take Grigori Mikhailych, for example—there's no getting rid of him. And even he . . . you know who I mean, don't you? They all think I have no soul, that I'm just something for their amusement.

FYODOR IVANYCH   You're smart—I like that! Well, what's the problem?

TANYA   Why Semyon wrote to his father, and he—his father, you know—saw me today. And right away he began to talk about his son being spoiled. Fyodor Ivanych, (*bows*) take the place of my father and speak with the old man, with Semyon's father. I could take them into the kitchen, and you could drop in and talk to the old man.

FYODOR IVANYCH (*smiling*)   So you want me to be a matchmaker? Why not? I can do it.

TANYA   Dear Fyodor Ivanych, take the place of my father, and I'll pray for you the rest of my life.

FYODOR IVANYCH   Fine, fine, I'll be there. I've promised and I'll do it. (*Picks up the newspaper.*)

TANYA   You'll be a second father to me.

FYODOR IVANYCH   Fine, fine.

TANYA   Then I have hopes of . . . . (*Exit.*)

FYODOR IVANYCH (*shaking his head. To himself*)   She's a sweet girl, a good girl. But just think how many like her are ruined! Just let her take one false step—and she'll start passing from hand to hand; and you'll never find her in the mire. Take dear Natalya, for example. She was also a good girl, and she also had a mother who brought her up with love . . . . (*Picks up the newspaper again.*) Well now, let's see what's up with Prince Ferdinand. How's he managing things in Bulgaria?

Curtain

ACT II

The stage represents the interior of the servants' kitchen. The three peasants, having taken off their things, are seated at the table and, perspiring, are drinking tea. Fyodor Ivanych is at the other end of the stage, smoking a cigar. The Old Cook is lying on the oven,[6] but he isn't visible until his first speech.

FYODOR IVANYCH   My advice to you is: Don't interfere with him. If this is what he wants, and if she wants it too, then give them your blessings. She's a good, honest girl. And don't pay any attention to the fact that she's so dressed up. This is how it's done in the city, and it can't be helped. But she's a smart girl.

SECOND PEASANT   Well, if he wants her—all right. He's the one who's going to have to live with her, not me. But she's just too elegant. How's she going to fit in with us? She won't even let her mother-in-law pat her.

FYODOR IVANYCH   My friend, it's not the elegance that counts, but the character. If she's got a good character, then she'll be obedient and respectful.

SECOND PEASANT   Well, it's all right with me if the lad has set his heart on her so much. After all, it's no fun living with someone you don't love. I'll talk it over with my old woman, and then give them my blessings.

FYODOR IVANYCH   Well, we're agreed then?

SECOND PEASANT   Why, I guess so.

FIRST PEASANT   You're real lucky, Zakhar. You came to put the deal across, and just look what a queen of a girl you've gotten for a daughter-in-law. Now you ought to wet the bargain, you know, so it'll all be according to regulations.

FYODOR IVANYCH   That's not at all necessary. (*An awkward silence.*) You see, I understand your peasant life very well. To tell you the truth, I'm thinking myself about where I should buy some land. I'd like to build myself a little house and live the life of a peasant. Maybe out your way.

[6] Russian ovens had a place on top for sleeping.

SECOND PEASANT   A very good thing!

FIRST PEASANT   Denifitively, if you've got the money, you can have all kinds of comforts in the country.

THIRD PEASANT   I should say so! Country life is always a lot freer—not like life in the city.

FYODOR IVANYCH   Well, will you take me into your commune if I settle in your village?

SECOND PEASANT   Why, of course. Treat the old men to some liquor, and they'll take you in at once.

FIRST PEASANT   If you open a tavern, so to speak, or an inn, you'll have a life such as you never dreamed of. You'll live like a czar, and no doubt about it.

FYODOR IVANYCH   We'll see about that later. All I want is a peaceful life in my old age. I've got a good life here too— and I'd hate to leave the place: Leonid Fyodorovich is a man of rare kindness, you know.

FIRST PEASANT   That's denifitively so. But what about our deal? Is it really hopeless?

FYODOR IVANYCH   He'd like to do it.

SECOND PEASANT   Looks like he's afraid of his wife.

FYODOR IVANYCH   He's not afraid; it's just that they don't see eye to eye.

THIRD PEASANT   Couldn't you try to help us? Otherwise, we won't be able to live. We have little land——

FYODOR IVANYCH   Let's first see what Tatyana can do. She's trying to help you, you know.

THIRD PEASANT (*drinking tea*)   Take pity on us! We have little land—there isn't enough room for a chicken, you know, let alone for cattle.

FYODOR IVANYCH   I wish it were up to me. (*To the Second Peasant.*) Well then, friend, so we're going to be matchmakers. The matter of Tanya is settled, isn't it?

SECOND PEASANT   I've already told you so, and I won't go back on my word, even if we don't wet the bargain. I just wish that our deal would go through.

(*The Woman Cook enters. She looks at the oven, makes signs in that direction, and immediately begins to speak to Fyodor Ivanych with animation.*)

WOMAN COOK   They've just called Semyon upstairs from the family kitchen. The master and that other fellow—the one that's bald and helps him call up spirits—have sat Semyon down and have told him to act in Kapchich's place.

FYODOR IVANYCH   Stop making things up!

WOMAN COOK   It's true. Yakov just told Tanya.

FYODOR IVANYCH   Well, this is certainly odd. (*The Coachman enters.*) What do you want?

COACHMAN (*to Fyodor Ivanych*)   I want you to tell them that I didn't hire out to live with dogs. Let somebody else live with them, but I'm not going to.

FYODOR IVANYCH   What dogs are you talking about?

COACHMAN   Why, they've brought three of Vasili Leonidych's dogs into our coachmen's room. They've messed up the place, they howl, and you can't get near them—they bite. They're vicious devils—likely to eat you up any minute. And wouldn't I like to break their legs with a stick.

FYODOR IVANYCH   Why, when did this happen?

COACHMAN   They brought them from the show today. They're some kind of expensive dogs—bedigreed, or something like that—who the hell knows? Either the dogs go, or the coachmen go. I want you to tell them that.

FYODOR IVANYCH   Yes, that's not right. I'll go ask about it.

COACHMAN   Why don't they bring them in here—to Lukerya?

WOMAN COOK (*excitedly*)   People eat here, and you want to keep dogs here? As it is——

COACHMAN   But I've got caftans, rugs, harness. And they're supposed to be kept clean. Well, why not take them into the porter's place?

FYODOR IVANYCH   I'll have to tell Vasili Leonidych about it.

COACHMAN (*angrily*)   Let him hang the dogs around his neck and walk around with them. But don't worry, he'd rather ride around on a horse. He's ruined Beauty for nothing. And what a horse that was! Eh, what a life! (*Leaves, slamming the door.*)

FYODOR IVANYCH   Just one mess after the other. (*To the peasants.*) Well then, friends, good-by for the time being!

PEASANTS   God be with you.

(*Fyodor Ivanych leaves. The moment he is out of the room, groans are heard on the oven.*)

SECOND PEASANT   He's a real smooth fellow—just like a yeneral.

WOMAN COOK   Why of course! He's got his own room; he gets his laundry free; sugar, tea—he gets it all from the master; and his food comes from the master's table.

OLD COOK   Why shouldn't the devil live so well—he's stolen a lot.

SECOND PEASANT   Who's that up there on the oven?

WOMAN COOK   Oh, just a man.

(*Silence.*)

FIRST PEASANT   Well, I saw you eating supper a while ago, and it was mighty good stuff.

WOMAN COOK   We can't complain. She's not stingy when it comes to food. White bread on Sunday, fish on holiday fasts—and if anybody wants to, he can have meat.

SECOND PEASANT   You mean somebody eats meat on fast days?

WOMAN COOK   Eh, why almost all of them do. The only ones who keep the fast are the coachman (not the one who was here, but an old fellow), and Syoma, and I, and the house-keeper; the rest all eat meat.

SECOND PEASANT   Well, and what about the master?

WOMAN COOK   Eh, what are you talking about? Why, he's even forgotten what a fast is.

THIRD PEASANT   Oh Lord!

FIRST PEASANT   That's the gentlemen's way. They've come to it by way of books. That's why they're smart!

THIRD PEASANT   White bread every day, I suppose?

WOMAN COOK   White bread? They don't know what your white bread is! You ought to see their food! What don't they have!

FIRST PEASANT   The gentlemen's food is light, of course.

WOMAN COOK   It's sure light, but they're great ones at stuffing themselves.

FIRST PEASANT   You mean they've got appetikes.

WOMAN COOK   That's because they wash it all down. They've got all those sweet wines, vodkas, fizzing liquors—a different kind for each course. They eat and wash it down, eat and wash it down.

FIRST PEASANT   So the liquor carries the food down in certain preportions.

WOMAN COOK   Oh, they're great ones at stuffing themselves —it's a caution! They don't just sit down, eat, cross themselves, and get up. No, they never stop eating.

SECOND PEASANT   Like pigs with their feet in a trough.

(*The peasants laugh.*)

WOMAN COOK   God bless us, as soon as they open their eyes, they have to have their samovar, teas, coffee, chicolate. No sooner have they finished two samovars than they need a third. And then comes lunch, then dinner, and then coffee again. They no sooner get up from the table than they've again got to have tea. And then snacks are served: candy, jams—and there's no end to it. They even eat when they're laying in bed.

THIRD PEASANT   Well, I'll be! (*Roars with laughter.*)

FIRST AND SECOND PEASANTS   What's the matter with you?

THIRD PEASANT   I'd like to live like that just one day.

SECOND PEASANT   Well, and when do they tend to their business?

WOMAN COOK   What business have they got? Just cards and

the piano—that's all the business they've got. It used to be that as soon as the young lady got up, she'd go right to the piano and start banging. And the one who lives here, the teacher, used to stand and wait for the piano. As soon as the one stopped, the other would let herself go. And sometimes they'd have two pianos, and then two or four of them would bang away at once. They'd bang away so that you could even hear them out here.

THIRD PEASANT   Oh Lord!

WOMAN COOK   And that's all the business they've got—either the piano or cards. The moment they get together, they start playing cards, drinking wine, and smoking—and so it goes all night. As soon as they get up, they start to eat again.

SEMYON (*enters*)   I hope you're enjoying yourselves!

FIRST PEASANT   Come and sit down.

SEMYON (*walking up to the table*)   Thank you very much. (*The First Peasant pours him some tea.*)

SECOND PEASANT   Where've you been?

SEMYON   Upstairs.

SECOND PEASANT   Well, what's going on up there?

SEMYON   I just can't figure it out. I don't know how to describe it.

SECOND PEASANT   But what is it? What kind of goings-on?

SEMYON   I just don't know how to describe it. They were testing some kind of power in me. But I don't understand it at all. Tatyana told me to do it. "We'll get the land for our peasants; he'll sell it," says she.

SECOND PEASANT   But how's she going to do it?

SEMYON   I can't get it out of her; she won't say. "Just do as I tell you," says she.

SECOND PEASANT   Do what?

SEMYON   Nothing right now. They sat me down, put the lights out, and told me to go to sleep. And Tatyana was hid nearby. They didn't see her, but I did.

SECOND PEASANT   Why was that? What was it for?

SEMYON   Who knows? I can't figure it out.

FIRST PEASANT   It's just a way of passing time, of course.

SECOND PEASANT   Well, it's clear we won't get to the bottom of this business. Now tell me, have you drawn much of your wages?

SEMYON   None. I've got twenty-eight rubles coming, I think.

SECOND PEASANT   Fine. Well, if, God grant, we get the land, I'll be taking you home, Syomka.

SEMYON   I'm all for that.

SECOND PEASANT   I think you've gotten spoiled. You won't want to do the plowing, will you?

SEMYON   Plowing? I'm ready for it any time. Mowing, plowing—these are the things you don't forget.

FIRST PEASANT   But still, after this city life, you won't find it much to your taste, so to speak.

SEMYON   I don't care about city life that much. The village is good enough for me.

FIRST PEASANT   Uncle Mitri here has his eye on your job, on this soft life.

SEMYON   Well, Uncle Mitri, you'd get tired of it soon enough. It looks easy, but there's an awful lot of running around. You get pretty tired.

WOMAN COOK   Uncle Mitri, you should just see their balls. You'd really be surprised!

THIRD PEASANT   Why? Do they eat all the time?

WOMAN COOK   No, not at all. You should see what goes on! Fyodor Ivanych took me to have a look. The ladies—they were really something! All dolled up—you never saw the likes of it! And naked down to here—and their arms were naked.

THIRD PEASANT   Oh Lord!

SECOND PEASANT   Whew, how filthy!

FIRST PEASANT   That's because of the climate, you know.

WOMAN COOK   So I looked in at them, Uncle. And what did I see? All of them were naked. Would you believe it, even the old ones had stripped—even our mistress, who has grandchildren, you know.

THIRD PEASANT   Oh Lord!

WOMAN COOK   And then, when the music struck up, when

they began to play, the gentlemen right away went up and embraced the ladies and started to whirl around.

SECOND PEASANT   Even the old women?

WOMAN COOK   Even the old women.

SEMYON   No, the old women just sit.

WOMAN COOK   You don't know what you're talking about. I saw them myself.

SEMYON   I tell you, it's not so.

OLD COOK (*sticking his head out and speaking in a hoarse voice*)   That's the polka-mazurka. Eh, you fool, you don't even know that! That's the way they dance.

WOMAN COOK   Look here, dancer, keep quiet. There's somebody coming. (*The Old Cook quickly hides.*)

GRIGORI (*enters. To the Woman Cook*).   Let me have some sauerkraut!

WOMAN COOK   I've just come back from the cellar, and now I've got to go back again. Who's it for?

GRIGORI   The young ladies want sour soup. Be quick about it! Send it up with Semyon. I haven't got the time to wait.

WOMAN COOK   First they eat sweet stuff until no more will go down, and then they want sauerkraut.

FIRST PEASANT   That's for cleaning them out, you know.

WOMAN COOK   Why yes, they'll make room in their stomachs, and then go at it again! (*Takes a bowl and leaves.*)

GRIGORI (*to the peasants*)   Well, haven't you made yourselves at home! You better look out. If the mistress finds out, she'll give you another overhauling, like she did this morning. (*Laughs and leaves.*)

FIRST PEASANT   She did denifitively kick up a storm this morning—it was awful!

SECOND PEASANT   It looked like he wanted to take our side this morning. But then, when he saw how she was raising the roof, he slammed the door, as much as to say: "Oh, go to hell!"

THIRD PEASANT (*waving his hand*)   It's the same all over. Sometimes my old woman flares up too, you know—and there's hell to pay! I just get out of the house. The hell with her! She's likely to let you have it with the poker any minute, you know. Oh Lord!

YAKOV (*running in with a prescription*) Syoma, run down to the drugstore—quick—and get these powders for the mistress!

SEMYON But he told me not to leave.

YAKOV You'll have plenty of time. Your business probably won't start till after tea. (*To the peasants.*) I hope you're enjoying yourselves!

FIRST PEASANT Why don't you join us? (*Semyon leaves.*)

YAKOV I really haven't got the time, but give me a cup for company's sake.

FIRST PEASANT Why, we were just talking about how your lady was carrying on this morning.

YAKOV Oh, she's a hot-tempered one—really awful. She gets so mad—she's just fit to be tied. Sometimes she even starts crying.

FIRST PEASANT There's something, so to speak, that I wanted to ask about. This morning she was saying something about a macrote. "You've brought a macrote, a macrote into the house," says she. What are these macrotes?

YAKOV Oh, those are macroves. They say they're a kind of bug from which, they say, all diseases come. She was saying that you have them on you. And, boy, didn't they wash and sprinkle the place where you'd been standing. There's a medicine from which they all die—the bugs, I mean.

SECOND PEASANT Well, where are they on us—these bugs?

YAKOV (*drinking tea*) They say they're so tiny, you can't even see them with glasses.

SECOND PEASANT And how does she know they're on me? Maybe there are more of those filthy things on her than on me.

YAKOV Why don't you go and ask her?

SECOND PEASANT I think it's all a lot of nonsense.

YAKOV Of course it's nonsense. The doctors have to invent something like this. Otherwise, why would anybody pay them? There's one that comes here every day. He comes, has a chat—ten rubles.

SECOND PEASANT   Are you serious?

YAKOV   There's one of them that gets a hundred.

FIRST PEASANT   What! One hundred rubles?

YAKOV   One hundred. You think a hundred is a lot for him? He gets a thousand if he goes out of the city. "Give me a thousand," says he, "and if you don't, you can go ahead and croak."

THIRD PEASANT   Oh Lord!

SECOND PEASANT   How come he can do this? Does he know some charm?

YAKOV   I suppose he does. I used to work for a general who lived a little ways out of Moscow. He was awfully hot-tempered and proud as anything—a real general. So once his daughter got sick. They sent for this doctor right away. "A thousand rubles and I'll come." Well, they agreed, and he came. Somehow or other, they got on the wrong side of the doctor. Well, my God, you should have heard him yell at the general! "Ah!" says he. "So this is all the respect you show me, eh? All right, I won't treat her!" And would you believe it? The general swallowed his pride and tried in every which way to bring the doctor around. "Sir, don't abandon us!"

FIRST PEASANT   And did they give him the thousand?

YAKOV   I should say they did.

SECOND PEASANT   That's real easy money. Just think what a peasant could do with it.

THIRD PEASANT   But I think it's all nonsense. Like the time my leg was festering. I doctored it, and doctored it—doctored away about five rubles, you know. Then I gave up doctoring, and it healed up all by itself.

(*The Old Cook on the oven coughs.*)

YAKOV   I see the poor fellow is back again.

FIRST PEASANT   Who might that man be?

YAKOV   Why he was our master's cook. He comes to see Lukerya.

FIRST PEASANT   So he was the chef. Well, does he live here?

YAKOV   No, they don't want him in here. He's one place in

the daytime—another place at night. If he's got three kopecks, he stays in a flophouse; but if he drinks himself broke, he comes here.

SECOND PEASANT   How did he come to this?

YAKOV   Why, he just got this weakness. And what a man he used to be! Just like a gentleman! Used to wear a gold watch, drew forty rubles a month in wages. And now look at him—he'd have starved to death long ago if it hadn't been for Lukerya.

(*The Woman Cook comes in with the sauerkraut.*)

YAKOV (*to the Woman Cook*)   Well, I see Pavel Petrovich is back again.

WOMAN COOK   Where else can he go? Maybe we should let him freeze to death?

THIRD PEASANT   Just see what liquor will do to a man! Liquor, you know . . . . (*Clicks his tongue in sympathy.*)

SECOND PEASANT   It's a fact, if a man is strong, he's stronger than a rock; if he's weak, he's weaker than water.

OLD COOK (*climbing down from the oven. His arms and legs tremble*)   Lukerya, let me have a little glass.

WOMAN COOK   Where you going? I'll give you a little glass!

OLD COOK   For Christ's sake! I'm dying. Friends, give me five kopecks.

WOMAN COOK   I tell you, get back on the oven.

OLD COOK   Woman, half a glass! I'm asking you in Christ's name, understand? In Christ's name!

WOMAN COOK   Forget it. Here's some tea!

OLD COOK   What's tea? What's tea? A stupid, weak drink. I want some liquor—only a swallow . . . . Lukerya!

THIRD PEASANT   Look how the poor fellow's suffering!

SECOND PEASANT   Well, why don't you give him some?

WOMAN COOK (*goes to the cupboard and pours out a glass*) Here, but this is all you're getting.

OLD COOK (*grabs the glass and, trembling, drinks*)   Lukerya! Woman! I'm drinking, but you must understand——

WOMAN COOK   Now, now, that's enough out of you! Get up on the oven, and don't let me hear another word out of you.

(*The Old Cook obediently climbs up on the oven and continues to grumble to himself.*)

SECOND PEASANT   How awful when a man gets this weakness!

FIRST PEASANT   Denifitively, it's a real human weakness.

THIRD PEASANT   There's no doubt about it.

(*The Old Cook lies down, continuing to grumble. Silence.*)

SECOND PEASANT   There was something I wanted to ask you. There's a girl from out our way working in the house—Aksinya's daughter. Well? What's she like? Is she, you know, an honest girl?

YAKOV   She's a fine girl. I can say nothing but good about her.

WOMAN COOK   I can give you the real story on her, Uncle, because I know what goes on around here. If you want to marry your son to Tatyana, get her away fast before she's ruined—because this is bound to happen.

YAKOV   Yes, she's absolutely right. Last year we had this girl Natalya. She was a fine girl. And she was completely ruined, just like that fellow. (*Points to the Old Cook.*)

WOMAN COOK   A whole lot of women go to ruin here. Everyone likes the light work and the good food. And before you know it, the good food has led her astray. And once she's gone astray, the masters don't want her. They get rid of her right away, and get a fresh one to take her place. That's what happened to poor Natalya. She went astray, and right away they threw her out. She had a baby, got sick, and last spring she died in the hospital. And what a fine girl she was!

THIRD PEASANT   Oh Lord! People are so weak. They should be pitied.

OLD COOK.   You just wait for the devils to pity anybody! (*Swings his legs over the edge of the oven.*) I roasted at the stove for thirty years. And then they didn't need me anymore—so, croak like a dog! You just wait for them to take pity!

FIRST PEASANT   This denifitively happens all the time.

SECOND PEASANT   While they ate and drank, they called you curly-head; when they finished eating and drinking—good-by scab-head!

THIRD PEASANT   Oh Lord!

OLD COOK   Much you know. What's *sauté à la Beaumont*? What's *bavasari*? The things I could make in those days! Think of it, the Emperor ate my creations. And now the devils don't need me anymore. But I won't knuckle under!

WOMAN COOK   Now, now, don't talk so much. I'll show you! Crawl back into the corner so that nobody'll see you. Because if Fyodor Ivanych or somebody else comes in, they'll throw both of us out.

(*Silence.*)

YAKOV   Do you know the village I come from, Voznesenskoe?

SECOND PEASANT   Of course I do. It's about seventeen versts from us, no more than that—less if you ford the river. Have you got some land there?

YAKOV   My brother has, and I send him money. I live here, but I'm dying to get back home.

FIRST PEASANT   Denifitively, that's understandable.

SECOND PEASANT   Then Anisim must be your brother.

YAKOV   That's right. He lives at the farther end.

SECOND PEASANT   I know the place—the third farm.

TANYA (*running in*)   Yakov Ivanych, what are you doing, sitting around here? She's calling you!

YAKOV   I'll be right there. What's up?

TANYA   Fifi's barking—wants to eat. And she's scolding you. "What a terrible person he is," says she. "He has no pity whatsoever," says she. "Her dinner time was long ago, but he hasn't brought her anything!" (*Laughs.*)

Yakov (*about to go*)   Oh, she's mad, is she? I hope I don't get into a mess because of this!

Woman Cook (*to Yakov*)   Take the sauerkraut along!

Yakov   Well, give it to me—quick! (*Takes the sauerkraut and leaves.*)

First Peasant   Who's this who's going to have dinner now?

Tanya   Why, the dog. That dog of hers. (*Sits down and picks up the teapot.*) Any tea left? I brought some along, just in case. (*Pours in more tea leaves.*)

Second Peasant   Dinner for a dog?

Tanya   Of course! They prepare a special chop for the dog, one that doesn't have fat. I wash the dog's linen.

Third Peasant   Oh Lord!

Tanya   It's like the story of the gentleman who was burying his dog.

Second Peasant   What's that?

Tanya   This is what happened. A man was telling how his dog died, the gentleman's, that is. It was winter, and he drove out to bury it. He buried it and was driving back, crying—the gentleman, that is. It was freezing cold; the coachman's nose was running, and he kept wiping it . . . . Let me fill your cups. (*Pours.*) His nose was running, and he kept on wiping it. His master saw this and said: "What is it?" he said. "What are you crying about?" And the coachman answered: "How can I help crying, sir? It was such a fine dog!" (*Laughs loudly.*)

Second Peasant   And I suppose that all the time he was thinking: "I wouldn't cry even if you croaked yourself." (*Laughs loudly.*)

Old Cook (*from the oven*)   That's true, that's so!

Tanya   Well, so the gentleman got home and right away said to his wife: "What a kind man our coachman is," said he. "He was so sorry for the dog that he cried all the way home. Call him in and give him some vodka and a ruble reward." And that's how much sense she shows when she talks about Yakov having no pity on her dog.

(*The peasants roar with laughter.*)

FIRST PEASANT   Well done!

SECOND PEASANT   That's real good!

THIRD PEASANT   Oh, my dear, that was sure funny!

TANYA (*pouring more tea*)   Have some more! Oh, it looks like we've got a fine life, but sometimes I can hardly stand cleaning up all this filth after them. Whew! It's better in the village. (*The peasants turn their cups upside down to indicate that they have finished drinking. Tanya offers them more tea.*) Have some more, Efim Antonych! Let me pour you another cup, Mitri Vlasevich!

THIRD PEASANT   All right, go ahead and fill it.

FIRST PEASANT   Well, clever girl, how's our business coming along?

TANYA   All right, not bad——

FIRST PEASANT   Semyon said——

TANYA (*quickly*)   Said what?

SECOND PEASANT   Why, we couldn't make heads nor tails out of what he said.

TANYA   I can't tell you anything now—just that I'm really working on it. Here's your document! (*Shows the document under her apron.*) If only a certain trick works—— (*Squeals with delight.*) How wonderful it would be!

SECOND PEASANT   Watch out, don't lose that document. It cost us a little something.

TANYA   Don't worry. You just want him to sign it, is that right?

THIRD PEASANT   What else? He just signs it, you know, and that's the end of it. (*Turns his cup upside down.*) I've had enough.

TANYA (*to herself*)   He'll sign it. Just you wait and see, he'll sign it. Have some more. (*Pours tea.*)

FIRST PEASANT   If you put across the accomplishment of the sale of the land, we'll get you married at the commune's expense. (*Refuses the tea.*)

TANYA (*filling a cup and offering it*) Have some more.

THIRD PEASANT If you do it, we'll get you married and, you know, I'll come to dance at your wedding. Though I never danced in my life, I'll dance then!

TANYA (*laughing*) I'll certainly be looking forward to that.

(*Silence.*)

SECOND PEASANT (*looking Tanya over*) All right, but you're not the type for peasant work.

TANYA Who, me? Maybe you don't think I'm strong enough? You should see me pull the mistress in. There's many a peasant couldn't pull her like that.

SECOND PEASANT Why, where do you pull her?

TANYA Well, there's this thing made of bone, like a jacket, and it goes up to about here. Well, you pull it in with cords, just like when you spit on your hands and tighten up a harness.

SECOND PEASANT In other words, you pull in the girth.

TANYA That's right, I pull in the girth. But, you know, you can't brace yourself against her with your foot. (*Laughs.*)

SECOND PEASANT Why do you pull her in?

TANYA Just because.

SECOND PEASANT Maybe she's taken some kind of vow?

TANYA No, it's for beauty's sake.

FIRST PEASANT You mean you lace in her belly so she'll look good.

TANYA I pull her in till her eyes pop, but she keeps saying: "More." You have to pull till your hands smart, and here you say that I'm not strong. (*The peasants laugh and shake their heads.*) But I've been jabbering too long. (*Runs off, laughing.*)

THIRD PEASANT What a girl! That was sure funny.

FIRST PEASANT And how neat she is!

SECOND PEASANT She's all right.

(*Sakhatov and Vasili Leonidych enter. Sakhatov is holding a teaspoon.*)

VASILI LEONIDYCH It wasn't exactly a dinner. It was a *déjeuner dînatoir*. And let me tell you, it was fine. The suckling-pig ham was marvelous. Roulier puts up a first-rate meal. I've just come back, you know. (*Sees the peasants.*) So the peasants are back again.

SAKHATOV Yes, yes, that's fine, but we came to hide something. Now where should we hide it?

VASILI LEONIDYCH Excuse me a minute. (*To the Woman Cook.*) Where are the dogs?

WOMAN COOK In the coachmen's room. We can't keep them in the servants' kitchen.

VASILI LEONIDYCH Ah, in the coachmen's room? Well, fine.

SAKHATOV I'm waiting.

VASILI LEONIDYCH Sorry, sorry. Well? Oh yes, where should we hide it? Well, Sergei Ivanovich, now here's my idea: Let's put it in the pocket of one of these peasants. How about him? Hey, there! Well? Where's your pocket?

THIRD PEASANT What do you want with my pocket? How do you like that? My pocket! I've got money in my pocket.

SAKHATOV Well, where's your bag?

THIRD PEASANT What do you want it for?

WOMAN COOK Watch your tongue! This is the young master.

VASILI LEONIDYCH (*roaring with laughter*) Know why he's so scared? I'll tell you why: He's got an awful lot of money. Well?

SAKHATOV Yes, yes, I understand. Now here's what we'll do: You talk with them, and while you're doing that I'll slip the spoon into his bag so that they won't know anything about it and won't be able to tip him off. Go ahead, talk with them.

VASILI LEONIDYCH All right, all right. Well, how about it, lads? Are you going to buy the land? Well?

FIRST PEASANT That's what we're proposing with all our hearts. But the deal just isn't getting anywhere.

VASILI LEONIDYCH Now don't you be stingy. Land is an important thing. I told you about raising mint. You could try tobacco, too.

FIRST PEASANT   That's denifitively so. We could raise all kinds of produces.

THIRD PEASANT   Sir, why don't you ask your father for us? Otherwise, how can we go on living? We have little land—there isn't enough room for a chicken, you know.

SAKHATOV (*having slipped the spoon into the Third Peasant's bag*)   C'est fait. We're all set. Let's go. (*Leaves.*)

VASILI LEONIDYCH   Now don't you be stingy. Eh? Well, good-by. (*Exit.*)

THIRD PEASANT   I told you we should have gone to the lodging house. So we'd have spent ten kopecks a head, you know, but at least we'd have had some peace. But this is a regular madhouse. "Give me the money," says he. What's the meaning of this?

SECOND PEASANT   He must be a little drunk.

(*The peasants turn their cups upside down, get up, and cross themselves.*)

FIRST PEASANT   And remember how he mentioned sowing mint? You have to consider this too.

SECOND PEASANT   Sure, raise mint! He should try and do a little work—he wouldn't be so fast to talk about mint. Well, thank you very much. And now, clever woman, where can we lay down here?

WOMAN COOK   One of you can sleep on the oven, the others on the benches.

THIRD PEASANT   God bless you! (*Prays.*)

FIRST PEASANT   If only God would grant the accomplishment of our business. (*Lies down.*) Then tomorrow we could get on the train after dinner and be home on Tuesday.

SECOND PEASANT   Are you going to put out the light?

WOMAN COOK   I can't. They'll be running in all night for one thing or another. Go ahead and lie down, and I'll turn it down some.

SECOND PEASANT How can you make ends meet when you've got just a little land? Why, I've been buying grain since Christmas, you know. And I'm running out of oat straw. If I could just get four desyatinas, I'd take Syomka home.

FIRST PEASANT You've got a family. You'll have no trouble working the land if you get it. If only the business can be accomplished.

THIRD PEASANT We should pray to the Queen of Heaven. Maybe she'll take pity on us.

(*Silence. Sighs. Then there is the sound of footsteps and voices, the door opens, and the following rush into the room: Grossmann blindfolded and holding Sakhatov's hand, the Professor and the Doctor, the Stout Lady and Leonid Fyodorovich, Betsy and Petrishchev, Vasili Leonidych and Marya Konstantinovna, Anna Pavlovna and the Baroness, Fyodor Ivanych and Tanya. The peasants jump up. After entering with quick steps, Grossmann stops.*)

STOUT LADY Don't you worry—I'm watching. I said I'd watch and I'm fulfilling my duty conscientiously. Sergei Ivanych, you're not leading him, are you?

SAKHATOV Of course not.

STOUT LADY Don't lead him, but, on the other hand, don't resist. (*To Leonid Fyodorovich.*) I know all about these experiments. I used to do them myself. I used to feel the emanation, and the moment I felt——

LEONID FYODOROVICH Please don't talk.

STOUT LADY Ah, I understand that very well! I've experienced it myself. The moment my attention was distracted, I could no longer——

LEONID FYODOROVICH Sh-sh.

(*They walk around, searching near the First and Second Peasants. Then they go up to the Third Peasant. Grossmann stumbles over a bench.*)

BARONESS   *Mais dites moi, on le paye?*

ANNA PAVLOVNA   *Je ne saurais vous dire.*

BARONESS   *Mais c'est un monsieur?*

ANNA PAVLOVNA   *Oh, oui.*

BARONESS   *Ça tient du miraculeux. N'est-ce pas? Comment est-ce qu'il trouve?*

ANNA PAVLOVNA   *Je ne saurais vous dire. Mon mari vous l'expliquera.* (*She catches sight of the peasants and then looks around and sees the Woman Cook.*) *Pardon.* What's this? (*The Baroness joins the group. Anna Pavlovna to the Woman Cook.*) Who let the peasants in?

WOMAN COOK   Yakov brought them in.

ANNA PAVLOVNA   Who told Yakov to do that?

WOMAN COOK   I don't know. Fyodor Ivanych saw them here.

ANNA PAVLOVNA   Leonid! (*Leonid Fyodorovich, being busy with the search, doesn't pay attention to her, merely says "sh."*) Fyodor Ivanych! What does this mean? Didn't you see me disinfect the whole hall? And now you've infected the whole kitchen for me. Black bread, kvas——

FYODOR IVANYCH   I thought it wouldn't be dangerous in here, and the men are here on business. There's no place close by for them to go, and they are from our village.

ANNA PAVLOVNA   That's just the trouble—that they're from the Kursk village where people are dying from diphtheria like flies. But the main thing is that I ordered them out of the house! Did I or did I not order them out of the house? (*Goes up to the group gathered around the peasants.*) Be careful! Don't touch them—they're all infected with diphtheria!

(*Nobody pays any attention to her. She walks away with dignity and stands motionless, waiting.*)

PETRISHCHEV (*sniffs loudly*)   I don't know about diphtheria, but there's definitely some other kind of infection in the air. Do you smell it?

BETSY   Stop your nonsense! Vovo, which bag is it in?

VASILI LEONIDYCH   In that one, over there. He's heading for it, he's heading for it.

PETRISHCHEV   What have we got here—a physical or spiritual emanation?

BETSY   Now's the time your cigarettes can come in handy. Go ahead and puff, closer to me. (*Petrishchev bends over her and puffs smoke at her.*)

VASILI LEONIDYCH   He's getting close, I tell you. Well?

GROSSMANN (*excitedly groping near the Third Peasant*)   It's here, here. I feel it's here.

STOUT LADY   Do you feel an emanation?

(*Grossmann bends down to the bag and takes the spoon out of it.*)

ALL   Bravo! (*General elation.*)

VASILI LEONIDYCH   Ah, so this is where our spoon was? (*To the Third Peasant.*) So that's the kind of fellow you are!

THIRD PEASANT   What do you mean by that? I didn't take your spoon. What are you trying to get me mixed up in? I didn't take it, I did not take it, and I don't know nothing about it. He can go ahead and say what he wants to! I knew when he came in that he was up to no good. "Let me have your bag," says he. But I didn't take it, so help me God, I didn't take it.

(*The young people crowd around him and laugh.*)

LEONID FYODOROVICH (*angrily to his son*)   You and your everlasting clowning! (*To the Third Peasant.*) Don't you worry, my friend! We know you didn't take it. It was only an experiment.

GROSSMANN (*takes off the blindfold and pretends to be coming to*)   A little water . . . please. (*Everybody fusses around him.*)

VASILI LEONIDYCH   Let's go to the coachmen's room. I'll show you this one bitch I've got there. *Épatante!* Well?

BETSY   What a nasty word. Can't you just say "dog"?

VASILI LEONIDYCH   Impossible. After all, how would it sound if I said that Betsy is a very *épatant* person? No, I'd have to use "girl." And that's how it is in this case. Well? Isn't that so, Marya Konstantinovna? Wasn't that good? (*Roars with laughter.*)

MARYA KONSTANTINOVNA   Well, let's go.

(*Marya Konstantinovna, Betsy, Petrishchev, and Vasili Leonidych leave.*)

STOUT LADY (*to Grossmann*)   Well? How do you feel? Are you rested? (*Grossmann doesn't answer. To Sakhatov.*) Did you feel the emanation, Sergei Ivanovich?

SAKHATOV   I didn't feel anything. Yes, it was well done, well done. A complete success.

BARONESS   *Admirable! Ça ne le fait pas souffrir?*

LEONID FYODOROVICH   *Pas le moins du monde.*

PROFESSOR (*to Grossmann*)   Would you mind? (*Hands him the thermometer.*) At the beginning of the experiment the temperature was ninety-eight point nine. (*To the Doctor.*) That's right, isn't it? Would you mind checking his pulse? Some loss is inevitable.

DOCTOR (*to Grossmann*)   Well, sir, let me take your pulse. We'll check it, we'll check it. (*Takes out his watch and holds Grossmann's wrist.*)

STOUT LADY (*to Grossmann*)   Excuse me, but that state you were in—couldn't that be called sleep?

GROSSMANN (*wearily*)   It's the same kind of hypnosis.

SAKHATOV   Do you mean to say that you hypnotized yourself?

GROSSMANN   And why not? Hypnosis can occur not only through association, say through the sound of a tom-tom—the way Charcot does it—but also if one just enters a hypnogenetic zone.

SAKHATOV   Granted, but still it would be desirable to define hypnosis more precisely.

PROFESSOR   Hypnosis is a phenomenon consisting of the conversion of one energy into another.

GROSSMANN   Charcot doesn't define it that way.

SAKHATOV   Now just a minute. That's your definition, but Libot himself told me——

DOCTOR (*letting go of Grossmann's wrist*)   Ah, fine, fine. And now the temperature.

STOUT LADY (*cutting in*)   No, excuse me! I agree with Aleksei Vladimirovich. And here's the best proof of all for you. When I lay unconscious after my illness, I was overcome by a compulsion to talk. In general I'm a reserved type, but now suddenly there was this compulsion to talk, talk, talk. And they told me that I talked so much that everyone was amazed. (*To Sakhatov.*) However, I interrupted you, I think.

SAKHATOV (*with dignity*)   Not at all. Please continue.

DOCTOR   The pulse is eighty-two; the temperature has gone up six-tenths.

PROFESSOR   So there's your proof! That's what it should be. (*Takes out a notebook and writes it down.*) Eighty-two, is that it? And ninety-nine point five? As soon as hypnosis is induced, there's always an intensification of the heart action.

DOCTOR   As a doctor I can testify that your prediction has been fully realized.

PROFESSOR (*to Sakhatov*)   You were saying . . . ?

SAKHATOV   I wanted to say that Libot himself told me that hypnosis is only a special psychic state which increases suggestibility.

PROFESSOR   That's so, but still, the most important thing is the law of equivalency.

GROSSMANN   Furthermore, Libot is far from being an authority, while Charcot has made a thorough investigation of the subject and has proved that hypnosis induced by a blow, by a trauma——

SAKHATOV   But I'm not rejecting Charcot's work.
I know him too. I'm just repeating what Libot told
me.

GROSSMANN (*getting excited*)   There are 3.000   (*all
patients in the Salpêtrière, and I took the whole   together*)
course.

PROFESSOR   Excuse me, gentlemen, we're getting
off the subject.

STOUT LADY (*cutting in*)   I can explain it in two words.
When my husband was ill, all the doctors refused——

LEONID FYODOROVICH   Well, let's go back to the house.
Baroness, if you please.

(*Grossmann, Sakhatov, the Professor, the Doctor, the Stout
Lady, and the Baroness leave, talking at the same time and interrupting each other.*)

ANNA PAVLOVNA (*pulling Leonid Fyodorovich by the sleeve
and stopping him*)   How many times have I asked you not to
give orders in the house! You've got no notion of anything except your own tomfoolery, and I'm left to worry about the house.
You're going to infect everybody.

LEONID FYODOROVICH   Who's going to do what? I don't know
what you're talking about.

ANNA PAVLOVNA   You don't, do you? People sick with diphtheria are sleeping in the kitchen, which is in constant contact
with the house.

LEONID FYODOROVICH   But I——

ANNA PAVLOVNA   You what?

LEONID FYODOROVICH   But I don't know anything about
these things.

ANNA PAVLOVNA   You should know, since you're the head
of the family. You can't do this sort of thing.

LEONID FYODOROVICH   But I didn't think I
thought . . . .

ANNA PAVLOVNA   I can't stand listening to you! (*Leonid
Fyodorovich remains silent. Anna Pavlovna to Fyodor Ivanych.*)

Get them right out of here! I don't want them in my kitchen! This is terrible. Nobody obeys me, anything to spite me . . . . I chased them out of there, and they let them in here. (*Becoming more and more upset and finally starts crying.*) Anything to spite me! Anything to spite me! And with my illness . . . . Doctor, doctor! Peter Petrovich! Even he's gone! (*Leaves, sobbing. Leonid Fyodorovich follows her out. Tableau. All stand for a long time without saying a word.*)

THIRD PEASANT   Oh, the hell with them! Stay around here and you're likely to end up in the police station at any minute. And I've never been taken to court. Let's go to the lodging house, lads!

FYODOR IVANYCH (*to Tanya*)   What do we do now?

TANYA   Now don't worry, Fyodor Ivanych. Let's take them to the coachmen's room.

FYODOR IVANYCH   But how can they go there? As it is the coachman's been complaining that the room is full of dogs.

TANYA   Well, then how about the porter's place?

FYODOR IVANYCH   And if she finds out?

TANYA   She won't know a thing about it. Now don't worry, Fyodor Ivanych. After all, we can't just turn them out at night. They couldn't find any place to stay this time of the night.

FYODOR IVANYCH   Well, do what you think best—as long as you get them out of here. (*Exit.*)

(*The peasants pick up their bags.*)

OLD COOK   See what the damned devils have done! It's their plushy life that makes them do this. The devils!

WOMAN COOK   Why don't you shut up? It's a good thing they didn't see you.

TANYA   Well, friends, let's go to the porter's place.

FIRST PEASANT   But how's our business coming along? How, so to speak, is the matter of the signature, the affixing of his name? Well, is there any hope?

TANYA   We'll know definitely in an hour.

SECOND PEASANT   Think you'll be able to put it across?
TANYA (*laughing*)   If God is willing.

Curtain

ACT III

The action takes place that evening in a small drawing room, where Leonid Fyodorovich's experiments are always conducted.

LEONID FYODOROVICH   Well, should we risk a séance with our new medium?

PROFESSOR   By all means. The medium is unquestionably a powerful one. Besides, it would be a good idea if we had the mediumistic séance this evening and with the same people. Grossmann will undoubtedly respond to the mediumistic energy, and then the connection and the unity of the phenomena will be even more apparent. You'll note that if the medium is as strong as he was a while ago, Grossmann will vibrate.

LEONID FYODOROVICH   In that case, you know, I'll send for Semyon and invite those who'd like to come.

PROFESSOR   Fine. In the meantime, I'll just jot down a few things. (*Takes out a notebook and writes.*)

SAKHATOV (*entering*)   Anna Pavlovna has them playing vint. I was the odd man and so . . . besides, I'm interested in the séance, so I thought I'd drop in. Well, are you having a séance?

LEONID FYODOROVICH   We are, definitely.

SAKHATOV   What, even without Mr. Kapchich's mediumistic power?

LEONID FYODOROVICH   *Vous avez la main heureuse.* Just think, that peasant I was telling you about turned out to be a real medium.

SAKHATOV   Is that so? Oh, why that's really interesting!

LEONID FYODOROVICH   That's right. We tried a little preliminary experiment with him after dinner.

SAKHATOV   And you're convinced?

LEONID FYODOROVICH   Completely. And he turned out to be a medium of remarkable power.

SAKHATOV (*incredulously*)   Is that so?

LEONID FYODOROVICH   It turns out that they've known about this for quite a while in the servants' quarters. When he sits down at the table, the spoon jumps right into his hand. (*To the Professor.*) Did you hear about that?

PROFESSOR   No, I didn't hear about this particular thing.

SAKHATOV (*to the Professor*)   But still, you too admit the possibility of such phenomena?

PROFESSOR   Of what phenomena?

SAKHATOV   Well, generally speaking, spiritualistic, mediumistic phenomena—supernatural phenomena as a whole.

PROFESSOR   Depends on what you want to call supernatural. When it wasn't a man but a piece of stone that attracted a nail to itself, then what did the spectators think the phenomenon was: natural or supernatural?

SAKHATOV   Yes, of course; but the point is that such phenomena as a magnet's attraction are constantly being repeated.

PROFESSOR   The same thing happens here. The phenomenon is repeated, and we subject it to investigation. Furthermore, we subject the phenomena under investigation to the laws common to other phenomena. You see, these phenomena seem to be supernatural only because their causes are attributed to the medium himself. But this is wrong, you know. The phenomena are produced not by the medium, but by a spiritual energy working through the medium—and that's a big difference. The whole matter depends on the law of equivalency.

SAKHATOV   Yes, of course, but——

(*Tanya enters and hides behind the portière.*)

LEONID FYODOROVICH   Just remember one thing, you couldn't count on anything for certain with Hume and Kapchich, and it's the same with this medium. There may be a failure, and then too, there may be a complete materialization.

SAKHATOV   Even a materialization? What kind of a materialization can there be?

LEONID FYODOROVICH   Why, it's like this, a dead person comes—your father or grandfather—takes you by the hand, gives you something. Or suddenly somebody rises into the air— this happened to Aleksei Vladimirovich the last time.

PROFESSOR   Of course, of course. But the most important thing is to explain all these phenomena and to subject them to general laws.

STOUT LADY (*enters*)   Anna Pavlovna said I could drop in.

LEONID FYODOROVICH   You're most welcome!

STOUT LADY   How very tired Grossmann got. Couldn't hold a cup. Did you notice how pale he got (*to the Professor*) the moment he came near it? I noticed it right off and was the first to mention it to Anna Pavlovna.

PROFESSOR   It was undoubtedly due to the loss of vital energy.

STOUT LADY   And it's my feeling that this should not be abused. You know, a hypnotizer suggested to a friend of mine —Verochka Konshin, you know her, of course—that she stop smoking. So her back began to ache.

PROFESSOR (*trying to get a word in*)   The measurement of the temperature and pulse obviously indicate——

STOUT LADY   Just a minute, please. So I told her it's really better to smoke than to suffer with nerves like that. Of course, smoking is harmful, and I'd like to give it up, but I just can't. Once I stopped for two weeks—but I couldn't keep it up.

PROFESSOR (*making another attempt to speak*) . . . indicate conclusively——

STOUT LADY   Please let me finish! I can do it in two words. You say there's a loss of strength? Well, I wanted to say that when I was travelling by carriage . . . . The roads were terrible then—you wouldn't remember that—but I noticed it. And, say what you will, all our nervousness is caused by the railroads. For example, I can't sleep while travelling—for the life of me, I just can't get to sleep.

PROFESSOR (*tries again, but the Stout Lady doesn't give him a chance*)   . . . a loss of strength——

SAKHATOV (*smiling*) That's right.

(*Leonid Fyodorovich rings.*)

STOUT LADY I'll miss one, two, three nights of sleep, and still won't be able to fall asleep.

(*Grigori enters.*)

LEONID FYODOROVICH Please tell Fyodor to get everything ready for the séance and tell Semyon to come here—the butler's helper, Semyon. Understand?

GRIGORI Yes, sir. (*Exit.*)

PROFESSOR (*to Sakhatov*) The measurement of the temperature and pulse indicated a loss of vital energy. The same thing'll also happen in connection with mediumistic phenomena. The law of the conservation of energy——

STOUT LADY Yes, yes. I only want to add that I'm very glad to see that a simple peasant has turned out to be a medium. That's wonderful. I always said that the Slavophiles——

LEONID FYODOROVICH Let's go into the drawing room for the time being.

STOUT LADY Just let me finish. I can do it in two words. The Slavophiles are right, but I always told my husband that there's no point to going off the deep end about anything. The golden mean, you know. Just how can you insist that there's nothing but good among the people when I myself saw——

LEONID FYODOROVICH Wouldn't you like to go into the drawing room?

STOUT LADY . . . a boy no bigger than this, and he's already drinking. I scolded him right off. And he was grateful to me for it later on. They're children, and I've always said that children need both love and severity.

(*All leave, talking. Tanya comes out from behind the portière.*)

TANYA   Oh, if it'll only work! (*Ties threads in preparation for her ruse.*)

BETSY (*hurrying in*)   Papa isn't here? (*Staring at Tanya.*) What are you doing?

TANYA   Why, I just came in, Lizaveta Leonidovna—I wanted to—I just came in . . . . (*Looks very confused.*)

BETSY   But isn't there going to be a séance here in a little while? (*Notices that Tanya is gathering up the threads, stares at her, and suddenly bursts out laughing.*) Tanya, so you're the one who's behind it all! Don't you deny it. And was it you the last time? It was, wasn't it?

TANYA   Dear Lizaveta Leonidovna!

BETSY (*delighted*)   Ah, that's a good one! And I never suspected! Why've you been doing it?

TANYA   Dear Lizaveta Leonidovna, don't give me away!

BETSY   Of course not, not for the world. I'm terribly glad! But how do you manage it?

TANYA   Why, it's like this—I hide, and then, when they put out the lights, I crawl out and do it.

BETSY (*pointing to a thread*)   What's this for? Oh yes, you don't have to explain; I get it. You take hold of——

TANYA   Dear Lizaveta Leonidovna, I'll tell you, but only you. Before this, I was just having some fun, but now I want to get some business settled.

BETSY   How? What? What business?

TANYA   Well, it's like this. You saw the peasants who came. They want to buy some land, but your father won't sell. He returned the document to them without signing it. Fyodor Ivanych says the spirits told him not to. So I got this idea.

BETSY   Ah, aren't you the clever one! Go right ahead. But just how are you going to do it?

TANYA   Why, this is what I was thinking: As soon as they put out the lights, I'll start rapping, throwing things around, pulling the threads over their heads. And at the end I'll throw the document about the land—I've got it—on the table.

BETSY   And then what?

TANYA Don't you get it? They'll be amazed. Here the peasants had the document, and suddenly it turns up on the table. And I'll tell Semyon that at this point he should——

BETSY That's right, Semyon is the medium today!

TANYA So I'll tell him to—— (*Laughs so hard that she can't finish.*) I'll tell him to squeeze anyone he gets his hands on. But not your father—he wouldn't dare do that. Let him squeeze any of the others until the document is signed.

BETSY (*laughing*) But that's not the way it's done. The medium doesn't do anything himself.

TANYA Oh, that's all right; it doesn't matter. Maybe it'll work all right, even so.

(*Fyodor Ivanych enters. Betsy makes signs to Tanya and then leaves.*)

FYODOR IVANYCH (*to Tanya*) What are you doing here?

TANYA Why I came to see you, dear Fyodor Ivanych.

FYODOR IVANYCH What is it you want?

TANYA I came to see you about that matter—the one I asked your help for.

FYODOR IVANYCH (*laughing*) I've made the match, and it's all settled. But we didn't wet the bargain.

TANYA (*squealing*) Is it really-truly so?

FYODOR IVANYCH It is. He said he'd talk it over with his old woman and then give you his blessings.

TANYA Did he say that? (*Squeals.*) Ah, I'll pray for you the rest of my life, dear Fyodor Ivanych!

FYODOR IVANYCH Well, all right, all right. There's no time for that now. I was told to get things ready for the séance.

TANYA Let me help you. How do you want things arranged?

FYODOR IVANYCH How? Why, like this: the table in the middle of the room, the chairs, the guitar, the accordion. They don't want a lamp—just candles.

TANYA (*arranging things with Fyodor Ivanych*) Is that right? The guitar here, the inkstand here . . . . (*Puts the objects in their places.*) Like that?

FYODOR IVANYCH   I wonder if they'll really use Semyon?

TANYA   I think so. They've used him once already, you know.

FYODOR IVANYCH   Amazing! (*Puts on his pince-nez.*) But is he clean?

TANYA   How would I know?

FYODOR IVANYCH   Well then, I'll tell you what you do.

TANYA   What, Fyodor Ivanych?

FYODOR IVANYCH   Go get a nail brush and some scented soap—take mine if you have to. Then cut his nails and scrub his hands till they're real clean.

TANYA   He'll do that himself.

FYODOR IVANYCH   Well, then just be sure you tell him. And tell him to put on some clean clothes.

TANYA   Fine, Fyodor Ivanych. (*Exit.*)

FYODOR IVANYCH (*sitting down in an armchair. To himself*) They're educated, educated—take Aleksei Vladimirovich, for example; he's a professor—but still, sometimes I've really got my doubts about them. The crude popular superstitions are being destroyed, superstitions about house-spirits, wizards, witches. And when you come to think of it, why this is as much a superstition as those others. Now is it really possible for the spirits of the dead to talk and play the guitar? Somebody's fooling them, or maybe they're fooling themselves. And I just can't understand this business with Semyon. (*Looking through an album.*) Now here's their spiritualistic album. Well now, is it really possible to take a picture of a spirit? And here's a picture of a Turk and Leonid Fyodorovich sitting together. An amazing human weakness!

LEONID FYODOROVICH (*entering*)   Well, is everything all set?

FYODOR IVANYCH (*getting up slowly*)   Yes. (*Smiling.*) Only I hope your new medium won't embarrass you, Leonid Fyodorovich.

LEONID FYODOROVICH   No, Aleksei Vladimirovich and I tested him. He's an amazingly powerful medium!

FYODOR IVANYCH   I wouldn't know that. But is he clean? You haven't told him to wash his hands. And this might cause some embarrassment.

LEONID FYODOROVICH   His hands? Oh, yes. You think they're dirty?

FYODOR IVANYCH   Why, of course. He's a peasant. And there'll be ladies present, and Marya Vasilevna.

LEONID FYODOROVICH   All right, tell him to wash up.

FYODOR IVANYCH   There was one more thing I wanted to tell you. The coachman Timofei came to complain that he can't keep things clean because of the dogs.

LEONID FYODOROVICH (*absentmindedly, while arranging things on the table*)   What dogs?

FYODOR IVANYCH   Why, Vasili Leonidych got three borzois today, and they were put in the coachmen's room.

LEONID FYODOROVICH (*annoyed*)   Tell Anna Pavlovna about it. Let her do what she wants to. I just haven't got the time.

FYODOR IVANYCH   But you know her weakness for Vasili Leonidych.

LEONID FYODOROVICH   Well, let her do what she wants to. All he does is cause me these annoyances. Besides, I just haven't got the time.

SEMYON (*enters, smiling. He is wearing a sleeveless jacket*) Did you call me?

LEONID FYODOROVICH   That's right. Show me your hands. Well, that's very fine. Now, my friend, you'll do just what you did before—sit down and abandon yourself to your feelings. But don't think.

SEMYON   Why think? It's only worse if you do.

LEONID FYODOROVICH   That's just it. The less consciousness there is, the more powerful it'll be. Don't think—just abandon yourself to your mood. If you feel like sleeping—sleep. If you feel like walking—walk. Understand?

SEMYON   Of course. There's nothing deep about it.

LEONID FYODOROVICH   And the main thing is, don't get

upset. You might be surprised by what you do. You must understand that just as we live, so the invisible world of spirits lives with us.

FYODOR IVANYCH (*explaining*)   Unseen beings. Understand?

SEMYON (*laughing*)   Of course. It's very simple the way you explain it.

LEONID FYODOROVICH   You might rise up in the air, or do something like that—so don't get scared.

SEMYON   Why should I? Anything like this could happen.

LEONID FYODOROVICH   Well, then I'll go call everybody. Is everything all set?

FYODOR IVANYCH   I think so.

LEONID FYODOROVICH   What about the slates?

FYODOR IVANYCH   They're downstairs. I'll bring them right up. (*Exit.*)

LEONID FYODOROVICH   Well, all right then. Now don't you get upset. Relax.

SEMYON   Should I take my jacket off? I'd feel more relaxed then.

LEONID FYODOROVICH   Your jacket? No, no, that's not necessary. (*Exit.*)

SEMYON (*to himself*)   She told me to do the same thing again, and she'll be throwing things around like she did before. I wonder how come she's not afraid to do this?

TANYA (*enters without shoes and in a dress the color of the wallpaper. Semyon roars with laughter*)   Sh-sh, they'll hear us! Here, fasten these matches to your fingers, like you did the last time. (*He fastens them on.*) Well now, do you remember what you're supposed to do?

SEMYON (*ticking off the items on his fingers*)   First of all, wet the matches. Then wave my hands. That's one thing. Another thing—chomp my teeth, like this. That's number two. But I forgot the third thing.

TANYA   The third thing is the most important of all. Now keep this in your head: As soon as the document falls on the table—I'll also ring a little bell—you start doing this with your arms. Spread them out as wide as you can and grab someone. Grab anyone who's sitting near you. And when you grab him, then squeeze. (*Laughs loudly.*) Doesn't matter if it's a gentleman or lady—remember, just squeeze and keep on squeezing, and and don't let go. Act like you're asleep, and chomp your teeth or bellow, like this. (*Bellows.*) And when I start playing the guitar, act like you're waking up. Stretch, you know, like this, and wake up. Think you can remember it all?

SEMYON   I'll remember it all right. But it's just so funny.

TANYA   And don't you laugh. But if you do, that won't be too bad. They'll just think you're doing it in your sleep. But remember one thing, don't really fall asleep when they put out the lights.

SEMYON   Don't worry. I'll be pinching my ears to stay awake.

TANYA   Now watch your step, Semyon dear. Just do everything I told you to, and don't be scared. He'll sign the document, you'll see. They're coming . . . . (*Crawls under the sofa.*)

(*Enter Grossmann, the Professor, Leonid Fyodorovich, the Stout Lady, the Doctor, Sakhatov, and Anna Pavlovna. Semyon stands at the door.*)

LEONID FYODOROVICH   Welcome, all unbelievers! Despite the fact that we have a new and unexpected medium tonight, I anticipate some very remarkable manifestations.

SAKHATOV   Very, very interesting.

STOUT LADY (*pointing to Semyon*)   *Mais il est très bien!*

ANNA PAVLOVNA   As a butler's helper, yes, but——

SAKHATOV   Wives never believe in their husband's projects. You don't put any stock in this at all, do you?

ANNA PAVLOVNA   Of course not. It's true that there's something special about Kapchich, but God alone knows what this is all about!

STOUT LADY   No, if you'll pardon me, Anna Pavlovna, you shouldn't talk like that. When I was still single, I had a remarkable dream. You know, there's the type of dream that doesn't seem to have a beginning or end. Well, I had a dream just like that——

(*Vasili Leonidych and Petrishchev enter.*)

STOUT LADY   And a lot was revealed to me in that dream. Nowadays these young people (*points to Petrishchev and Vasili Leonidych*) reject everything.

VASILI LEONIDYCH   But I never reject anything, I tell you. Well?

(*Betsy and Marya Konstantinovna enter. They start a conversation with Petrishchev.*)

STOUT LADY   But how can one reject the supernatural? They say it's contrary to reason. But reason may be stupid. So what then? Now on Sadovaya Street—did you hear about it?—something appeared every night. My husband's brother—what would you call him?—not *beau-frère,* but in Russian—oh, I can never remember those Russian names for in-laws. Well, he went there three nights in a row and still didn't see anything. So I said——

LEONID FYODOROVICH   Now who's going to stay?

STOUT LADY   I, I!

SAKHATOV   I!

ANNA PAVLOVNA (*to the Doctor*)   Are you staying too?

DOCTOR   Yes, just once I'd like to see what Aleksei Vladimirovich sees in this. You can't reject things without any proof either.

ANNA PAVLOVNA   So I should definitely take them tonight?

DOCTOR   Take who? Oh, yes, the powders. Yes, please take them. That's right, take them. I'll drop in again.

ANNA PAVLOVNA   Yes, please do. (*Loudly.*) *Messieurs et mesdames,* when you get through, please come to see me. You can relax after your emotional experience and we'll finish the vint.

STOUT LADY   Of course.

SAKHATOV   We'll do that!

(*Anna Pavlovna leaves.*)

BETSY (*to Petrishchev*) Stay, I tell you. I promise you there'll be some unusual things happening. Want to bet on it?

MARYA KONSTANTINOVNA Don't tell me you believe this?

BETSY I do today.

MARYA KONSTANTINOVNA (*to Petrishchev*) And what about you?

PETRISHCHEV "I believe not, I believe not the cunning vows." But if Lizaveta Leonidovna so commands——

VASILI LEONIDYCH Let's stay, Marya Konstantinovna. Well? I'll think of something real *épatant*.

MARYA KONSTANTINOVNA No, don't you make me laugh. I haven't got much self-control, you know.

VASILI LEONIDYCH (*loudly*) I—shall—stay!

LEONID FYODOROVICH (*sternly*) All I ask is that those who stay refrain from turning this into a joke. This is a serious matter.

PETRISHCHEV Hear that? Well, let's stay. Vovo, sit down here, and see that you don't lose your nerve.

BETSY Yes, you're laughing, but just wait and see what happens.

VASILI LEONIDYCH But what if something did really happen? Wouldn't that be great? Well?

PETRISHCHEV (*trembling*) Oh, I'm scared, I'm scared. Marya Konstantinovna, I'm scared! My little trembles are legging.

BETSY (*laughing*) Quiet!

(*All sit down.*)

LEONID FYODOROVICH Sit down, please. Sit down, Semyon!

SEMYON Yes, sir. (*Sits down on the edge of the chair.*)

LEONID FYODOROVICH Sit the way you're supposed to.

PROFESSOR Sit properly in the middle of the chair. Relax completely. (*Gets Semyon settled. Betsy, Marya Konstantinovna, and Vasili Leonidych burst out laughing.*)

LEONID FYODOROVICH (*raising his voice*) I ask those who

remain not to misbehave, but to treat this matter seriously. Otherwise, there may be evil consequences. Vovo, do you hear me? If you can't behave, then leave.

VASILI LEONIDYCH   Quiet everybody! (*Hides behind the Stout Lady.*)

LEONID FYODOROVICH   Aleksei Vladimirovich, hypnotize him.

PROFESSOR   No, let Anton Borisovich do it. He has a lot more experience and power in this matter. Anton Borisovich!

GROSSMANN   Ladies and gentlemen. I'm not a spiritualist myself; I've just studied hypnosis. It's true that I've studied hypnosis in all of its known manifestations, but that which is called spiritualism is something I know nothing about. On putting a subject into a trance, I can expect certain familiar hypnotic phenomena: lethargy, abulia, anaesthesia, analgesia, catalepsy, and all sorts of suggestive states. But here we're proposing to investigate not these but other phenomena, and so it would be desirable to know the nature of these expected phenomena and what scientific significance they have.

SAKHATOV   I fully concur with Mr. Grossmann's opinion. Such an explanation would be very, very interesting.

LEONID FYODOROVICH (*to the Professor*)   I know you won't refuse to give us a brief explanation, Aleksei Vladimirovich.

PROFESSOR   I'd be glad to explain if it's of interest. (*To the Doctor.*) And would you please take his temperature and pulse? My explanation will, of necessity, be superficial and brief.

LEONID FYODOROVICH   Yes, brief, brief.

DOCTOR (*taking out a thermometer and giving it to Semyon*) There now, my good fellow! (*Adjusts the thermometer in his mouth.*)

SEMYON   Yes, sir.

PROFESSOR (*getting up, turning to the Stout Lady, and then sitting down*)   Ladies and gentlemen! The phenomenon we are investigating generally appears, on the one hand, as something novel—on the other, as something transcending the natural order of things. Neither the one view nor the other is correct. This phenomenon is not new, but as old as the world itself—and not supernatural, but always subject to the same eternal laws to which everything in existence is also subject. This phenomenon has usually been defined as a communion with the spiritual world. Such a definition is not exact. According to this definition, the spiritual world is juxtaposed to the material world, but this is not correct—there is no such juxtaposition. Both worlds are so tightly contiguous that it's absolutely impossible to draw a demarcation line separating one world from the other. We say that matter is composed of molecules——

PETRISHCHEV   The matter is dull! (*Whispering, laughter.*)

PROFESSOR (*stopping, and then continuing*)   Molecules are composed of atoms, but atoms, having no extension, are really nothing more than points of application of forces. That is, strictly speaking, not of forces, but of energy—of that same energy which is as much a unity and as indestructible as matter. But just as matter is one while its forms are different, even so it is with energy. Until recently we have known of only four forms of energy capable of conversion. We know about the dynamic, thermal, electrical, and chemical forms of energy. But these four forms far from exhaust all the possible varied manifestations of energy. The forms of energy manifestation are manifold, and one of these new, little-known forms of energy is now being investigated by us. I am speaking of mediumistic energy. (*Again whispering and laughter in the corner where the young people are sitting. The Professor stops and then, after looking about sternly, continues.*) Mediumistic energy has been known to humanity since time immemorial: predictions, presentiments, visions, and many other things—all these are nothing else but the manifestations of mediumistic energy. The phenomena produced by it have been known since time immemorial. But the energy itself has not been recognized as such until very recently, until we recognized the agent whose vibrations produce mediumistic phenomena. And just as the phenomena of light remained inexplicable until we recognized the existence of an imponderable substance, an ether—even so mediumistic phenomena seemed mysterious until we recognized the now undeniable truth that in the interstices of ether particles there is another imponderable substance which is even more elusive than ether and is not subject to the law of three dimensions— (*Again whispering, laughter, and squealing. The Professor again looks about sternly.*) And just as mathematical calculations have irrefutably confirmed the existence of an imponderable ether which produces the phenomena of light and electricity, even so a brilliant series of most precise experiments by the great Herman Schmidt and Joseph Schmatzhofen have definitely confirmed the existence of that substance which fills the universe and which can be called spiritual ether.

STOUT LADY   Yes, now I understand it all. I'm so thankful—

LEONID FYODOROVICH   Yes, but couldn't you—abbreviate this—a little, Aleksei Vladimirovich?

PROFESSOR (*not replying*)   And so, as I've had the honor of informing you, a series of strictly scientific experiments and investigations has defined the laws of mediumistic phenomena for us. These experiments have shown us that the immersion of certain individuals in a hypotic state, which differs from normal sleep only in the fact that immersion in a trance not only does not reduce physiological activity but, on the contrary, always intensifies it, as we saw a while ago—it has been shown that the immersion in this state of any subject whatsoever invariably produces certain perturbations in the spiritual ether, perturbations which are very much like those produced by the immersion of a solid body in a liquid. And these perturbations are what we call mediumistic phenomena——

(*Laughter, whispering.*)

SAKHATOV   That makes good sense and it's understandable. But let me ask you one thing. If, as you put it, the immersion of a medium in a trance produces perturbations of the spiritual ether, then why do these perturbations always manifest themselves, as it's commonly assumed in spiritualistic séances, through the activity of dead people?

PROFESSOR   Why, because the particles of this spiritual ether are nothing else but the spirits of the living, the dead, and the unborn. So every shock to this spiritual ether invariably causes a certain movement of its particles. These particles are nothing else but the spirits of people coming into contact with each other by means of this movement.

STOUT LADY (*to Sakhatov*)   What's so hard about understanding this? It's so simple. Thank you very, very much!

LEONID FYODOROVICH   It seems to me that everything's clear now, and we can go ahead.

DOCTOR   The fellow's condition is quite normal: temperature—ninety-eight point nine, pulse—seventy-four.

PROFESSOR (*takes out a notebook and writes it down*)   A confirmation of what I've just had the honor of communicating to you is the fact that the immersion of a medium in a trance invariably produces, as we shall soon see, a rise in temperature and pulse, just as in any case of hypnosis.

LEONID FYODOROVICH   Yes, yes. Excuse me, but I'd just like to answer Sergei Ivanych's question as to how we know that the spirits of the deceased are contacting us. We know because the spirit who comes tells us so straight out—it's as simple as my talking to you. He tells us who he is, and why he's come, and where he is, and whether he's happy. The Spaniard Don Castillos was at the last séance, and he told us everything. He told us who he was, and when he died, and that he was suffering because he had taken part in the Inquisition. Furthermore, he informed us of what was about to happen to him at the very moment that he was talking with us—namely, that at the very moment he was talking with us he was about to be reborn on earth. And so he couldn't finish the conversation. But you'll see for yourself——

STOUT LADY (*interrupting*)   Oh, how interesting! Maybe the Spaniard was born in our house and is a baby right now.

LEONID FYODOROVICH   That's very possible.

PROFESSOR   I think it's time to start.

LEONID FYODOROVICH   I only wanted to say——

PROFESSOR   It's late already.

LEONID FYODOROVICH   Well, all right. So let's begin. Please start hypnotizing the medium, Anton Borisovich——

GROSSMANN   How would you like me to do it? There are quite a few methods in common use. There's Brede's method, and there's the Egyptian-symbol method, and there's Charcot's method.

LEONID FYODOROVICH (*to the Professor*)   I don't think it matters, does it?

PROFESSOR   Not at all.

GROSSMANN   In that case I'll use my own method, the one I demonstrated in Odessa.

LEONID FYODOROVICH   Please do!

(*Grossmann waves his hands over Semyon. Semyon closes his eyes and stretches out.*)

GROSSMANN (*watching him intently*)   He's falling asleep . . . he's asleep. A remarkably quick appearance of hypnosis. Apparently the subject has already entered an anaesthetic state. A remarkably and unusually receptive subject, and he could be used in some interesting experiments! (*Sits down, gets up, and again sits down.*) You could now stick needles in his arms and he wouldn't react. If you wish——

PROFESSOR (*to Leonid Fyodorovich*)   Do you notice how the medium's trance is beginning to affect Grossmann? He's starting to vibrate.

LEONID FYODOROVICH   Yes, yes. Can we put the candles out now?

SAKHATOV   But why does the room have to be dark?

PROFESSOR   Why? Because darkness is one of the conditions necessary for the manifestation of mediumistic energy, just as a certain temperature is a necessary condition for certain manifestations of chemical or dynamic energy.

LEONID FYODOROVICH   But not always. Many, including myself, have witnessed manifestations by candlelight, and even in broad daylight——

PROFESSOR (*interrupting*) Is it all right to put out the candles?

LEONID FYODOROVICH Yes, yes. (*Puts the candles out.*) Ladies and gentlemen, your attention please.

(*Tanya crawls out from under the sofa and takes hold of a thread attached to a candelabrum.*)

PETRISHCHEV I really liked that Spaniard—the way he took a header right in the middle of a conversation; like the French say: *piquer une tête.*

BETSY No, you just wait and see what's going to happen!

PETRISHCHEV I only hope that Vovo doesn't start grunting like a pig.

VASILI LEONIDYCH Want me to do it? I'll suddenly——

LEONID FYODOROVICH Ladies and gentlemen, please don't talk. (*Silence. Semyon wets a finger, rubs it over the matches on his hand, and waves his hands.*) A light! See the light?

SAKHATOV A light? Yes, yes, I see it, but permit me to——

STOUT LADY Where? Where? Ah, I didn't see it! There it is. Ah!

PROFESSOR (*whispering to Leonid Fyodorovich and pointing to Grossmann, who is moving about*) Just see how he's vibrating. It's a double force.

(*The light appears again.*)

LEONID FYODOROVICH (*to the Professor*) It must be he.

SAKHATOV Who's *he?*

LEONID FYODOROVICH Nicholas the Greek. That's his light. Isn't that so, Aleksei Vladimirovich?

SAKHATOV Who's this Nicholas the Greek?

PROFESSOR A certain Greek who was a monk in Constantinople at the time of Constantine. He visited us the last time.

STOUT LADY Well, where is he? Just where is he? I don't see him.

LEONID FYODOROVICH You can't see him yet. Aleksei Vladimirovich, he's always partial to you. Talk to him.

244 The Fruits of Enlightenment

PROFESSOR (*in a peculiar voice*)   Nicholas, is that you?

(*Tanya raps against the wall twice.*)

LEONID FYODOROVICH (*delighted*)   It's he! It's he!

STOUT LADY   Oh, my God! I'm leaving.

SAKHATOV   How can you assume it's he?

LEONID FYODOROVICH   Why, the two raps. It's an affirmative answer. Silence means "no." (*Silence. Repressed laughter from the corner where the young people are sitting. Tanya throws a lampshade, a pencil, and a pen-wiper on the table. Leonid Fyodorovich continues in a whisper.*) Take note, ladies and gentlemen, here's the lampshade. And something else. A pencil! Aleksei Vladimirovich, a pencil!

PROFESSOR   Fine, fine. I'm keeping my eye on both him and Grossmann. Do you see what I see?

(*Grossmann gets up and examines the objects which have landed on the table.*)

SAKHATOV   Excuse me, but I'd like to see if the medium isn't doing all this himself.

LEONID FYODOROVICH   You think so? Then why don't you sit down next to him and hold his hands? But you can be sure that he's in a trance.

SAKHATOV (*starts for Semyon, catches his head on the thread which Tanya is lowering, and stoops in fright*)   Y-e-e-s! It's strange, strange! (*Goes up to Semyon and takes him by the elbow. Semyon bellows.*)

PROFESSOR (*to Leonid Fyodorovich*)   See how Grossmann's presence affects him? It's a new phenomenon—I've got to jot it down. (*Runs out of the room, writes it down, and then returns.*)

LEONID FYODOROVICH   Yes . . . . But we shouldn't leave Nicholas without an answer. We have to start——

GROSSMANN (*gets up, walks up to Semyon, raises and drops his arm*)   It would be interesting to produce a contracture now. The subject is in a state of complete hypnosis.

PROFESSOR (*to Leonid Fyodorovich*)   Do you see what I see?

GROSSMANN   If you wish——

DOCTOR   Well, sir, let Aleksei Vladimirovich handle it. This is becoming serious.

PROFESSOR   Leave him alone. He's in a trance.

STOUT LADY   I'm really glad now that I decided to come. It's frightening, but still I'm glad, because I always told my husband——

LEONID FYODOROVICH   Please be quiet.

(*Tanya passes the thread over the head of the Stout Lady.*)

STOUT LADY   Oh, my God!

LEONID FYODOROVICH   What is it? What is it?

STOUT LADY   He grabbed me by the hair!

LEONID FYODOROVICH (*whispering*)   Don't be afraid. It's nothing at all. Give him your hand. His hand is usually cold, but I like it that way.

STOUT LADY (*hiding her hands*)   Absolutely not!

SAKHATOV   Yes, this is strange, strange!

LEONID FYODOROVICH   He's here and wants to communicate. Who wants to ask him something?

SAKHATOV   If you don't mind, I will.

PROFESSOR   Please go right ahead.

SAKHATOV   Do I believe or not?

(*Tanya raps twice.*)

PROFESSOR   An affirmative answer.

SAKHATOV   If you don't mind, I'll ask another question. Do I have a ten ruble bill in my pocket? (*Tanya raps several times and passes the thread over Sakhatov's head.*) Aha! (*Sakhatov grabs the thread and breaks it.*)

PROFESSOR   I'd like to ask those present not to ask any vague or flippant questions. He doesn't like it.

SAKHATOV   Excuse me, but I've got a thread in my hand.

LEONID FYODOROVICH   A thread? Keep it. That happens quite often. Not only threads—but even silk cords, and very ancient ones too.

SAKHATOV   No, but where did the thread come from? (*Tanya*

throws a cushion at him.) Excuse me, but something soft just hit me in the head. Let's have some light. There's something here that doesn't——

PROFESSOR   We beg you not to disturb the manifestation.

STOUT LADY   For God's sake, don't disturb it! I want to ask it something too. May I?

LEONID FYODOROVICH   Go right ahead and ask.

STOUT LADY   I want to ask about my stomach. Can I do that? I want to ask if I should take aconite or belladonna? (*Silence. There is whispering among the young people. Suddenly Vasili Leonidych cries out like an infant: "Whah, whah!" Laughter. The girls and Petrishchev rush out, holding their noses and mouths and snorting.*) Ah, Nicholas must also have been reborn!

LEONID FYODOROVICH (*furious, in an angry whisper*)   Nothing but nonsense from you! If you can't behave, leave!

(*Vasili Leonidych leaves. Darkness. Silence.*)

STOUT LADY   Oh, what a pity! Now I can't ask him. He's been reborn.

LEONID FYODOROVICH   Not at all. That was Vovo's nonsense. *He* is here. Go ahead and ask him.

PROFESSOR   This happens quite often—these jokes, this ridicule. They're a most common phenomenon. I think that *he* is still here. Anyway, we can ask. Leonid Fyodorovich, why don't you?

LEONID FYODOROVICH   No, please, you ask. This nonsense of Vovo's has upset me—it's so unpleasant! He's so tactless!

PROFESSOR   All right! Nicholas, are you still here? (*Tanya raps twice and rings a little bell. Semyon begins to bellow and spreads his arms. He seizes Sakhatov and the Professor and starts to squeeze them.*) What an unexpected manifestation! The force operating on the medium himself. This has never happened before. Leonid Fyodorovich, you observe this. It's inconvenient for me—he's squeezing me. And see what Grossmann is doing. This calls for full attention.

(*Tanya throws the peasants' document on the table.*)

LEONID FYODOROVICH   Something fell on the table.

PROFESSOR   See what it is.

LEONID FYODOROVICH   A sheet of paper! A folded sheet of paper. (*Tanya throws a traveller's inkstand on the table.*) An inkstand! (*Tanya throws a pen on the table.*) A pen!

(*Semyon continues to bellow and squeeze.*)

PROFESSOR (*out of breath*)   Just a minute, this is a completely new phenomenon. It's not the elicited mediumistic energy that's at work here, but the medium himself. But open the inkstand and put the pen on the paper, and he'll write something—he'll write something.

(*Tanya comes up behind Leonid Fyodorovich and hits him on the head with the guitar.*)

LEONID FYODOROVICH   He hit me on the head! (*Looking at the table.*) The pen isn't writing yet; the paper's still folded.

PROFESSOR   See what kind of paper it is. Do it quick. Obviously it's a double force that's producing these perturbations —his and Grossmann's.

LEONID FYODOROVICH (*goes out with the paper and immediately returns*)   Extraordinary! This paper is the peasants' contract—the one I wouldn't sign this morning and returned to them. Apparently *he* wants me to sign it.

PROFESSOR   Of course, of course! Go ahead and ask him.

LEONID FYODOROVICH   Nicholas, do you really want me to——

(*Tanya raps twice.*)

PROFESSOR   Hear that? He obviously does!

(*Leonid Fyodorovich takes the pen and goes out. Tanya raps, plays the guitar and accordion, and again crawls under the sofa. Leonid Fyodorovich returns. Semyon stretches and coughs.*)

Leonid Fyodorovich   He's coming to. We can light the candles.

Professor (*hurriedly*)   Doctor, doctor—quick—the temperature and pulse. You'll see that they've gone up.

Leonid Fyodorovich (*lighting the candles*)   Well, what do you have to say for yourselves, unbelievers?

Doctor (*going up to Semyon and inserting the thermometer in his mouth*)   Well then, my good fellow, had a nap, didn't you? Well then, keep this in your mouth and let me have your hand. (*Looks at his watch.*)

Sakhatov (*shrugging*)   I can confirm the fact that the medium couldn't have done all of these things. But what about the thread? I'd like an explanation of the thread.

Leonid Fyodorovich   The thread, the thread! We had much more important phenomena than thread tonight.

Sakhatov   I don't know. At any rate, *je réserve mon opinion.*

Stout Lady (*to Sakhatov*)   No, what do you mean by *je réserve mon opinion*? And how about the baby with the little wings? Didn't you see him? At first I thought I was only imagining things, but later it was as clear, as clear as if he were alive——

Sakhatov   I can only speak of what I've seen. I didn't see this at all.

Stout Lady   What do you mean? It was absolutely clear. And on the left a monk in black was bending over him——

Sakhatov (*walking away*)   What an imagination!

Stout Lady (*to the Doctor*)   You must have seen it. It was ascending on your side. (*The Doctor pays no attention to her and continues to check Semyon's pulse. She addresses Grossmann.*) And that light, that light coming from it—especially around its little face. And its expression was so gentle, so tender, somehow so heavenly! (*Smiles tenderly.*)

Grossmann   I saw a phosphorescent light, objects moving around, but I didn't see anything else.

Stout Lady   Now stop this! You're just saying that. It's

because you scientists of Charcot's school don't believe in life after death. But now no one, no one in the world can shake my faith in a future life. (*Grossmann walks away from her.*) No, no, say what you will, but this is one of the happiest moments in my life. When I heard Sarasate[7] play and this . . . . Yes! (*Nobody pays any attention to her. She goes up to Semyon.*) Well, tell me, my friend, how did you feel? Was it very hard on you?

SEMYON (*laughing*)   That's right.

STOUT LADY   But still, it was bearable?

SEMYON   That's right. (*To Leonid Fyodorovich.*) Can I go now?

LEONID FYODOROVICH   Yes, go on.

DOCTOR (*to the Professor*)   The pulse is the same, but the temperature is lower.

PROFESSOR   Lower? (*Thinks and then suddenly finds an explanation.*) That's the way it should be—there should have been a drop! The double energy, intersecting, should have produced something in the nature of an interaction. Yes, yes.

LEONID FYODOROVICH   I'm just sorry that there wasn't a complete materialization. But still . . . . Ladies and gentlemen, won't you please go to the drawing room.

STOUT LADY   I was particularly impressed when he flapped his little wings and I saw him rise.

GROSSMANN (*to Sakhatov*)   If one were to stick to hypnosis alone, one might produce a real case of epilepsy. It might be a complete success.

SAKHATOV   Interesting, but not fully convincing! That's all I have to say.

(*all speaking together as they leave*)

[7] A Spanish violinist and composer who visited Russia.

(*Fyodor Ivanych enters.*)

LEONID FYODOROVICH (*holding the document*)   Well, Fyodor, that was some séance—amazing! Looks like I'll have to give the peasants the land on their own conditions.

FYODOR IVANYCH   Is that so?

LEONID FYODOROVICH   Well, why not? (*Shows him the document.*) Just think! This document which I returned to them turned up on the table. I've signed it.

FYODOR IVANYCH   But how did it get there?

LEONID FYODOROVICH   Why, it just got there. (*Leaves, followed by Fyodor Ivanych. Tanya crawls out from under the sofa, laughing, as Grigori comes to the door unobserved.*)

TANYA (*to herself*)   Oh, my God, my God! I really got scared when he grabbed the thread. (*Squealing.*) But it came out all right anyway: he signed it!

GRIGORI   So you're the one who's been fooling them!

TANYA   What's it to you?

GRIGORI   And do you think the mistress is going to praise you for this? No, you've had your fun, and now you're in a jam. Unless you do what I want you to, I'll tell her all about your tricks.

TANYA   I'm not going to do what you want me to, and there's nothing you can do about it.

Curtain

ACT IV

The setting is the same as in Act I. The First and Second Footmen (both in livery), Fyodor Ivanych, and Grigori are in the entrance hall.

FIRST FOOTMAN (*with gray side-whiskers*)   This is the third house we've visited today. Thank God everybody we're visiting lives in the same part of the city. You used to have open house on Thursdays, didn't you?

FYODOR IVANYCH   Yes, then it was changed to Saturday so

that it'd be on the same day as the Golovkins' and the Grade von Grabes'——

SECOND FOOTMAN   It's so nice at the Shcherbakovs'. They treat the footmen so well—it's just like they were having a ball.

(*The Princess and Young Princess come down the stairs. Betsy is seeing them off. The Princess glances at her notebook and then at her watch. She sits down on a low chest, and Grigori puts on her overshoes.*)

YOUNG PRINCESS   Yes, be sure and come. Because if you don't, and Dodo doesn't, then nothing will come of it.

BETSY   I don't know. I definitely have to go to the Shubins. And then comes the rehearsal.

YOUNG PRINCESS   You can make it. Yes, do come. *Ne nous fais pas faux bond.* Fedya and Coco will be there.

BETSY   *J'en ai par dessus la tête de votre Coco.*

YOUNG PRINCESS   I thought I'd find him here. *Ordinairement il est d'une exactitude*——

BETSY   I'm sure he'll come.

YOUNG PRINCESS   When I see him with you, I always think that he's just proposed or is about to do it.

BETSY   Well, I suppose I'll have to go through that experience sooner or later. And it's so unpleasant!

YOUNG PRINCESS   Poor Coco! He's so in love.

BETSY   *Cessez, les gens.*

(*The Young Princess sits down on the sofa and speaks in a whisper. Grigori puts on her overshoes.*)

YOUNG PRINCESS   Till tonight then.

BETSY   I'll try to make it.

PRINCESS   Be sure to tell your papa that I don't believe a thing but that I'll come to see his new medium. He should let me know when. Good-by, *ma toute belle.* (*Kisses her and leaves with the Young Princess. Betsy goes upstairs.*)

GRIGORI   I don't like to put overshoes on old women—they can't bend over at all, they can't see anything because of their bellies, and so they keep sticking their feet everywhere except into the overshoes. It's another matter with a young woman— it's a pleasure to take her little foot in your hands.

SECOND FOOTMAN   Isn't he the particular one!

FIRST FOOTMAN   It's not for the likes of us to be particular.

GRIGORI   Why shouldn't we be particular? Aren't we human beings too? They've got the idea that we don't understand anything. When they were talking just now, they looked at me and right away said "lyeh zhon."

SECOND FOOTMAN   And what does that mean?

GRIGORI   That's French for "Don't say it. They'll understand." They say the same thing at dinner, but I understand. You say there's a difference between them and us. I say there isn't any.

FIRST FOOTMAN   There's a big difference for those who know what's what.

GRIGORI   There's no difference whatsoever. Today I'm a footman, but tomorrow maybe I'll be no worse off than they are. Fine women sometimes marry footmen—such things happen. I'm going to go have a smoke. (*Exit.*)

SECOND FOOTMAN   That young fellow of yours sure has a lot of gall.

FYODOR IVANYCH   He's not good for much—not fit for service. Worked as a clerk and got spoiled. I advised against taking him, but the mistress liked him; he makes a fine appearance when they go out.

FIRST FOOTMAN   I'd like to see him in our count's service. He'd put him in his place. Oh, how he hates this kind of sleek fellow. If you're a footman, then be a footman—be a credit to your calling; but this pride is out of place.

(*Petrischev runs down the stairs and takes out a cigarette.*)

PETRISHCHEV   (*deep in thought*)   Yes, yes. My second is

round. Choc-o-late. My all is . . . . Yes, yes . . . . (*Coco Klingen, wearing pince-nez, enters and walks in his direction.*) Ah, Coco-late, Choco-late! Where're you coming from?

COCO KLINGEN   From the Shcherbakovs. What do you keep up this nonsense for all the time——

PETRISHCHEV   No, listen to this: a charade. My first is white, my second is round, and my all is brown.

COCO KLINGEN   I've got no idea of what it is. And I haven't got the time.

PETRISHCHEV   Why, where else do you have to go?

COCO KLINGEN   What do you mean "where else?" I've got to be at the Ivins for singing practice. Then to the Shubins, and then to the rehearsal. You're supposed to be there too, aren't you?

PETRISHCHEV   Of course, definitely. Both at the re-hear-sal and the re-him-sal. I was a savage before and now I'm both a savage and a general.

COCO KLINGEN   Well, and how was last night's séance?

PETRISHCHEV   A riot! There was a peasant there. But the main thing is that it was all in the dark. Vovo cried like an infant, the professor did the explanations, and Marya Vasilevna provided the footnotes. It was a lot of fun! Too bad you weren't there.

COCO KLINGEN   I'm afraid, *mon cher*. You somehow manage to keep out of trouble with your jokes. But I've always got the feeling that if I barely say a word they'll immediately twist it into a proposal. *Et ça ne m'arrange pas du tout, du tout. Mais du tout, du tout!*

PETRISHCHEV   You'll be safe—as long as you don't add a verb to your proposition. Why don't you go see Vovo, and then we'll go to the re-them-sal together.

COCO KLINGEN   I just can't understand how you can run around with such a fool. He's so stupid—a real nothing!

PETRISHCHEV   But I love him. I love Vovo, but "with a strange love"; "to him the people's path will not be overgrown

. . . ." [8] (*Goes into Vasili Leonidych's room. Betsy comes down the stairs, seeing the Lady off. Coco makes a deep bow.*)

BETSY (*shakes his hand. Sideways to the Lady*)   Have you met?

LADY   No.

BETSY   Baron Klingen. Why didn't you come yesterday?

COCO KLINGEN   Just couldn't make it. Too busy.

BETSY   What a shame! It was very interesting. (*Laughing.*) You should have seen the manifestations. Well, how's our charade coming along?

COCO KLINGEN   Oh, fine! The verses for *mon second* are ready. Nick did them, and I did the music.

BETSY   How do they go? Let me hear them.

COCO KLINGEN   Pardon me—how? Oh yes! The knight sings to the Nereid. (*Sings.*)

> *Na*ture is so beautiful,
> I'll *na*me you all its charms.
> *Ne*reid, *Ne*reid! *Nay, na, nay!*

LADY   *Mon second* is *na,* but what's *mon premier*?

COCO KLINGEN   *Mon premier* is *Maty,* the name of a savage girl.

BETSY   You see, *Maty* is a savage girl who wants to eat the object of her affection. (*Laughs loudly.*) She walks around and pines and sings:

> Ah, my appetite!

COCO KLINGEN (*cutting in*)

> I don't feel right.

BETSY (*continuing*)

> I want someone to eat.
> I walk with saddened mind . . . .

[8] The first quotation is from Lermontov's "Native Land," the second—from Pushkin's "To Myself I Raised a Monument Not Built With Human Hands."

COCO KLINGEN

> But no one do I find . . . .

BETSY

> No flesh to chew, no meat.

COCO KLINGEN

> Behold, a raft I see.

BETSY

> It's heading straight for me.
> On it two generals are.

COCO KLINGEN

> Generals we are.
> Fate has brought us from afar,
> And left us on this isle bizarre.

And again the refrain:

> Fate has brought us from afar,
> And left us on this isle bizarre.

LADY   *Charmant!*

BETSY   But just think how stupid it is.

COCO KLINGEN   But that's the charm of it.

LADY   Who's playing *Maty*?

BETSY   I am. I had a costume made, but mama says it's indecent. But it's no more indecent than a ball dress. (*To Fyodor Ivanych.*) Well, is the man from Bourdier around yet?

FYODOR IVANYCH   Yes, he's in the kitchen.

LADY   Is *matinee* the word?

BETSY   You'll have to wait and see. I won't spoil your fun by letting it out. *Au revoir.*

LADY   Good-by! (*They bow to each other. The Lady leaves.*)

BETSY (*to Coco Klingen*)   Let's go see mama. (*She and Coco Klingen go upstairs.*)

(*Yakov comes out of the butler's pantry, carrying a tray with tea and pastry. Puffing and panting, he walks through the hall.*)

YAKOV (*to the footmen*) Best regards to you! (*The footmen bow. Yakov to Fyodor Ivanych.*) Couldn't you tell Grigori Mikhailych to give me a hand? I'm just worn out with getting things ready . . . . (*Goes upstairs.*)

FIRST FOOTMAN That's a hard-worker you've got there.

FYODOR IVANYCH He's a good man, but the mistress doesn't like him, you know. He doesn't make a good appearance, she says. And on top of that, they lied about his letting some peasants into the kitchen yesterday. I hope she doesn't fire him. He's a real nice fellow.

SECOND FOOTMAN What peasants were those?

FYODOR IVANYCH Why, some peasants from our Kursk village came to buy land. It was late at night, and some of the people here are from the same parts. One of the peasants is also the father of the butler's helper. Well, so they were taken to the kitchen. And as luck would have it, there was some mind-reading going on last night, and they'd hidden something in the kitchen. So all the company came in; the mistress saw them— and there was hell to pay. "What!" says she. "These people may be infected, and you let them into the kitchen!" She's awfully scared of this infection business. (*Grigori enters.*) Grigori, you go and give Yakov Ivanych a hand, and I'll stay here and take care of things. He can't get it done all alone.

GRIGORI He's clumsy, that's why he can't get it done. (*Exit.*)

FIRST FOOTMAN This is some new fashion they've got nowadays—these infections! So yours is afraid too?

FYODOR IVANYCH It's scared the daylights out of her. All we do nowadays is fumigate, wash, and sprinkle.

FIRST FOOTMAN I thought I smelled something real strong. (*With animation.*) It's just disgraceful how they sin on account of these infections. Perfectly disgusting! They've even forgotten God. Here a while back, the daughter of Princess Mosolov died. The Princess is our master's sister. And what do you suppose happened? Neither the mother nor the father so much as stepped into the room—so they never said good-by to her. And the daughter kept crying and begging for her parents to come say good-by—but they didn't go in the room! The doctor had discovered some kind of infection. And yet her maid and a nurse took care of her—and nothing happened to them. They're both alive.

(*Vasili Leonidych and Petrishchev come out of the former's room, smoking cigarettes.*)

PETRISHCHEV   Well, let's go. I'll just go get Coco-late—Chocolate.

VASILI LEONIDYCH   Your Coco-late is a blockhead! I tell you, I just can't stand him. He's a nothing, a real loafer! Doesn't do anything except run around. Well?

PETRISHCHEV   Well, just wait. I want to say good-by to him, anyway.

VASILI LEONIDYCH   All right, I'll go have a look at the dogs in the coachmen's room. One of them is so vicious, the coachman says he almost ate him up. Well?

PETRISHCHEV   Who ate whom? You mean to tell me the coachman ate the dog?

VASILI LEONIDYCH   Oh, you and your eternal jokes. (*Puts on his things and leaves.*)

PETRISHCHEV (*deep in thought*)   Vi-o-let, choc-o-late . . . . Yes, yes. (*Goes upstairs.*)

(*Yakov runs downstairs and across the stage.*)

FYODOR IVANYCH (*to Yakov*)   What else do they want?

YAKOV   There aren't any sandwiches. I told—— (*Disappears into the butler's pantry.*)

SECOND FOOTMAN   And then our young master got sick. So right away they sent him to a hotel with his nurse, and he died there without his mother.

FIRST FOOTMAN   They've just got no fear of sin! It's my feeling that you can't hide from God nowhere.

FYODOR IVANYCH   That's what I think too.

(*Yakov runs upstairs with the sandwiches.*)

FIRST FOOTMAN   And you've got to remember that if you're going to be so afraid of everything, then you'll have to shut yourself up in a room—just like in a prison—and simply stay there.

TANYA (*enters and bows to the footmen*)   Hello! (*The footmen bow.*) Fyodor Ivanych, I have to have a word with you.

FYODOR IVANYCH   Well, what is it?

TANYA   Why, the peasants have come back, Fyodor Ivanych.

FYODOR IVANYCH   Well, so what? I gave the document to Semyon, you know.

TANYA   I gave them the document. And I can't tell you how thankful they are. Now all they want to do is pay the money.

FYODOR IVANYCH   Where are they?

TANYA   Out by the porch.

FYODOR IVANYCH   Well, I'll tell him.

TANYA   There's one more thing I wanted to ask you for, dear Fyodor Ivanych.

FYODOR IVANYCH   What's that?

TANYA   Well, you see, Fyodor Ivanych, I can't stay here any longer. Ask them to release me.

(*Yakov runs downstairs.*)

FYDOR IVANYCH (*to Yakov*)   Now what?

YAKOV   Another samovar and some oranges.

FYODOR IVANYCH   Ask the housekeeper. (*Yakov runs out.*) Why do you want to leave?

TANYA   Well, you know how it is. Now my chance has come.

YAKOV (*running in*)   There aren't enough oranges.

FEODOR IVANYCH   Serve what there is. (*Yakov runs out.*) You've picked a bad time. You can see for yourself what a rush——

TANYA   Now you know very well, Fyodor Ivanych, that there's never an end to this rush—no matter how long one waits.

You know that very well. And this matter of mine is very important—it's for keeps. You've already done me a big favor, dear Fyodor Ivanych; now be like a father to me, pick the right time, and tell her. Otherwise, she'll get mad and won't let me have my papers.

FYODOR IVANYCH But what are you in such a hurry about?

TANYA Well, everything's been settled, Fyodor Ivanych. I'd like to go to godmother's and get ready. The wedding's not far off, the first week after Easter. Tell her, dear Fyodor Ivanych!

FYODOR IVANYCH Run along now. This isn't the place to talk about it.

(*The Elderly Gentleman comes downstairs and, without saying a word, departs with the Second Footman. Tanya leaves. Yakov enters, on his way upstairs with the oranges.*)

YAKOV It's a real dirty shame, Fyodor Ivanych. Now she wants to fire me. "You smash everything," says she. "You've neglected Fifi and let the peasants into the kitchen against my orders." And you know yourself that I didn't have any idea of what the story was. Tanya just told me to take them into the kitchen, and I don't know who said they could go.

FYODOR IVANYCH Did she really talk about firing you?

YAKOV Just now. Try to talk her out of it, Fyodor Ivanych! Here my folks have just been getting on their feet, and if I lose this job, who knows how long it'll be before I find another. Please, Fyodor Ivanych!

(*Anna Pavlovna and the Countess with false teeth and hair come downstairs. The First Footman helps the Countess with her things.*)

ANNA PAVLOVNA Of course, definitely. I'm deeply touched.

COUNTESS If it weren't for my poor health, I'd come to see you more often.

ANNA PAVLOVNA You really should try Peter Petrovich. He's brusque, but no one can give you such peace of mind. Everything is so simple and clear with him.

COUNTESS   No, I'm just so used to my own doctor.

ANNA PAVLOVNA   Take better care of yourself.

COUNTESS   *Merci, mille fois merci.*

(*Grigori, excited and with rumpled hair, rushes out of the butler's pantry. Semyon is pursuing him.*)

SEMYON   You keep away from her!

GRIGORI   I'll teach you how to fight, you scum! Oh, you rat!

ANNA PAVLOVNA   What's the meaning of this? Where do you think you are, in a tavern?

GRIGORI   This coarse peasant is making life impossible for me.

ANNA PAVLOVNA (*angrily*)   Have you two gone out of your minds? Can't you see who's here? (*To the Countess.*) *Merci, mille fois merci. A mardi.* (*The Countess and the First Footman leave. Anna Pavlovna to Grigori.*) What's this all about?

GRIGORI   I may be only a footman, but I've got my pride. And I'm not going to let every peasant who comes along push me.

ANNA PAVLOVNA   But what happened?

GRIGORI   Why, your Semyon has gotten brave from having been around gentlemen. He's trying to pick a fight.

ANNA PAVLOVNA   What's this? Why's he doing that?

GRIGORI   Why, who knows?

ANNA PAVLOVNA (*to Semyon*)   Just what's the meaning of this?

SEMYON   Why does he keep pestering her?

ANNA PAVLOVNA   But what happened between you two?

SEMYON (*smiling*)   It's like this. He keeps grabbing Tanya, the maid, and she doesn't like it. So I pushed him aside with my arm—like this, just a little.

GRIGORI   I'll say he pushed me aside—nearly broke my ribs. And he tore my coat. And you know what he said? "The power has come over me, just like yesterday." And then he began to squeeze me.

ANNA PAVLOVNA (*to Semyon*) How dare you fight in my house?

FYODOR IVANYCH Allow me to inform you, Anna Pavlovna . . . I should tell you that Semyon has certain feelings toward Tanya and they're engaged. But Grigori—well, why not tell the truth?—behaves indecently and dishonorably toward her. And so, I suppose Semyon got mad at him.

GRIGORI That's not it at all. It's out of spite, because I found out about all their tricks.

ANNA PAVLOVNA What tricks?

GRIGORI Why, at the séance. It wasn't Semyon who was doing all those tricks yesterday; it was Tatyana. I saw her myself —crawling out from under the sofa.

ANNA PAVLOVNA What's this about crawling out from under the sofa?

GRIGORI My word of honor! She's the one who brought the document and threw it on the table. If it hadn't been for her, the document wouldn't have been signed, and the land wouldn't have been sold to the peasants.

ANNA PAVLOVNA Did you see her yourself?

GRIGORI With my own eyes. Have her come in. She can't deny it.

ANNA PAVLOVNA Call her.

(*Grigori exit. There is a commotion off-stage. The Doorman's voice is heard: "You can't go in, you can't go in!" The Doorman appears, and the three peasants rush in past him. The Second Peasant is in front. The Third Peasant stumbles, falls, and clutches his nose.*)

DOORMAN You can't come in. Get out!

SECOND PEASANT We don't mean no harm. Do you think we've come to cause trouble? No, we came to pay the money.

FIRST PEASANT Denifitively so. Since by the signing with the affixing of the signature, the deal has been closed, we just want to present the money with our gratitude.

ANNA PAVLOVNA   Wait, just wait with your thanks. It was a swindle. The matter isn't finished. The land isn't sold yet. Leonid! Leonid Fyodorovich! (*Doorman exit. Leonid Fyodorovich enters but, on seeing Anna Pavlovna and the peasants, starts to leave.*) No, no, please come here! I told you the land shouldn't be sold on credit, and everybody else told you so too. And here they've swindled you like a real stupid man.

LEONID FYODOROVICH   Swindled me? How? I don't understand what this swindling is that you're talking about.

ANNA PAVLOVNA   You ought to be ashamed of yourself! You've got gray hair, and still they cheat you and laugh at you as if you were a boy. You begrudge your son a paltry three hundred rubles that he needs to maintain his social standing, but you let them cheat you out of thousands, like a fool.

LEONID FYODOROVICH   Now just calm down, Annette.

FIRST PEASANT   We only came about your receiving the sum, you know———

THIRD PEASANT (*taking out the money*)   For God's sake, take it so we can go!

ANNA PAVLOVNA   No, you just wait. (*Tanya and Grigori enter. Sternly to Tanya.*) Were you in the small drawing room during the séance last night?

(*Tanya, sighing, looks around at Fyodor Ivanych, Leonid Fyodorovich, and Semyon.*)

GRIGORI   Don't beat around the bush. I saw you there myself.

ANNA PAVLOVNA   Speak up! Were you? I know everything, so you'd better make a clean breast of it. I won't do anything to you. I just want to expose him (*points to Leonid Fyodorovich*) —the master . . . . Did you throw the document on the table?

TANYA   I don't really know what to say. All I ask is that you let me go home.

ANNA PAVLOVNA (*to Leonid Fyodorovich*)   You see, they've made a fool of you.

(*Betsy enters, unnoticed.*)

TANYA   Let me go home, Anna Pavlovna!

ANNA PAVLOVNA   No, my dear. You may have caused a loss of several thousand rubles. He sold land which shouldn't have been sold.

TANYA   Let me go home, Anna Pavlovna!

ANNA PAVLOVNA   No, you'll have to answer for this. You can't go around swindling like that. I'll have you up before a justice of the peace.

BETSY (*stepping forward*)   Let her go, mother. If you take her to court, you'll have to take me along too. I was in on everything that she did last night.

ANNA PAVLOVNA   Of course, if you had anything to do with it, it couldn't have been anything but the worst nastiness.

PROFESSOR (*entering*)   Good day, Anna Pavlovna! Good day, Lizaveta Leonidovna! Leonid Fyodorovich, I've brought you the report of the Thirteenth Congress of Spiritualists in Chicago. Schmidt's speech was amazing.

LEONID FYODOROVICH   Ah, that's very interesting!

ANNA PAVLOVNA   I can tell you something a lot more interesting. It turns out that this girl has been making fools of both you and my husband. Betsy's trying to take the blame, but that's just to tease me. An illiterate girl has been fooling you, and you believed it all! There weren't any of your mediumistic phenomena last night. She (*pointing to Tanya*) was the one who was doing it all.

PROFESSOR (*taking off his overcoat*)   What do you mean?

ANNA PAVLOVNA   I mean she's the one who was playing the guitar in the dark, hitting my husband on the head, and performing all your nonsense. She's just confessed.

PROFESSOR (*smiling*)   And just what is that supposed to prove?

ANNA PAVLOVNA   It proves that your mediumism is a lot of nonsense, that's what it proves.

PROFESSOR   Just because this girl wanted to trick us—because of this, mediumism is a lot of nonsense, as you deign to express it? (*Smiling.*) That's a strange conclusion! It may well be that this girl wanted to trick us—that happens quite often; and it may be that she really did do something; but what she did, *she* did; and what was a manifestation of mediumistic energy— was a manifestation of mediumistic energy. It's even very probable that what this girl did evoked—solicited, so to speak—the manifestation of mediumistic energy, gave it a definite form.

ANNA PAVLOVNA   Here comes another lecture!

PROFESSOR (*sternly*)   You say, Anna Pavlovna, that this girl, and also perhaps this charming young lady, did something. But the light which we all saw, and the rise in temperature the first time, and the drop in temperature the second time, and Grossmann's excitement and vibration—well now, did the girl do all this too? And these are facts, facts, Anna Pavlovna. No, Anna Pavlovna, there are things which must be investigated and fully understood before one can start talking about them—things that are too serious, too serious——

LEONID FYODOROVICH   And the child that Marya Vasilevna saw so plainly! Why, I saw it too . . . . Now the girl couldn't have done this.

ANNA PAVLOVNA   You think you're clever, but you're a fool!

LEONID FYODOROVICH   Well, I'm going. Aleksei Vladimiro-vich, let's go to my room. (*Goes into his study.*)

PROFESSOR (*shrugging and following him*)   Yes, we still have a long way to go before we catch up with Europe!

(*Yakov enters.*)

ANNA PAVLOVNA (*in Leonid Fyodorovich's direction*) They've swindled him like a fool, but he doesn't see a thing. (*To Yakov.*) What do you want?

YAKOV   How many people should I set the table for?

ANNA PAVLOVNA   How many? Fyodor Ivanych, take the silver from him! And out with him right away! He's the cause of all this trouble. He'll send me to my grave. Yesterday he almost starved my little dog to death, and it had never done him any harm. As if this wasn't enough, he then brought the infected peasants into the kitchen—and here they are again. He's the cause of all this trouble. Out wth him, out with him right away! Discharge him, discharge him! (*To Semyon.*) And if you ever dare to start a brawl in my house again, I'll teach you a thing or two, you nasty peasant!

SECOND PEASANT   Well now, if he's a nasty peasant, then there's no need to keep him on. Pay him up and let him go, and that'll be the end of it.

ANNA PAVLOVNA (*listening to him but staring at the Third Peasant*)   Just look, this one has a rash on his nose—a rash! He's sick; he's a reservoir of infection! I told you yesterday not to let them in—and here they are again. Chase them out!

FYODOR IVANYCH   Then you're not accepting their money?

ANNA PAVLOVNA   Money? Take the money, but out with them, out with them this very minute—especially that sick one. He's all rotten!

THIRD PEASANT   You're wrong, lady, you're absolutely wrong. Ask my old woman, you know. I'm not rotten. I'm as sound as a bell, you know.

ANNA PAVLOVNA   He dares to argue about it! Out with them, out with them! They're trying to spite me! No, I can't stand it, I can't! Send for Peter Petrovich. (*Runs out, sobbing. Yakov and Grigori leave.*)

TANYA (*to Betsy*)   My dear Lizaveta Leonidovna, what do I do now?

BETSY   Don't worry about it at all. Go with them, and I'll take care of everything. (*Exit.*)

(*The Doorman enters.*)

FIRST PEASANT   How is it, honorable sir, with respect to the reception of the sum?

SECOND PEASANT   Take the money so we can go.

THIRD PEASANT (*fidgeting with the money*)   If I'd known it was going to be like this, I wouldn't have come for anything in the world. This'll dry you up worse than the syph.

FYODOR IVANYCH (*to the Doorman*)   Take them to my room. The abacus is there, and I'll take the money there. Well, go along.

DOORMAN   Let's go, let's go.

FYODOR IVANYCH   And don't forget to thank Tanya. If it hadn't been for her, you wouldn't have the land.

FIRST PEASANT   Denifitively. She put the matter into motion, just like she proposed.

THIRD PEASANT   She's made men of us. What would we be without her? We have little land—there isn't enough room for a chicken, you know, let alone for cattle. Good-by, clever girl! When you come to the village, you'll find a real welcome in my house.

SECOND PEASANT   As soon as I get home, I'll start getting things ready for the wedding and brewing the beer. Just be sure and come.

TANYA   I'll come, I'll come! (*Squealing.*) Isn't this just wonderful, Semyon?

(*Peasants leave with the Doorman.*)

FYODOR IVANYCH   The best of luck! But look out, Tanya, when you have your own little house, I'm coming to visit you. Will I be welcome?

TANYA   Like a father, dear Fyodor Ivanych! (*Hugs and kisses him.*)

Curtain

Rinehart Editions